C000221300

RUNNING
FROM THE SPILLS

A Manchester Childhood

Andrew Barton

Copyright © 2012 Andrew Barton

The moral right of the author has been asserted.

Apart from any fair dealing for the purposes of research or private study,
or criticism or review, as permitted under the Copyright, Designs and Patents
Act 1988, this publication may only be reproduced, stored or transmitted, in
any form or by any means, with the prior permission in writing of the
publishers, or in the case of reprographic reproduction in accordance with
the terms of licences issued by the Copyright Licensing Agency. Enquiries
concerning reproduction outside those terms should be sent to the publishers.

Matador
9 Priory Business Park,
Wistow Road, Kibworth Beauchamp,
Leicestershire. LE8 0RX
Tel: (+44) 116 279 2299
Fax: (+44) 116 279 2277
Email: books@troubador.co.uk
Web: www.troubador.co.uk/matador

ISBN 978 1780881 454

British Library Cataloguing in Publication Data.
A catalogue record for this book is available from the British Library.

Typeset in 11pt Bembo by Troubador Publishing Ltd, Leicester, UK
Printed and bound in the UK by TJ International, Padstow, Cornwall

Matador is an imprint of Troubador Publishing Ltd

RUNNING
FROM THE SPILLS

For my wife and children

The Prologue

MANCHESTER
August 1965

Climbing a tree is an exact science. Like chess, you have to plan your moves ahead and, like running a marathon, you have to pace yourself. If you climb too quickly, you make a mistake and then you fall and you have to hope that the branches and the leaves on the way down break that fall or you'll end up in the hospital.

If you climb too slowly then you start to think too much about what can happen and your hands start to shake and you lose your nerve completely. Not so bad if you are on your own and you can get back down again, but I have seen lads half way up a tree, lose their nerve and have to get rescued by their dads. Not recommended, especially in front of your friends. So for these reasons, on this day like all other days I climbed my tree, quite fast and all alone.

My favourite tree is an old apple tree and it is in the orchard next to the farm buildings that have become yet another building site. I can still climb it for now, but not for much longer because soon the builders will be chopping it down and all the other trees in the orchard too, so they can build yet more houses. They will plant new trees but it will be years before they'll be strong enough to take our weight. By then it will be too late.

It's a good way to be on my own. When there are arguments in the house, if I run my fastest I can be at the bottom of my tree in thirty seconds flat.

I feel the rough bark on my fingers and today, like most other days,

I am climbing away from my father's shouting and my mother's crying, each fork in the branch, each nodule in the trunk helping me upwards, into a more peaceful state. Almost as if the tree is a friend, and is welcoming me inside her leaves, hiding me away in the secret rooms of her dark green foliage. I climb in stages like a mountaineer, searching by sight and by touch for the holds and grips that I know through experience are always there, each limb that I clamber upon as familiar as my own limbs, thick and enveloping lower down, thin and tremulous further up, occasional bunches of near ripe apples, green and shiny, bouncing off my face as I go. Then upwards through the last few branches I ascend in a rush, until I burst through the top of the canopy back into the light of a cloudless sky.

I can see for miles in all directions. There is always elation coming through the topmost leaves into the silence, but looking down is always a shock and my body tenses and my hands grip tighter, especially if there is a breeze. A strong breeze can make the whole tree move and it's like being on a swing boat ride, but fifty feet up. I wriggle my arse into the same crook of a branch that I always settle into and watch everything going on down below from my perch.

To the north and the west, I can skim my eyes across to the rest of Manchester, long lines of terraced rooftops, huge red brick factories and warehouses, railway viaducts and tall chimneys, like giant red cigarettes with thin blue smoke spiralling upwards. In amongst the industry stands the occasional church, their once pristine steeples discoloured from years of absorbing soot and grime.

I can also see my own estate, newer houses with little patches of green lawns and concrete driveways, sitting alongside the older houses, eating up all the spare ground and encroaching into the fields. Some are occupied already, like our own, and some are still in the process of being built, surrounded by mud and machinery and piles of bricks and sand.

I look down and the people on the ground are like ants. I can see people washing cars and mowing lawns and little kids chasing the ice cream van, its chimes of 'Greensleeves' carrying across the still warm air. I can hear disembodied bursts of adult laughter, groups standing in driveways and gardens and far below, I can see Billy and Vic and Linton walking three abreast up Queens Road on their way to meet me at the site.

To the south and to the east I can see right across to the hills and the moors in the distance. If I cling to the top of the tree, swinging slightly in the breeze, and close my eyes, I pretend that I live in those hills amongst the caves and the rocks and the underground chambers, and not on a shitty old housing estate like everybody else.

Chapter 1

MANCHESTER
November 2002

I heard the news that Myra had died as I drove, with my son beside me, to my own mother's deathbed.

'One of the infamous Moors Murderers, Myra Hindley died last night' the radio announced as we cut through the mists of that wet, grey dawn on our way to the hospital. The newsreader's voice was monotone, his clipped BBC tones showing no sign of any emotion, the sound of his words almost lost in the whirring and slapping of the windscreen wipers. Then, as the gist of his message sunk in I felt the skin on my face tighten and my lips go dry, and for a moment all sound vanished except for the asthmatic breathing of my son in the passenger seat beside me. Out of the corner of my eye I felt him glance at me, then study me harder than he normally would, made curious by my reaction to the bulletin. Up ahead a woman and a boy stepped out in a hurry onto the zebra-crossing in front of us, causing me to brake hard. My tyres screeched on the wet tarmac and made them both jump and the woman gave me a cold, hard stare through the rain. I knew I had been concentrating more on the radio than the road, so I raised a conciliatory hand and I tried smiling at the boy, her son I presumed, but I received just a blank look in return. He wore no hat and his dark, wet hair was plastered to his head and he looked white and thin as if he had been ill. I waited until they were clear across and watched them disappear down an old, cobbled street adjacent to the main road. Only then did I pull away.

I could hear properly again and the radio was still droning on about Myra and then they cut from the studio to a spokesman outside the hospital where she had died; another emotionless, disembodied voice, giving the sparest of details.

'We can confirm that Myra Hindley, date of birth the 23rd July 1942, died in West Suffolk Hospital at 16:58 yesterday, the 15th November 2002, following respiratory failure.

Myra Hindley was convicted of murder at the Central Criminal Court on the 6th May 1966 and was serving a whole life tariff. She had been in hospital since the 12th November 2002. Myra Hindley's next of kin have been informed. There will be a coroner's inquest as there always is when a prisoner dies whilst in custody.'

So at last Myra the old witch was dead, hated and reviled by all save a few bleeding hearts and assorted do-gooders; that deluded old fool Lord Longford foremost amongst them. It had been a severe chest infection following a heart attack that got her in the end; a drawn out death and no more than she deserved, many would be thinking. All over Manchester, where I had arrived that morning, there would be old mothers, my own mother amongst them had she not been on death's door herself, that would have relished this woman's decline and seen it as some kind of belated justice. A lot of people would have wished her pain and terror as she herself had inflicted pain and terror. Her final laboured breaths, oozing froth from her diseased lungs, signalling the end to her time on earth would have been too clinically well managed and thereby too merciful for many of her enemies. They would have liked her gradual, drug-laden slide into oblivion to be filled with dread and forboding, for her to be convinced as she went, that the devil was waiting for her and that she would get no forgiveness, only eternal damnation on the other side.

It was strange that I still thought of her as Myra, by her given Christian name and not by Hindley, which was how those who hated her less thought of her. In Manchester, just after they had been captured, when we were still young, exactly the age in fact that Myra and her accomplice Ian Brady liked their victims, we all thought of her as Myra, as if she was an old friend and a confidant and not our deadly pursuer. Sometimes even the police had called her Myra, completely baffled as they were, by her propensity for such cruelty; it was almost as if they had made her an animal to explain the unexplainable, to try and accept her inhumanity, and, like a zoo-keeper would a wild beast, hide the divide in a pretence at familiarity. On first name terms with a predator.

I had listened to all this as I drove to the hospital where my own mother lay dying. There would be an unwanted symmetry in their passing, although I was comforted by the difference in age. Not only had my mother's life been blameless and loving, it had also been many years longer. At the age of seventy six she was slowly succumbing to pneumonia after a fall downstairs and a broken hip and she was not to know, thankfully, that she would not be returning to her home of fifty years. I was, in my own mind, preparing to engage with those two contrasting emotions of sorrow and relief that my own mother's final days would bring me, and I was daunted by the prospect.

Beside me, my thirteen year old son Alex had slumped back into his own world, a scowl of concentration on his features, the dull thump of music coming from behind his earphones. I had been surprised when he had agreed to come with me, and that his mother had urged him to, but I had accepted his offer gratefully because as he had grown up and not seen his grandmother so much, I was pleased that he was loyal enough to want to say goodbye. Our own relationship, that of father and son, had grown distant since he had gone to secondary school and I was hoping to regain some lost ground. So far it didn't look promising. We had hardly spoken since we had left London, as he worked his way through his repertoire of music and electronic games, giving only monosyllabic answers or the occasional grunt in response to my efforts at conversation. Yet in a way I didn't mind, I even relished the silence. Besides, I had valuable time. The only upside on this most desperate of filial duties was that I was able to spend some time with my own son, alone and without the added complications of peers and siblings around, to hopefully make friends again, as hard as that might prove to be.

Then when the news came through, my mind went back to 1966, and it occurred to me that I had been the same age as the boy sitting beside me when the murders had happened. Those feelings from my childhood came back in a rush and I suddenly felt a great tenderness for my son. Was his life an amalgam of confusion and happiness and fears like my own had been at that time? Was his distance, his aloofness towards me, just a guard, a defence against potential betrayal, even desertion? I realised then, in a rush of sudden regret, that I didn't really know him anymore.

I remembered a time three years before when Alex had been about ten years old and we had still all been together, one big and not so happy family. Alex and I had spent a morning on our own while his mother and his sisters had gone shopping and we had actually had a nice morning, watching a film, and even playing scrabble, which we hardly ever did. But after a while I had had enough. The others should have been back an hour ago and I wanted to go out myself. When I halted the scrabble (with me ahead by the way) what at first became banter, then mild reproach, finally turned (with the help of his tricky little tongue) into direct criticism of my parenting skills.

"You're never here, you never do anything with me and you just don't care," was spat out in a flow of condemnation that surprised me with its depth of feeling and, because there was truth in what he said, instead of seeking to understand his anger I merely gave into some of my own.

"Look, I have to work all hours at the moment, Alex."

"Not all hours. Sometimes you go to the pub," he replied. The truth, but irritating nonetheless.

"How often do I go to the pub?"

"More often than you spend time with me."

"I'm sorry you feel that way, but it's not true."

"Yes it is."

4

I felt the sharp taste of annoyance rising up through my throat, and I tried one last time to get his sympathy, at least, but I was dealing with an unsympathetic foe.

"Look I have to work. I don't necessarily like what I do but I have to do it for all our sakes. That's a fact of life and you will find out yourself one day."

"It's because you do a crap job." No beating around the bush with my boy. He didn't know it but he had gone straight to the nub of the problem.

"That's enough," I said in a raised voice.

"That's why you have no time and no money." God he sounded like his mother.

"Alex," I managed to whisper as the red mist rolled in from my temples.

"That's why you're poorer than Sam's dad and Josh's dad."

In that split second that I looked at him I could see in his eyes that he knew he had gone too far and that he wanted to retract. He knew what was coming and it was too late to stop it. In a blur I raised my hand and brought it crashing down on his leg with far more force than I had intended to use. With certainly far more than was warranted. In my rage I had raised the lily white skin on his left thigh and turned it claret red as he had begged for mercy and screamed that he was sorry. I ignored his cries for forgiveness, but at least I didn't hit him a second time. That would have been too much. I stalked off in a foul mood to my study, where I turned on the TV to watch the news. Already, despite the echoes of self-justification rebounding around my head, the certainty that I had been right to hit my own son, and so hard as well, had started to wane and a mixture of misery and guilt had set in.

The midday news had just started and the main item was an incident that had taken place in the occupied territories of the Middle East. There was vivid footage showing a Palestinian man and his son, both clearly terrified, caught in crossfire between warring PLO militants and Israeli soldiers, somewhere in the West Bank. The man was trying desperately to protect his own son, even going so far as to cover him with his own body, but the boy was hit by a stray bullet and sadly did not survive. The father's distress at losing his son was heartbreaking. As I sat watching this footage, with the cries of my own son still ringing in my ears and my own sense of having betrayed his love, I made a pact with myself to never, under any circumstance, deliberately hurt him again.

Well so far, physically at least, I had not broken this pact, although I confess to occasionally being sorely tested. As he had grown in height and weight, so his character had blossomed, and with it his natural intelligence and assertiveness. I suppose if they were to analyse it a child psychologist would say that my son had leadership skills. That is if they could be discovered buried deep within this attitude that he carried, as these skills, if that is what they were, were mainly used to dominate his mates at the PlayStation or to troubleshoot their computer problems for them. He could be geeky and arrogant and rude, and above all clever, and what is more, cleverer than me, but still I didn't hit him. I kept to my pact in that sense at least.

At that moment in the car, driving in Manchester again, I wanted to reach out to him in some way, tell him that I would never leave him, take him in my arms like I could do at will when he was a kid. But I knew this wasn't the time. If I had stopped the car there and then and tried just to hug this spotty youth who had grown four inches in the last year and whose voice was starting to crack, and who had God knows what else going on inside and outside of his body, well he would have jumped out of the car and run all the way back to North London.

So I resisted the temptation and concentrated on the once familiar streets of my home-town. All around me as we drove were the very same suburbs of east Manchester that had been the communities of the children and their killers. Through Gorton and Ashton, with their old red-bricked terraces, darkened by age and factory smoke and dwarfed by the white concrete new buildings of regeneration. The old cobbled streets, once so common but no longer practical, were bisected by new smooth, dark, four-lane highways taking fast cars into the city centre. Intermittently there were old bombsites and slum clearance; land that had not been built on and was now covered in long, wild grass, regular squares of green, like unplanned nature reserves amidst the new hotels and leisure centres of the new city. We drove through Victorian high streets established now as Manchester's multi-cultural identity, past curry houses and Asian delicatessens, the street markets ringing to the shouts and cries of Urdu and Bengali, and then into quieter, less colourful residential areas like Didsbury and Cheadle, until eventually we turned through a once-imposing gateway, its classical lines blurred and diminished by the relentless erosion of time and weather. Then down into an avenue of beech trees that was the driveway of the St. Nicholas' Hospital. We pulled up into a large gravel forecourt and as we climbed from the car I looked up at more Victorian architecture, purpose-built and institutional, a facade of red and grey brick, grand but austere and unwelcoming. I smelt a bonfire of wet foliage in the terraced gardens below us and I sniffed its acrid pall for several moments, savouring the familiar sharpness, then, still stretching joints aching from the long journey, we climbed the old stone steps that led inside, to where my mother was waiting.

Later I sat by her bedside, and in my own hand my mother's hand lay resting. White-boned and blue-veined, her skin cool now after years of heat, but still red in colour, raw from the rituals of washing that had dominated her whole life. Washing clothes, washing dishes, washing children, always up to her arms in warm water through cold Manchester days.

I looked down at my mother sleeping just as once she had looked down at me, at those high cheekbones and that strong jaw that had, amidst the hard work and disappointment, given her great beauty. I traced the lines of her features with my fingers, light strokes of reassurance, just as once, a lifetime ago, she had done for me, and for herself.

Her hair was the same brilliant white that it had been for years, but was sparse on her scalp and I knew she would have hated the thinness of it. Every other week I paid thirty pounds for a young girl to come to her house from the local salon to cajole those fine wisps into a sort of covering and now that same girl was visiting the hospital. On a previous visit I had seen her chatting away to my mother, even though she was barely conscious, and I never considered asking her to miss an appointment. I liked the everyday routine of it and it pleased me the way this girl, who had no relationship with my mother, nor any obligation, had not given up on her and who, like me, still found her beautiful.

"She keeps asking for Stevie. That's all she says," said my sister Sandra, who was standing right behind me. She had always stood in the presence of our mother as if she was still on her guard, ready to run, although I couldn't for the life of me remember Sandra running from anyone or anything.

"What did you say?" I said, not looking up, my eyes still on my mother's hair.

"What could I say? Deep down she knows but still she asks. I said nothing, like I always do."

Sandra glanced at me and she looked tired all of a sudden.

"What about our George?" I said. "He should be here by now."

"He's on his way. He had to sort out his kids. It was his turn to have them." Sandra gave me one of her defensive looks. "Life does go on you know." Then in a stage whisper so typical of our Sandra she gave vent to her true feelings. "She's been threatening to die for weeks. I almost wish it was over and done with."

My hand stopped for a moment and rested on my mum's left cheek, but she made no sign that she was feeling my touch. Her skin still shone but was tinged with yellow and was flaccid in repose; her mouth, once routinely anointed with the brightest red lipstick, was clear and cleansed and slightly open, allowing low, shallow breaths to escape. Her eyelids were closed in a deep sleep, the wrinkled hoods covering a blue-eyed brightness that had not diminished in old age. Not for the first time, I wondered at the peace that sleep brought and the likeness between sleeping and dying, the short little breaths, the flickering of her facial muscles, the low pulse in her neck like that of a tiny bird. I wondered, did my mum still have dreams? Did the small form under the covers ever return to a child's body, with its child's strength, to leap up again and run through green fields and pick blackberries as she had loved to tell us about when we were kids? Or did she in her deep sleep remember what it was like to carry her children and comfort us when we were hurt, or feel love for her husband, even desire for him and then the pain that would surely come with all of it. The pain of loss and abandonment and broken promises? I looked down at my dying mother and thought about all of these things.

In the corner of the hospital room Alex sat quietly saying nothing, not complaining, just looking at his grandmother, and I was suddenly mindful that he hadn't eaten, nor had we even checked into the hotel. There was no question that my sister would invite me to stay, although she still lived close by in Stockport. She had never offered, and I had never asked her because we just weren't close enough. We never had been. She was five years older than me and we had never narrowed that distance.

I stood up. "C'mon son we need to go."

"Where to?" gasped Sandra in an incredulous tone. "You can't go now; she could go at any minute. George isn't here yet either. Don't leave me here on my own, for Christ's sake."

"It's all right," I said. "We won't be long. She's not going just yet."

"How the bloody hell do you know? You're not the doctor."

I knew because there was something missing. It would have been pointless to tell our Sandra because she would have laughed in my face and thought me mad or delirious but, as I had sat and looked at my mother, who wanted to die but seemed for some reason to be just holding on, it came to me. In a moment of blinding realisation, as her fingers gripped mine, she had taken me back to snow and ice and another person's final breath, and it had all become clear. Like crystal, as my elder brother would have said. In that moment I knew there was something I must find, something that should have been with her but wasn't and it may have sounded melodramatic, but I was sure that my mother would refuse to die until I had found it.

"The key to Mum's house. Is it still in the wall?" I was short with my sister but I didn't want any more debate with her.

"Yes it is. Of course it is. At least I think so. I haven't been there for weeks since she came in. She's got a key somewhere."

"Yeah," I replied more softly because I felt her confusion. "But I don't want to go through her stuff now. Don't worry, I'll get in."

"Why now? This is not the time. Alex doesn't want to go there now, surely?"

"Actually I would quite," said Alex, answering for himself and not cowed by his Aunt Sandra. I nodded at him, glad of his support.

"See?" I said. "We won't be long. It's just to get some air." I saw my sister's disbelieving look but chose to ignore it. "We'll be back before you know it."

Then I remembered the news bulletin.

"Did you hear about Myra Hindley?"

"No. What?"

"Oh. She died, that's all. Yesterday evening. Down south somewhere, Suffolk or Cambridge. Lungs and heart I think they said. Riddled with disease."

"Oh. Well I knew she was ill. They expected it by now. Good riddance I say. Mum would be pleased. I think she'd quite like to get hold of her on the other side."

I looked down at my old mum shrinking away before my very eyes, enveloped by her bed and her drips, slowly leaving us.

"No chance," I said. "They'll be in different places. They'll never meet up."

The old house, number forty six Tatton Drive, where we had all grown up, and where mum had lived, eventually on her own, until her final trip to the hospital a month ago, stood cold and dark and full of memories. It was mid-afternoon and the old road was suspended in a limbo of half light, the dying embers of a fine November day. In such a shade the old houses looked timeless to me, the small front gardens still neat and well-kept, the roofs and the doors and windows symmetrical and orderly. But underneath this veneer of familiarity there were differences. Double-glazing on most, pebble dash or new paint on many and almost all that had a driveway had a new car in it. Cars had still been quite rare in the sixties. I also knew that it would be different around the corner on the old council estate, which led down to the river and where we had spent so much of our time.

We got in through the back door, that much-crossed threshold, memories of sneaking out at dawn to secret meetings, or back at dusk from rivers and fields and derelict buildings, late and in trouble, flowing back to me. We acted like thieves scrabbling around in the half light for a back door key that I was sure would be there, where it had been for more than forty years, and within seconds I found the crack in the brickwork where it lay. Alex and I crept in and, as we wandered through the old rooms, keeping the lights off so as not to alert the neighbours (I had no desire to see any of them), I could see my son's distaste for it all in his posture and in the tightness of his mouth, although he was gracious enough not to criticise directly. Yet I too would have admitted that I found the state of the place pretty awful. I couldn't help but feel a cold blast of resentment towards my sister, who historically had never even visited my mother, let alone taken any responsibility towards supporting her. I knew my resentment was unjust – my own contact, or lack of it, bordered on neglectful, but at least I had geography as my excuse.

The house was in darkness and smelt damp, like wet cardboard, so immediately I went from room to room, drawing all the curtains and opening up the windows. The inward burst of winter light, thin as it was, transformed the place, diluting those shadowy blocks of gloom and lighting up the furniture and walls. The air blew papers from the shelves but also washed the dust from the fabric of the curtains.

Then, as my eyes became accustomed to my surroundings, I began to recognise furniture and pictures and even kitchen appliances that had never been replaced, objects that I had grown up with over the years, but which now, without my mother present, seemed slightly unfamiliar, out of context. Even the old sliding door that my dad had put up between the kitchen and the dining room, in the days when he was around and inclined to do such things, seemed archaic. I wandered into the old kitchen, through that sliding door, and felt again the cramped but warm sensation of endless hours spent as my mother cooked or washed, the clanking of the washing machine a constant accompaniment in our over-populated house, or where she just sat and smoked cigarettes and listened to Jimmy Young and Mrs Dale's Diary on the radio, alone with her thoughts. On some days she was happy for me to be there and would kiss me a lot; too much sometimes. On other days she would be sad, her blue eyes brimming and she couldn't wait for me to leave the house.

The old telly, with its small grey screen and its flickering picture through which I'd strained to watch Wagon Train and Rawhide and Errol Flynn films, was gone. It had been replaced by mum's one concession to modern technology, a big screen Sony number, which now stood in pride of place in the corner. In the other corner the old gramophone was still there, the HMV, around which our Sandra and our Stevie had both in their turn danced to their favourite records. Stevie loved Buddy Holly and Elvis. Sandra always preferred the Beatles and the Searchers and sometimes there had been conflict around that record player over what should be played.

The maroon settee on whose raised ornate pattern I had run my fingers over and over so that I could still recall it now, thirty years on, and where we had all lain as kids with the mumps and measles and chicken pox, was still there, but a lot of the chairs had gone. There was no need for so many chairs once all the family had left, and I wondered whether mum had been lonely in her final years. God knows none of us had visited her much in the old home and she had always been willing to visit us in London, or at least she had until my marriage had taken a dive. I hadn't seen her much in the last few years. She still had her neighbours, a lot had died, a few had moved but she still had a couple who had been there since we were kids, so maybe she had been all right. A bit late to start worrying about it now, I thought to myself.

What I had really come back to see, what I was searching for, was in the corner of the room, just as it had always been: the old bureau made of mahogany, its wood black with age and feeling like old used leather when I touched it. As I ran my fingers along the outline I recalled my mother and the hours that she had spent sitting in front of it, a cigarette jammed between her bright red lips, writing letters to her friends overseas. She had been a great letter-writer and when I was younger I had often played in the room on rainy days with her in the corner scribbling away, not minding the noise I made, for what seemed like hours. The desk was the only piece of furniture that she had professed to care about, her family heirloom she called it, and she said that it had travelled all round the world in the possession of numerous colonising relatives, and she was never sure how it had ended up with her, but she was very glad it had. The outside was a simple design, robust and solid, but I knew from past experience that this gave no indication of the intricacies that lay inside.

With a deep breath I turned the small brass key and it moved in the lock with a musical click and an ease that surprised me. Then I rolled, from either side of the top drawer, the long wooden supports, at the same time using the tips of my fingers to pull down the writing desk to sit neatly in place on top of them.

Inside, just as she would have left it, was a silk scarf that had belonged to my mother. It was a rich pattern of blues and greens and reds and she had loved it because it was a present from her eldest son and she had worn it often to protect her hair from the cold northern wind. I felt a quick stab of guilt as I remembered being embarrassed, because it was garish and out of place and she drew attention to herself by wearing it. I scrunched the material up in my right hand and felt it melt in my grip, and I pushed it against my face to smell the scent of her again, her favourite perfume, that smell of rose blossom, and peaches too possibly, a scent I could never place, with a name I had never discovered, although it had stayed with me always.

With the desk top down, the bureau opened up to reveal a treasure of woodcraft, of ornate carved trees and plants, on which were painted humming birds and birds of paradise, all entwined, in exotic greens and blues and yellows. Above was a catacomb of drawers, different sizes, row upon row, containing letters and photographs, important documents and memorabilia. My mother had never been a hoarder to my knowledge, but she had kept a stack of personal letters, tied with a plain white ribbon, that I resisted looking at. I would be interested to look at a later stage, but for now I was looking for something else.

I knew there was a secret door in the back of the desk because I had seen my mother use it, and I needed to find the small catch that would unlock that door. It took me ten minutes, but I found it. I reached my hand around the space from where the door protruded and, with my fingers at full stretch and feeling the velvet of the compartment, I touched cool metal and leather and carefully extricated them from their hiding place. In fact there were two pieces there, both small and surprisingly heavy, and, with a slight tremble of expectation in my aching hand, I laid both items on the leather base of the desk and studied them closely. Many years had passed since I had seen them last and there was no change, no obvious deterioration of any kind, both ornate in their way but with very specific designs. Once they had been readily available for all to see, but latterly my mother, as she became older and more fearful, had hidden them away for fear of losing them to burglars. I remember in the dark times of my childhood, when she and I were mourning our losses together, how often she had gone to her desk, and had sat, head bowed, gently stroking these inanimate objects, seeking comfort, even reconciliation. These precious items were, for a reason that was clear to me at least, something that she needed with her in her final hours.

There was a call from the back of the house so I quickly wrapped them back up in the scarf and put them in my breast pocket for safekeeping. I walked through the sliding door and out into the kitchen, where my son was studying something intently on the wall by the back door.

The wallpaper was peeling and Alex's head was at an angle as he attempted to decipher some writing.

"Hey, Dad," Alex said. "There's writing under this paper. Can I peel some off and see what it is?"

"Blimey," I said. "I know what that is. That's our measurements as we were growing up. My father used to do it every year to make sure we were growing properly. Do you see?"

'July 1965. Michael. Height: five feet two inches. Aged twelve years and six months.' I read it carefully, my father's old scrawl barely discernible after years under paper.

"That was your height when you were twelve?" said Alex.

"That's what it says."

He sounded puzzled. "You weren't very big, were you? Last year when I was twelve, I was at least three inches above you."

"Well, remember every generation gets bigger. Better nourishment. Rationing had only just finished when I was born. And my mum and dad had it even tougher. World wars and all that."

"I bet you weren't that heavy either," my son persisted.

"Thin as a rake, I was. Mind you, we were out all day. We never stopped running or riding bikes."

"Yeah, all right, Dad. I've heard it all before."

"It's true though, Alex. We went out after breakfast and didn't come back until after tea. It used to drive mum spare I can tell you. You should try it."

"As if she would let me," he countered. "Can you see her putting up with that? I don't think so!"

"It was different then. We covered miles, went everywhere. There was nothing we wouldn't try and do."

"Yeah, well, maybe it was easier for you. Less traffic. Fewer weird

15

people about. Anyway, we're restricted now by over-protective parents who read too many papers and watch too much TV."

"I know, I know," I conceded, "every generation is different. Besides, you have a lot more to entertain you in different ways. Look at all the technology you have. Computers and phones; we just didn't have any of that stuff. As for travel, this generation can go more or less where they please. In a couple of years you can go all round the world, well when I was a kid Blackpool was the end of the world."

"Some people still think it is," said Alex and I gave a short laugh.

"Yeah well. Things change and thank God for it but we had our moments too."

"So what sort of things did you get up to that were so wonderful?"

"Oh all sorts. Like you wouldn't believe."

"Round here though, Dad? It's not exactly Disneyland, is it? Just houses, houses and more skanky houses."

I gave him a look but left it at that.

"It was different once. When we first came here there were only a few houses. To us it was the most dangerous, most exciting place you could grow up in."

"What, round here? You are joking," he said, genuinely bemused. "It's boring. I think you're going soft."

I couldn't help laughing although he wasn't being deliberately funny. It was just the smugness of youth, that we've all carried at one time or another, that can be so irritating but wasn't this time for some reason. My laugh annoyed him though.

"C'mon, Dad" he said, "I want to go. I'm getting claustrophobic in this house. I need some air."

"Ok," I said. "We've got some time. We'll take a walk down to the river."

"Where's the river?" he said.

"Not far."

"What's there?"

"Oh it's just a place where we hung out as kids. Where lots of things happened, which led to other things happening. Strange things sometimes, funny things other times."

My son looked at me curiously. I could tell he was interested despite himself.

"What do you mean strange things and funny things?"

"It's hard to explain." I was taunting him a little; I couldn't help myself.

His next question surprised me.

"Does it have anything to do with Myra Hindley? The one they were talking about on the radio? The one that just died? Boy you had a weird look on your face when they were reading that news out today."

"I didn't think you had heard the news," I replied. "Plugged in as you were to all your equipment."

"I heard. What did she do then? Why the big smile now she's dead?"

I sighed. I wasn't in the mood to talk about her, but he was going to press me, I could tell.

"A lot of people used to think like you," I told him. "In my time as well. They used to think the world was boring and safe and predictable. That nothing bad could happen to you."

"Exactly," he grunted.

"That was until Myra came along. She and her boyfriend changed everything. They changed things for me, and all the people I knew, and they changed things for every last person that came after us, including you, although you haven't realised it yet. Things were never the same after those two had done their work."

"What did they do that was so bad?"

"Look, I thought you wanted to get outside."

"I do. Will you tell me what happened to you when you were a kid?"

"Alright," I said. "Let's walk, and we'll talk as we go."

"I suppose so," he muttered, returning to his non-committed, disinterested persona, but then spoiling the effect by suddenly exclaiming, "Hey, Dad, what about Gran? We should get back."

I thought of her little treasures wrapped in her scarf and secreted in my jacket pocket, a reassuring nudge against my chest.

"Don't worry she'll wait for us," I said confidently.

"Daaad," groaned my son. "Don't be stupid."

"We've got some time, I promise. Learn to trust your old dad. I'll show you a few places and tell you some of my adventures from when I was a boy. Maybe you'll learn something."

In August 1965, I stood at the same point in the kitchen, on the threshold of the back door, close to where my son and I now stood, waiting for a knock on the glass pane.

When eventually the knock came, a short sharp rap on the glass, I tried to get there first but my mum beat me to it and I groaned inwardly. It was the first time that my new friend Billy Skinner had come to call for me and he wouldn't be used to dealing with my mother. I had hoped, this first time, to save him the trouble until they got a bit more acquainted, but I was not quick enough. She could be quick on her feet when she wanted to be, my mum. She opened the door to this cheeky looking kid, tall for his age, handsome with a mop of fair hair on his big head, ruddy faced from hours outside and teeth not so white, bared in a big smile. I was to discover that Billy used this smile on most of the mothers around about, but more work was needed with mine.

"Hello," I heard him say, "Can Mikey come out?"

I closed my eyes and waited.

"There's nobody called Mikey living here," said my mother in her imperious tone.

"Eh," said Billy confused, "number forty six?"

"There is somebody called Michael living here," she continued, oblivious to Billy's confusion and my embarrassment. I was trying to squeeze around her into the doorway, so Billy could see me at least, but she was doing a good job of blocking me out.

"Mum," I pleaded, but she ignored me and carried on.

"He may even on rare occasions be addressed as Mike, but Mikey…, never!"

18

"Oh," said Billy, quick on the uptake because he was bright when he wanted to be.

"Can Michael come out then?" he persevered but the smile was now gone from his face. I knew I had to get out of there fast or I would lose the first friend I had made since we had arrived from the other side of Manchester.

"That is better," said my mum and, with a flourish as if she was introducing me on stage, she stepped back and finally allowed me through.

"What's your name then?" she said, more friendly now that she saw how pleased I was to see him.

"Billy." A pause as he thought and then he continued, "You might prefer to call me William though." His grin had returned, much to my relief.

He could be witty like that, Billy, when he wanted to be and it made my mum laugh.

"Don't be late for your tea," she said, "and where are you going by the way?"

"Where are we going, Billy?"

"To the swing down at the Ladybrook," he said.

"Don't get wet," said my mother and shut her kitchen door behind her. Then she opened it again for a moment to shout after us.

"And don't talk to any strangers." She meant it as well; she wasn't half joking any more like she had been with my name.

"Bloody hell," I whispered under my breath, "just go in will you."

"We won't," said Billy. He gave a big wave as she finally disappeared back into the house.

As we loped down our road at a half run towards the Ladybrook river, me along the pavement and Billy up and down on the low garden walls like a mountain goat, he said to me, "She's a bit odd your mum, i'nt she?"

I thought about agreeing with him but managed not to. Odd was not a nice enough word for her.

"No," I said. "She's not odd, just different that's all."

Anyway, thoughts of my mother left me immediately for, as we stepped off the estate and into the fields, up ahead on the path that led to the rope swing, groups of lads made their way, jumping and leaping and skylarking in the distance like white-chested monkeys. Friend or foe we weren't sure, but all those years ago Billy had raced on ahead to find out, his big red face turning occasionally, to check that I was still with him.

Chapter 2

THE ROPE SWING
1965

In that long summer of 1965, the Ladybrook drew us to its banks like bees to the honey pot. Its murky brown waters were for us the clearest, deepest pools and its sparse ecology a lost world of exotic wildlife. In the foliage through the densest parts, we collected grasshoppers the size of shrimps, and black and yellow furry caterpillars, the hairs of which, if handled wrongly, left angry red rashes on our sticky little fingers. In the shallows where the sunrays shone through the branches overhead and lit the waters in a creamy glow, there lurked bloodsucking leeches which stuck to our pale skins as we waded, like Amazon explorers, into unknown lands. Occasionally a yell of "LEECH!" would be heard and whoever was carrying the matches would fumble in their pockets for the magic cure. Then, as the victim made suitable grimaces, the rest of us would watch with fascination as the leech would forsake its warm red meal and curl pointlessly around the matchstick. It never failed. Then we would pop open the leech and watch its red gunge spurt out like a bloody pimple. This happened a lot but we never grew tired of doing it.

Under the banks of the river lived long brown rats which occasionally we saw swimming but more often we heard them as they scuttled along their rat runs in search of food. We had the greatest respect for them because on the (thankfully rare) occasions that we came face to face with them, it was evident that they were not afraid of us. They didn't run away in fright, but merely looked at us for a moment then turned and sought an alternative course; that is if we hadn't scarpered away before them.

In the river were minnows and the sticklebacks, with their sharp little spines, and the much bigger, but harmless, gudgeon, which the more patient among us could catch with their hands, especially on hot days when they seemed sleepier than usual. Older lads told us of encounters with eels, long black watery snakes that could bite off your fingers, and although we suspected that these stories were exaggerated, we became very wary of eels as well.

So most days, rain or shine, we could be found down by the river, by the Ladybrook, which downstream became the Mickerbrook and then eventually became the Mersey, the famous river Mersey, which we had heard was more like a sea than a river. We came in search of adventure and capture and possession of living things.

That first time that Billy brought me there was a hive of activity, mainly centred around the rope swing and the constant queue of lads that were waiting their turn to go on it. Just like the others, I wore only a pair of shorts which were wet and sticking to my skin, because every time we swung away from the bank, just at the highest point of the swing, right up in the treetops, we would let go and drop the ten feet or so into the water, making a huge splash.

There were five of us, five lads, friends I suppose, and we were all yelling in our high-pitched Manchester voices. Billy Skinner was the self-appointed leader on account of the fact that he was the biggest and toughest. I'm not sure if this fact was proven but the others seemed to think so and the whisper was that Billy would get physical if anyone challenged him too strongly, so for now that was good enough for me. Then there was Victor Roberts, who was small and wiry and with a bit of a tongue on him, and who sometimes rubbed up Billy the wrong way because he didn't always accept him as leader, as everyone else seemed to. Then there was Mr fancy name himself, Linton Mannering, whose dad was a policeman. He was quite mild and easy-going but always seemed on the edge of the group, as if he was tempted to join in but was wary of getting into trouble, probably on account of his dad being what he was. He did have a tendency to talk about him too much for our liking. He was a real detective working in the middle of Manchester with real criminals and Lint was not afraid to remind us of that and tell us the hot news from down the station, some of which we didn't believe anyway. He was alright really.

Last but definitely not least there was Mr 'Fat Boy, Edmund Pybus, who we all just called by his last name, Pybus. Apparently his parents named him after the mountaineer Edmund Hillary, who got to the top of Mount Everest in the year before he was born, but you couldn't meet anybody less likely to get up a mountain than Pybus. I think his parents were quite rich because he was the only one of us who had the full Man United strip; it must have cost them a fortune and every day he wore the red shirt and white shorts, and every day they seemed to get smaller on him until his big stomach stuck out and the material pressed hard against the rest of his flesh. This day, because it was so warm, Pybus had managed somehow to peel his shirt from his body, possibly sealing his fate for what was about to unfold.

We were not sure who had put the rope up originally but it hung from a branch of a big oak tree that stood a few feet back from the bank from the river. This branch extended out halfway across the water a distance of about ten feet. If we let go of the rope it fell back over the middle of the river because it was as thick as a tow rope, and we had to hook it back in using a long stick because there was a drop between the bank and the water of about five feet. Once the rope was in hand, those of us brave enough to do it ran along the bank between the tree and the drop, and parallel to the river, and then as the rope was at its furthest length and your feet were about to leave the ground, you pushed off, right out into the middle, into thin air. Then as the rope swung back on itself, it brought you back down the centre of the river in a big arc at great speed and then, as it reached its furthest point downstream, it flipped you back onto the bank, where you could land safely on both feet. It took me a while to pluck up the courage to jump off that bank, but once I did it was the best feeling of my young life so far, to hurtle through the void, yelling louder than Tarzan, toes skimming the water, arms straining on the rope, faces on the bank a blur of colour and noise as they cheered you on.

Then the four of us jumped onto the swing at the same time with Pybus watching us nervously from the bank and we leapt out into the middle and made one heck of a splash. Then we waded out of the water onto little sand spits, like beaches in the shallows, and clambered back up to the top, hauling ourselves along the roots of the oak and other foliage that protruded out of the bank itself. But on my third go I hit a rock or something in the river as we went in, right in the middle of my back, and I got winded; those few seconds of panic when you think you'll never get your breath back. I felt like I was going to be sick so the others helped me out and left me to lie down in the undergrowth for a while to recover.

The hum of the hot spring day was all around me in the noise of the insects and in the smell of the nettles and the cow parsley and, as I sucked on a blade of grass, I began to feel better again. My eyes wanted to close but I could still see light through the inside of my eyelids, little red blood vessels like lines on the map, dappled though it was through the leaves on the trees. So I opened them up again. The sun felt strong on my face and chest. Up in the blue ocean that is the sky, a jet like a silver minnow left a trail behind. Silent, thirty thousand feet away, with a man inside who has a family, maybe a boy like me whom he kissed every time he left for the airport in case he didn't come back because, as everyone knew, flying was a dangerous job.

From my place in the half shade I could hear the high-pitched banter of the other boys wafting downstream in audible bursts, like birdsong. Billy had taken to baiting Pybus as usual.

"Go on, Pybus, you soft get," he was saying "If you want to be in this gang, you've got to use the swing."

"I'm going to do it," he protested, "I'm just working up to it that's all."

"Go on, Pybus," joined in Linton. "There's nothing to it."

"Not for you maybe," said Pybus. "What if the rope snaps?"

"Then you'll end up in the bleedin' river, won't you!" shouted Billy.

"I'll call the rozzers and tell them there's going to be a flood, shall I?" said Vic, mouth wide open in pleasure, grinning at Pybus's predicament.

I wandered back along the bank and into the discussion.

"It won't snap, Pybus," I said. "Look how thick the rope is."

"Yeah and look how big he is," said Vic.

"C'mon," growled Billy, getting visibly more impatient.

"Look, Pybus," I said, "the river's not deep, if you go in we'll rescue you, won't we lads?"

There were mumbles and mutterings but no real commitment at my suggestion. Then in that moment, from way across the other side of the river, we heard a noise. It was distant and could have been laughter or it could just have been some bird or animal but as I turned round again I could see that the others, their purpose temporarily forgotten, were straining to identify the source of that sound.

Then Linton said very quietly, but loud enough for everyone to hear, just one word. "Spills."

"What?" I said.

"Spills," said Linton again. "I bet that's them on the other side."

"Shut up, Linton," said Billy, "the Spills are nowhere near us. Now c'mon, Pybus, before I throw you in myself."

"The Spills are always near us," continued Linton, ignoring Billy. He spoke like he was the Prophet of Doom. "You just can't see them, that's all. They could be over there now, watching us from the trees."

They all turned and looked nervously across the river to the opposite bank, which suddenly looked very close.

"Who are the Spills?" I asked. The effect on the others was starting to make me feel nervous too and I knew nothing about these 'Spills'.

"They come from up there and they're right mean, tough kids," said Linton and he pointed with an extravagant gesture to the top of the hill across the river. Beyond the fields and standing on top of the hill were new blocks of flats, white concrete and about a dozen in number, rising out of the summer haze like some kind of space city from a science fiction comic.

"Says who?" said Billy scornfully.

"Says my dad," said Linton.

"Oh no," said Vic, "not your bloody dad again! He's not Dixon of Dock Green is he by any chance? He seems to know everything that's going on. The poor criminals must be terrified of him."

Linton carried on, ignoring Vic.

"He says they're all thieves, even the young ones. They're dead wary of them down at the station. He says they come from the slums in Manchester and there you have to be dead tough. They've been given new houses out here because their slums are falling down. All the people over this side are dead upset about it but there's nothing they can do, they're here now and they're not going back and there are hundreds of them. Up there. The overspill estate my dad calls it. Overspill from Manchester. That's why they're called the 'Spills'."

We all looked across the river to the top of the hill in silence. Billy was the first to speak.

"I ain't scared of no Spills," he said.

"Nor me," said Vic.

I said nothing because suddenly I had an uneasy feeling. Although we were having a good time and it was hot and it was the holidays, everything suddenly felt different. My sick feeling had gone but suddenly my head began to throb, and I shivered, as if a cold blast of air had blown across my bare skin. There was a moment of silence between us as we all thought our own thoughts, but that was broken by Billy.

"PYBUS WILL YOU GET ON THAT BLEEDING SWING " he shouted, so loudly and with such violence that we all jumped, and Pybus immediately wrapped his big red legs around the rope and prepared to push off.

The rest of us on each corner of his body, were ready to help swing him out into the middle of the river and we all yelled "CHARGE" as we launched him. Pybus screamed in abject terror as he passeed over the Ladybrook like some huge fleshy missile, and then he forgot to let go. Strangely, I thought of all the fish, the sticklebacks and the gudgeon, the tench and the dace, under the surface of the river looking up at the huge cloud that was Pybus swinging above them. To them it was probably like the atomic bomb about to go off. Out of the corner of my eye I could see Linton looking up at the branch of the old oak tree creaking and groaning under the weight of its passenger, but then the momentum was lost and Pybus came to a slow but inevitable halt, clinging for dear life to the rope and suspended several feet above the deepest pool. He was just hanging there, rolling slowly in a series of three hundred and sixty degree spins, red faced, half naked, the rolls of fat around his middle quivering with the effort of holding on. On the bank we were creased up with laughter, Vic was actually on the ground with his legs in the air he was laughing so much.

But then a noise from the other bank made us stop. Around us on our bank the air was still, the ambient sounds, the chirrups, the buzzes and the hums had ceased; even the birds have stopped their singing. But from the other side came the sounds of laughter, deep voices and swearing in heavy Manchester accents, and the cracking and snapping of wood breaking in the undergrowth. Then on a little sandbank across the river, and right behind the dangling Pybus, four lads appeared, about our ages or maybe a little older.

They stood there just looking, saying nothing, wearing unfriendly smiles and we stared back saying nothing either. I was nervous; these lads looked really tough. I heard Linton mutter under his breath, "Spills, I bloody knew it" and I could see Billy move slowly away from the bank. Pybus, meanwhile, still spinning around on the rope swing, only more slowly now, looked wild-eyed from one bank of the river to the other, as if he was watching a particularly nerve-racking game of tennis. All I could hear was the groan of the rope on the tree and my own breathing, shallow and wheezy.

Then *smack*. The smallest of the group threw the first stone and hit Pybus right in the middle of his naked back, and he squealed like a puppy, half in pain, half in terror. *Smack*. Another stone, this time on his leg.

"Oy!" I shouted, "Leave him alone!"

"Shurrup or you'll get some en all!" yelled back the smallest Spill and, as he said it, half a brick went whizzing past my head like a bullet.

"Pybus, I should let go of the rope or you're going to get killed," said Linton from behind the tree. Another hit, this time right on his big arse. There came a huge squeal from the victim and much laughter from the other side.

"You're too easy a target, yer fat bastard," shouted another Spill, this one much taller and thinner than his mate, but with a meaner look, and his pale face and neck covered in angry red spots.

"Let go of the rope you big dick," shouted Billy, from behind the same tree as Linton, but Pybus either couldn't or wouldn't hear us, stuck in the middle of this battle of stones and catcalls as he was. It was fear in slow motion for us but for our poor mate out there on the swing above the water, it must have been an eternity of terror.

"Cop that fat boy," said another Spill with red hair, his naked torso thin but muscled and white as marble, and he chucked a big black stone at the target. He caught Pybus right on the side of the head and there was a sickening hollow sound, like one beat on a drum, and then a thin but spectacular fountain of blood. Everyone stopped, the enemy as well, and gazed in awe at the trajectory of the blood as it spurted from his head down onto his chest and legs in bright red lines, like dripping paint.

And still he didn't let go of the swing.

But when he saw what had happened, the seriousness of his predicament, Pybus let out the most bloodcurdling shriek, like the cry of a wounded animal. It was a scream of pain and fear, but worse than that, it was a scream of abandonment that sent ice down my spine and a jagged spear into my own conscience.

I forgot my own dread of the Spills and waded into the river. By this time the missiles had ceased to fly: the Spills had their blood and now they were losing interest, but I still had to get Pybus safely back. I waded in chest deep across to him and clasped my puny white arms around his huge calves. Then in a voice that was not like my own I said, "Let go of the rope, I've got you."

To my surprise and relief he did let go but he was so heavy that in so doing we both fell headlong into the water. Spluttering and retching, we scrambled to the bank, where the other lads helped us ashore, which was just as well because by this time I was exhausted and Pybus was paralysed with pain and shock. At the top of the bank, however, he quickly regained his composure and stood mopping his cut head with his Man United shirt, still dripping but no longer crying. Billy had found his voice and was shouting promises of vengeance at the Spills, who had already disappeared back into the undergrowth from where they had come, laughing and crowing.

"Hey," said Linton, "Do you think if Pybus had been wearing his United shirt they would have left him alone? My dad says Spills are all Man U. fans because their slums were quite close to Old Trafford."

"Probably not," said Vic. "They're mad bastards that lot. You could have had Georgie Best on that swing; they still would have chucked stuff at him."

"No," said Billy who was seething with rage, his blue eyes narrowed and fists clenched and a lot more aggressive than he had been when the Spills were in view. "That lot don't care. Pybus was defenceless on that swing, but they didn't care. Well it's bloody war now!"

When I got home, mum and dad were arguing again. I sat in the lounge and ate my tea with our George, tomato sandwiches and a ring doughnut, which was my favourite, and tried to watch *Robin Hood*, which was the one where he and Little John entered the archery competition in disguise and won it (of course) with some great shooting. But it was hard to concentrate when I could hear the murmur of unhappy voices in the kitchen on the other side of the sliding door, waiting for one of them to suddenly shout or scream so as not to jump when it happened, but always getting caught out. I always jumped more than our George, which was annoying in itself. And then the voices, trying to regain some form of control, would hush again and Robin

Hood might get a word in. This argument though, on the evening of the day when I first met the Spills, was a 'baddun' and George and I couldn't help listening, Robin Hood forgotten, the sandwiches and doughnuts tasteless in our misery. It was all about being trapped and broke and no life and no fun and facing up to responsibility and family and it was more mum going on at dad, or so it seemed, until with a volume of shouts and swear-words dad got up and left the house, slamming the back door behind him. From the front window I saw him walk down the road, and even though I couldn't see his face, I could tell by the way he held his body that he was angry, and because there was something in the way that he left that frightened me, I myself got up and, without saying anything to our George or my mum, (Stevie and Sandra weren't in yet), I went after him.

He took the same route that Billy and I had taken earlier that day – down through the estate, out onto the wasteland and across the field down to the Ladybrook. And I followed him, although I didn't really want to, at a distance so he wouldn't see me and send me back. I tracked him all the way.

Everything had changed down at the river, even since this afternoon when we had all played in hot sunshine until the Spills had arrived. The heat was still there in the air, but the brightness had gone. In the sky, blue had been replaced by black. Huge lumbering rain-filled clouds circled slowly overhead like giant balloons ready to burst all over us and the river itself was brown and bubbly, still at this afternoon's level, but its flow was faster and more urgent, compared to its languid course earlier on.

I called out to my dad because I suddenly had an urge to tell him what had happened this afternoon in this very place, but when he turned around, even from twenty yards away, I could see the exasperation on his face. I reached him just as the rain came: huge great drops, intermittent at first, then growing more persistent. I saw one drop on his brown hair, fall slowly down his forehead and on to his cheek like a big tear. Then another and then another, making him blink.

"Go home, kid," he said not unkindly.

"But, Dad…"

"No arguments." His voice was suddenly sharper, not interested in any negotiation.

"Come home, Dad," I pleaded, "you'll get soaked."

"I'll be back, soon I promise. Now go on, beat it."

I looked at him, not moving, taking a chance. This time he shouted at me.

"GO HOME. Michael, for Christ's sake. Just leave me alone."

His voice crackled and his face distorted as he brought it almost to my level. I could see the raindrops on his skin and his pink scalp through his hair as he bent down to me, his face in mine. I could see that he had clenched his fists at his side. I saw the whiskers on his throat and his Adam's apple bursting through his skin.

And I saw something in his eyes, like a light coming through that wasn't his. I saw it although I didn't know what it was at the time.

Then I turned and started to run for home. I didn't look back, just ploughed head down into the rain towards the houses, small yellow lights, shimmering behind sodden windowpanes.

Up ahead, coming towards me out of the gloom from the direction of the houses, was a tall figure I didn't recognise and I momentarily braced myself to change direction.

Then I heard my brother's voice, deep-toned and concerned, carrying across the noise of the rain. "Is that you, our kid?"

"Stevie," I called out. "Stevie." And with relief I abandoned my escape plan and went to him.

"Are you alright, soft lad?" he said not unkindly. "Charging off like that and giving your mum a fright."

"I went after dad," I answered defensively.

"There's kids disappearing from all over Manchester and you're out here on a stormy night, chasing around like a mad dog."

"He was upset," I persisted. "I think they had another row."

"He's grown up enough to look after himself." He looked down at me his own hair sopping wet, tears of rain rolling down his cheeks.

"And you are still young enough to fall into the wrong hands. That's the truth of it."

I wasn't convinced of that, but I said nothing because I suddenly felt really tired. I just stood there quietly in the protective shadow of his big body, head bowed, half asleep.

I heard him say, "You look like a drowned rat, our kid," and I felt his strong arms grip under mine and then, like our coalman does when he lifts a sack of coal off his lorry, heave me around onto his back.

"Grip your arms around my neck," he said gruffly and he shuffled his weight to accommodate me. "You're getting heavier," he muttered as he set off towards the lights, "soon it'll be you carrying me."

Then with the smell of his soapy neck against my nose, and the touch of his soft wet hair against my eyes, I let him piggy-back me home.

Chapter 3

THE RAFT

That next morning found me in the kitchen with my mother and two of her friends, Mrs Robinson from number 38 and Mrs Williams from Wilmslow Road. She was having a break from the hoovering, and the three of them were sitting at the kitchen table drinking tea and smoking Gold Leaf cigarettes while Jim Reeves crooned to them about blue skies from a radio in the background. They were laughing and chatting about their friends and their husbands and their lives in general.

My dad was a changed man from the night before. It was almost as if his dash to the river in the rain, with me in pursuit, had never happened. He had muttered "sorry" to me (which he never did) for sending me back and that I was a good boy for sticking by him, but he and mum were talking normally and that was very unusual after an argument. Usually one or the other, or both together, sulked for days. He came through from the garage, where he was working on his old BSA motorbike, for a cup of tea and he grinned at the four of us sitting there, and ruffled my hair with his oily hand. He was in a good mood because it was his day off and he wasn't due back at work until early the next day. It was good to be near him when he was like that.

"Four old gossips together," he laughed, "and our Mike the biggest one of the lot," and the three women laughed too. I felt really happy to be in amongst them and treated like an adult, but most of all I was happy that they were talking again. It was horrible when they were fighting.

Then my dad went back out to his bike and the news came on the radio and they talked about Lesley Ann Downey, who had been missing since last Boxing Day, and how more kids had now disappeared, including a lad with glasses and another lad who had disappeared from a market over Ashton way. Then straight away the mood changed around our table, and the atmosphere turned solemn and sad and the women lowered their voices. My mother started to twist her hair around her forefinger, over and over, like a little girl would do. She had started that little habit a few months back when she had given up smoking for a short time and she twisted her hair to give her hands something to do, but now she was smoking again and she was still twisting her hair. I think she was slowly pulling it out because it definitely seemed thinner. I saw Jean Robinson giving her an odd look, like she knew something was not right.

Anyway, I knew when I was not wanted. They wanted to talk about the children and I was no longer included in the discussion so I took the hint and left the table. I had things to do anyway.

When my mother looked up from her conversation to see me with my jacket on she immediately said, "And where do you think you are going, young man?"

"Out with Billy," I answered her.

"Not too late please, and nowhere on your own."

"Ok Mum."

"And no lifts in any cars," I heard her say to me with a chorus of assent from her two friends as I ran out the door, finally free of her worrying.

We raced past the old oak tree, its spindly black branches still dripping last night's rain, and turned down the cinder track that led to the old farm. Almost overnight, it seemed, it had become yet another new housing estate; they had already dug out great big foundation holes, which were full of dirty brown water from the heavy rain, and beyond these man-made lakes there were new houses in various stages of development, quite a few of them covered in scaffolding. In the brief few days that we had spent at the river, a lot of the old farm buildings had disappeared. The cowsheds and the barns, in whose stalls and lofts we had played Japs and Commandos and hide and seek, were now mounds of rubble waiting to be cleared. Only the farmhouse was still standing; they hadn't got to that yet, and that morning we explored it for the last time.

The story went that the farmer had left several years before. He had once owned all the land around but had sold it off piece by piece to the building companies, who developed it as they went. As the farmer sold the furthest acres first, so they had built almost in a circular fashion, starting at the outer ring and then moving ever inwards until only the buildings remained. But this was the final phase. This was to be the showpiece of the whole estate, an enclave of detached homes, expensive and exclusive.

In the farmhouse we wandered through empty rooms covered in old peeling wallpaper, patterns of red roses on a light blue background or Roman temples in green pastoral landscapes, our small voices amplified in the hollow halls, shrieking and laughing, talking of ghosts and war and things in the cellar that murdered careless children. We climbed up the old wooden stairs to the bedrooms, little square box rooms where once the farmer and his family had slept, and I looked out of the small-paned window out over the new estates. That old farmer must once have looked out of that same window and seen all his own land, uninterrupted views of rural Cheshire, his cows grazing and his ewes giving birth to lambs and seen his crops waving in the westerly breeze. All I saw now, as I stood where he had once stood, was a land slowly being swallowed up. The country lanes and the honeysuckled pathways of his children's memories were streets and roads and crescents and closes, a matrix of loops and connections that made sense to older people, but not to crows or bees or children.

It was a sad place, the old farm, piece by piece of it disappearing as the days went by. I had asked my mum what happened to the old farmer and she told me that his wife died, his children left home and he got lonely looking after the animals all by himself. So he sold it all off and moved into a bungalow in Anglesey, quite near to where we sometimes go on our holidays actually, and he never had to worry about money again because the builders paid him loads of it for his very expensive land. She also said that he didn't have to worry about cold early mornings and cold late nights anymore and crops failing and animals getting sick and all that goes with being a farmer, but she thought he was probably sad and regretful just the same, although it was nice to be near the sea.

"Did you see those foundation holes full of water?" asked Billy.

"Yeah I saw them from the top of the farmhouse," I replied. "They looked deep."

"They looked pretty dangerous to me," said Linton in his doom and gloom voice.

"I'm not saying we should swim in them. Just have a look, that's all," reasoned Billy. "Come on. We can chuck stuff in them."

As we followed Billy, there were lots of kids of all ages engaging in a wide variety of activities, as if we were in a huge adventure playground and not on a supposedly secure building site. A group of older lads from over Queens Road way were gathered around a huge bonfire, big red flames against the charcoal-coloured clouds, the old wood from the buildings with lethal-looking nails curling in the heat and making loud cracks and hissing sounds. They let us stand around feeling the intense heat of it while they melted old roof felt back into liquid tar, stirring it in old paint pots with big sticks. Then we got our hands on it and with smaller sticks we let it drip onto the ground in shiny black patterns and waved them around like sparklers on bonfire night, forgetting that if we got it on our clothes there would be hell to pay.

As we walked past old pig sties, a gaggle of younger kids flew out screaming and shouting "RAT", half laughing half fearful, and, sure enough, right behind them a little Jack Russell emerged with a big, grey, very angry rat in its jaws. The rat was half the size of the dog and it was debatable whether the battle was over yet, although the dog seemed none too worried. The littluns were in a right state; one in particular, a lad of about eight wearing spectacles with one of the lenses blacked out.

"Tell your dog to piss off and stop following us," said the spectacled lad to his mate.

"What can I do?" said the lad in question, "we brought him down here for protection and that's what it thinks it's doing."

"That rat will eat your dog if he's not careful," said Billy.

"You wanna bet mate?" said the little kid, snot on his nose and holes in his jumper. He sniffed. "You just watch."

Sure enough, after more dodging, the dog, who by now had lost interest in his catch, sank his needle-like teeth deep into the rat's neck, and gave one vigorous shake of his head. The rat, in his death throes, gave one drawn out squeak and then fell limp and the dog took it away to eat it or bury it or whatever dogs do.

They had dug the new foundation holes for the next section of houses: big holes in the ground made by the bulldozers and the diggers, deeper than all of us there and filled almost to the brim with brown, deadly-looking water that had been topped up by last night's rain.

"They're going to have to drain that lot out," said Linton.

There was a gradual slope into the hole from where the bulldozer had emerged on the last day they had worked, and in the wet clay of the gradient, vivid scars had been made by the claws of the digger bucket and the caterpillar tracks of the machine. The clay smelt worse than cow muck even though no animals had been there and a few days ago, before they had dug it all out, it had been six feet under the surface.

The wind was blowing the water and it made a corrugated pattern on the brown, oily surface. To me it looked like a big lake, the coldest, most forbidding and unwelcoming lake there could ever be, and Billy and I walked carefully down that slope to look over it, like explorers gazing over an inland sea.

"It reminds me of Skegness," said Linton. "The water in that place is always the colour of cow shit."

"Let's make a raft," said Billy completely out of the blue.

"What for?" I said, not fancying the idea at all.

"To sail the seven seas," said Billy, like Francis Drake or Thomas Cook. "Will you look at that water, it looks just like the real sea. We could cross to the other side." He motioned to the far bank, which seemed like miles away but was in fact only about twenty yards across. Though far enough, if you're on a rickety old raft.

"We could make it easily," Billy went on, starting to like his own idea. "There's loads of wood. There are whole doors lying around for God's sake. We could nail them together. C'mon. Then we could sail across to the other side."

"It looks dangerous to me," said Linton. "You don't know how deep that water is for a start."

"It's as deep as a bloody foundation hole," Billy shouted back at Linton, losing patience at our lack of enthusiasm.

"Alright," I said. "Come on, Lint. Let's give it a go. We'll get the doors."

"I saw some nails and a hammer in one of those old cowsheds," said Billy. "I'll be back in a minute." And he shot off back up to the farm.

Linton and I carried two of the wooden doors, which had once belonged to the pig sties and had not yet ended up on the fires, down to the edge of the water.

After a while, Vic appeared over a mound of earth pulling his little cart, that he called a bogie, behind him and looking like some war refugee on a bombsite. He was looking very pleased with himself.

Billy returned with, not one hammer, but two and a whole load of other tools as well. His eyes went straight to Vic's cart. "Bloody Hell!" he exclaimed. "Look at all those bottles he's got. He's got a small fortune there, the jammy get."

In the passenger part of his bogie, where Vic normally sat when he was whizzing down some hill somewhere, were row upon row of empty corona bottles. All stacked neatly, end to end, were old lemonade bottles, cherryade, limeade, dandelion and burdoch and several of my favourites: American cream soda. All empty, all worth three pence each.

"Where did you find that lot, Vic?" asked Linton.

"I've been in every building, all over the site, and it's huge," said Vic, obviously flushed with the success of his venture. "You want to see it on the other side. Scaffolding's up all round the top floors and Joe Fenner and his mates are all leaping off it into the sandpit. They're mad that lot. And they started the dumper truck up. They got it stuck in the mud. The builders will go mad."

"How much is that lot worth then?" I asked him.

"About ten bob," came the proud reply.

"Look at them," said Billy, "there's concrete and shite all over them. Shops will never take them like that."

"I'll clean them up. Won't take long."

"They'll be after you, those builders," said Billy.

"They won't know."

"They will, when I tell them."

"You wouldn't," Vic persisted. "Anyway, they don't care. What's ten bob to them? They earn a fortune."

"What you going to do with the money?" Billy asked for all of us because we were all curious.

"I'm going to buy some pop."

"Yeah."

"And some bubble gum."

"Yeah."

"And some ciggies."

"You never will," said Linton.

"Yes I fookin' will," said Vic aggressively again.

"You want to steer clear of them. My dad says they'll kill you," said Linton.

"That's bollocks," said Vic. "My grandad started when he was nine and he's sixty four now. He says he's never felt better."

"Does he cough?" persisted Linton.

"Well yeah. Course he does, he's old. All old people cough."

"That'll be the fags, you mark my words," said Linton.

"Well thank you, Dr Kildare," said Vic, sneeringly. "I'll pass on your opinion to my grandad, shall I? He'll be cock-a-hoop with that, you sad get."

"Just saying," said Linton quietly under his breath.

"I'll have a smoke with you," said Billy, still on the original conversation. "What about you, Mike?"

"I'm not sure," I said.

"Count me out," said Linton.

"We already have," said Vic, with real scorn in his voice.

"C'mon, Mike. It'll be a laugh."

I was thinking about my mum, who would be really upset if I started, even though she smoked like a chimney herself.

"No," I said finally. "You go." I turned it into a joke to get them off my back. "I'm short enough as it is. I don't want to stunt my growth any more."

Thankfully that was enough and they left me alone.

"Please yourself," said Vic. "Anyway, I'm going up the parade to cash this lot in. Are you coming, Bill?"

"No. I'm going to finish this raft. If you get some, come and find me. I'll be down here."

"Alright, see you later," said Vic and he wandered off, one hand on the steering mechanism, which was a piece of old rope, towing his cargo carefully behind him over the undulating landscape. One of his wheels was squeaking but even that couldn't drown the cacophony of clinking that came from all the pop bottles.

"That back wheel of his is going to fall off," said Lint. "I'd better tell him."

"No. No. Leave it," said Billy with a grin. "He'll be alright. C'mon, let's get on with this raft."

We had found two oil drums, because Linton, who knew about these things, said that you needed them for the ballast. He couldn't explain why exactly, but he thought if we tied the doors to the two empty drums, the raft would float better than if we just tried to float the doors, especially if we were going to ride on it. I admired Linton for knowing all this stuff and not being bigheaded about it, but it still seemed to annoy Billy that he knew something that the rest of us did not. Luckily there were loads of empty drums around, some with their caps discarded nearby. Even Billy and I understood that it might be useful to have these drums watertight if we were going to float them on this treacherous sea. We sniffed long and hard the sweet aroma of paraffin coming out of the opening, and then, with light heads, placed the caps back into the hole. Mine was a tight squeeze and I had to bang it with my fist to get it back in.

Just then, right on cue, our kid appeared with his blond curls and 'butter wouldn't melt' look.

"What do you want?" I said in not a very welcoming manner.

"What's that?" he said, seeing the raft for the first time.

"It's the Loch Ness Monster's better half, what do you think it is?" I said.

"Never you mind," said Billy. "What do you want kid?"

"Mum says our Michael is to come for his tea."

"Alright," I said, "I'm coming. Now piss off."

"I'll tell Mum you're down here swearing. And you're making a boat."

"Listen, you little get, if you tell I'll batter you. This is nothing to do with you."

"C'mon," said Billy, "we'll all of us go for our teas and we'll meet back here in one hour. Then we'll do the big launch. Alright?"

There were nods of assent from Linton and me.

"Alright," we agreed.

"Nobody goes alone," said Billy. "We all wait for each other." He looked hard at us both. "Deal?!"

"Deal!" We all said in unison.

One hour later, I was on our homemade raft in the middle of a brown choppy sea that was the flooded foundation holes, and I was scared.

We had had our tea in front of the telly watching Richard the Lionheart fighting Saladin and his Saracen hordes. The tinned pears were alright but the main part was mince on toast and I hated that. Our mum did it because she was tired and it was easy, but to me it was not like a tea at all. We had to eat it quickly because my dad had just woken up and he was in a foul mood, and arguing with my mum about nothing as usual. His hair was all over the place and his eyes were like little cracks in his face and he was snarling to himself. He was always like this when he had had a drink at lunchtime and slept in the afternoon. He would be grumpy until he got out again in the evening. The trouble was all of us had to suffer. I wished Stevie would get home because I think my dad was a bit wary of our Stevie and he was not so argumentative when he was around, but Stevie was at the football, probably having a few pints after the game and he wouldn't be home for hours. Our Sandra was working in Timothy Whites in Manchester, but she was due home soon. Anyway I couldn't stand the bickering, the two of them going on and on, so as soon as I had scoffed my tea I headed for the door. Our kid was on at me again to tag along; he was just as sick of the arguing as I was, so surprising myself and him I said yes. I felt sorry for him, always stuck at home with these two and the look on his face was sheer pleasure, which made me feel guilty.

We went back to the building site and it was deserted. Everyone was still having their tea and we wandered down to the lake where our new raft sat at a tilt, the dirty brown water lapping at the oil drums underneath it. There was no sign of the others.

Suddenly I felt really for myself, and I had this overwhelming urge to sail the raft out into the middle of the lake and just sit there on my own away from everybody and everything. The water no longer looked dangerous, but welcoming; the wind had dropped, and it now looked more like a pond than a lake.

Our kid didn't want to help me launch it, moaning on about how dangerous it would be, and to wait for the others like I had promised. But we had been down at the lake for ages, and they probably weren't going to turn up now since it was getting dark, and by the morning it would probably be too late, because we'd be somewhere else. George was only nine and he was a weed, but I needed his help; I couldn't launch it on my own. So together we shifted the raft, oil drums and all, slowly down the little mud ramp that had suddenly became quite a convenient little causeway. What had started as a slow struggle, with the two of us straining to push the thing towards the edge of the water, suddenly became an uncontrollable rush, as the craft tipped over the edge of the muddy slope and hurtled downwards. With its own weight giving it the momentum to hit the lake at speed, it immediately reached a depth of water that would support it. I knew that if I didn't seize my moment, the raft would be out in the middle with nobody on board, and all our hard work wasted, so instinctively I leapt. There was a split second when I thought that I would miss it and fall flat on my face in the shallows, but I just managed to get enough of my body on to the old doors, on from my waist up with my legs hanging over the edge. My weight made it lurch in the water and rear up like a surfboard, but only for a moment and then all of me was on board, dragging myself up, and into the middle of the platform. I lay there panting, as if I had run across a field and not merely jumped on a raft. I heard my brother call to me from the side.

"Are you alright, our kid?"

But I just said quietly, not necessarily so that he could hear, "Go away will you." Just for my own satisfaction, that's all.

I lay on my back and looked up at the grey sky and thought about my mum and dad and while I did this the raft spun me around in a slow circular motion, as if I was in a gentle whirlpool, and as I circled so my anger went. The doors creaked on the drums, but whereas earlier I was nervous of the lake, now it was different. Not exactly brave all of a sudden but just that I didn't care too much either way; not in that moment, at least, when I was spinning quietly.

However, things were about to change. Something happened in the motion of my raft that gave me a clue. A sudden lurch as if it had run aground made me sit upright immediately, as if I had been shouted awake by some angry teacher. I was smack bang in the middle of the lake. Quickly I calculated that I was probably at the furthest most point from the edge, not far in real terms, probably only about ten yards, but in between my craft and the shore the muddy brown water was starting to look angry again. The wind was starting to get up and was blowing ripples across the surface, and as I had lain contemplating my family situation, the light had started to go. With it went my feeling of well-being. The raft had grown less stable and I kneeled in the middle of it, trying to keep level. It was starting to bob like a cork and I had to grip the edge because I was in serious danger of falling off the damn thing. Instead of it moving forward, it now refused to move anywhere except on the point of its own axis, that is to say, the raft was beginning to upend itself, taking me with it, only slowly in real time, but fast enough, when I seemed to be the only person left in the world. I thought about our kid. Where had he gone? I had told him to leave me alone, but this time he had taken me at my word. It was too embarrassing to think that I was going to have to yell for him to come and rescue me, but I was close to doing it. When the raft lurched again, I started to feel panic, the initial feeling of blood flowing quickly to my face, of going red and hot, and my voice turning dry, with the taste of metal inside.

I would bloody kill that Linton when I got hold of him, with his fancy ideas of ballast and weight. I'd give him oil drums. I looked around wildly, not daring to let go of the edge, my knees starting to hurt, and then I saw Billy standing there. He just stood watching me, with a nasty look on his face.

"You bastard!" he yelled by way of a greeting.

"Billy," I said, pleased to see him despite his obvious hostility. "Billy, I'm sinking."

"GOOD!" he screamed at me. "I hope you bleeding drown."

"Billy, I'm serious. This pile of shite is sinking. Help me."

"You cheat! We had a deal. Launch it together we said. Nobody goes alone."

"Billy. I'm sorry. I didn't think. It just sort of carried me off. Bloody Linton," I finished. I knew it wasn't really Linton's fault, but I was somehow trying to divert Billy's anger.

Billy turned to walk away.

"No!" I yelled after him. "Billy please. It's sinking and I can't swim. Fetch my dad, will you?"

"Fetch yer own bleedin' dad! You can fookin' drown for all I care!" He shouted this, without bothering to look back.

"If I drown it'll be your fault!" I yelled back at him, my words carrying across the grey water with a strange hollow tone. "Have that on your conscience." But he ignored all my pleas and stormed off up the muddy banks back up the building site, and again there was an eerie quiet around the lake, as the light faded into dusk. My imagination started to play tricks on me and I thought about the people who would one day occupy the show homes that would be built where I had drowned.

In my panic, as I lay spread-eagled on the pig sty doors like some waterborne sacrifice, I swore I would come back and haunt them; I'd come up through their posh floors and expensive carpets, covered in slime and moaning and groaning like the creature from the Black Lagoon. "Please God save me" I begged aloud rather than prayed, as the raft lurched and rolled, "I'm going to slip below this brown water with its oil painting stains of petrol dripping from the eight gallon drums and never be heard of again. Have mercy on me. Please, I'm only a kid," I implored him. But no saviour came.

To add to my woes there were other oil drums now appearing from nowhere, encircling me like mines around a lonely destroyer in the North Atlantic, and there were goosebumps on my naked white arms from the freezing bloody cold.

Then a rogue drum hit my raft and it wobbled and nearly capsized so I had to sit down to steady it and grip one of the handles still attached to one of the doors. The freezing water soaked straight through my trousers, and finally I started to cry.

Then, as I blubbed my first blub, thankfully no more than that, there came, striding over the horizon in wellington boots, with a raincoat over his old blue suit flapping in the bitter wind, my dad, with Billy gleefully following behind. If Billy had been angry that was nothing compared to how my dad looked as he strode across that building site. There was a look on his face that would break glass and if you could have seen him, well, you would not have swapped places with me for a million quid. I was about to be murdered.

He strode out to the middle of my mountainous sea, his pace slowing as the water rose to his knees, then to his waist and finally almost to his chest. Then he picked me off the raft and carried me back to the bank under his arm like a piece of carpet, and then dropped me so that I fell headlong onto the muddy ground. Then, without a word, my dad carried on, without breaking stride, up the cinder track to go home and change before returning to the pub, from where, I found out later, he had been summoned by my mother. I should have thought more about the inconvenience to him of being called away from his mates and his beer at the Railway Arms on his one precious night off, but I didn't. As I lay in the mud and watched him go back up the lane, my one overriding feeling was of relief. I had survived.

I lay there for a moment and then I got to my feet.

Billy just stood there looking at me. He had a sort of strange expression that I had not seen before but I didn't register it. I was too pleased with myself.

"Well, Billy boy," I said. "It looks like I got away with that. I suppose I owe you …"

But before I could finish, Billy's clenched fist came away from his body as if on a spring and socked me right on the chin. I fell straight back into the mud from where I had just got up.

"OWWW!" I yelled. "What was that for?" I moved to get up but Billy kneeled down and put his hand against my chest. He was stronger than me and he held me down easily. He motioned to smack me again and I winced, but he pulled his fist away at the last moment. Then he laughed, a mean, triumphant, in control sort of laugh. He bent his face almost right into mine, so that our foreheads glanced off each other and I could see the ice in his eyes and the curl in his lips. I could also smell tobacco on his breath.

"If you ever cross me again, I'll batter you black and blue. Your own mother wouldn't recognise you."

"It was only a raft, Billy."

He screamed in my face.

"YOU CHEATED ME! Now promise me you'll never do it again or I'll kill you I swear!"

I looked up at him, red faced, spittle on his lips, his tobacco smell starting to make me gag, and both fists clenched ready to start laying back into me.

"Alright. Alright. I promise," I said quickly, before he hit me again.

"Yeah. Then what?" said my brother Stevie, trying hard to undo his boot laces as he sat on his bed, a little the worse for wear after a day out with his mates watching Man United at Leeds. It had been a good result both on and off the pitch and he had carried his excitement home with him to the point where he had felt the need to tell me all about it. However, as soon as I woke up, I told him about my adventures with Billy and we had gone off track.

I told Stevie how I had wandered home muddy and cold and pissed off to get a telling off from our mother, who blamed me for having such a 'pathetic excuse for a father' (at least that was how she put it) and that "he could go to hell" for all she cared, she was sick of the lot of us.

"HAVE A BATH AND GO TO BED!" she shouted at me when I asked her for something to eat and I knew it was probably better to get out of her way, so I did as I was told. Our George was already asleep in his little box room because he's a bloody goody goody, and our Sandra was out with that weird boyfriend of hers, probably up at Alderley Edge doing black magic and dancing naked, which is what I think she liked to do in her spare time.

I continued the story of Billy and me and the raft.

"Well I promised him again. Then he got off me and let me go."

"Did you hit him?"

"No."

"Why the hell not?"

"He would have hit me back. Even harder. Besides, he's a mate."

47

"Some mate he is," said my brother. "He won't respect you if you don't have a go back. Even if you can't beat the bastard, you have to show you're not scared of him. Otherwise he will take endless liberties with you. He'll make your life hell. Take my word for it, kid. It's human nature."

"At school the teachers say that it's stronger to walk away. Don't retaliate, they say."

"That's a load of old crap. Bloody teachers, what do they know? They don't have to put up with it all. Listen, our kid. You get a reputation as somebody who won't fight and you'll have every man jack of them after you. You'll have little ones after you. You'll even have the girls after you. I tell you, if that happens, I'll batter you myself."

I laughed. He could always cheer me up, our kid. Even when he was being serious, it could come out as amusing.

"If you want, I'll give you some boxing lessons. Or I'll send you to train with Frankie O'Hara. He'll sort you out."

"I'm not a coward, Stevie," I said. "You know that, don't you?"

"Sure I do. How could a half-brother of mine be a yellow belly? No kid, I see you have plenty of courage; it's just knowing when to use it, that's the tricky bit. But you mark my words. This Billy lad thinks he has the edge on you. Sooner or later you are going to have to show him otherwise or he'll just dominate you."

"Billy and I are doing a milkround together tomorrow. I'm not going to fight with him and knacker that arrangement. I want to earn some money."

"Do it on your own."

"Mum won't let me. And his mum won't let him. They're scared we'll disappear into thin air like all those other kids if we go on our own. Especially in the middle of the night, which is about when we have to start. I have to get up in a couple of hours."

"Alright, fair enough," my brother finally conceded. "Just don't take any nonsense from him, that's all I say. In fact, don't take any nonsense from anybody no matter who they are."

"Alright Stevie," I said. "I promise. No more nonsense from anyone."

There was a moment of silence and I thought that he had fallen asleep but no such luck. He was in one of his storytelling moods and he had a lot to tell about his journey to Yorkshire that day to watch the football. I settled back down and listened in that half state between sleep and wakefulness.

My brother talked like they had been to war, slurring his words, half with the remnants of the booze that he had drunk, half with the excitement of recalling it. He told the story right from the beginning. From when they'd arrived at Leeds railway station a bit late after the main crowd had gone through, and he described how the four of them had approached the stadium. He could tell a story could our Stevie; he was a natural at building tension, I'll give him that. They were late and they moved quickly through the streets, coats done up tight to their necks, heavy boots clicking on the cobbled streets that ran to the ground. They walked off the pavements, just in the road, ready for the ambush that might come from the maze of alleyways and narrow streets of back to backs that lined their route. The streets were quiet, an eerie silence, occasional twitching curtains in lounge rooms, but no family yells from open hallways, no kids outside despite the good weather. The sun was warm on their bare heads, but there were cold gusts of wind blowing old bits of paper around. In Yorkshire, even late August days can cut you in two. It reminded my brother of those cowboy films where the four outlaws are walking down the main street and no townsfolk dare show their faces. They all knew that they looked a handy crowd, not to be messed with, and it felt good to be feared.

The match had already started and they could hear the noise now, coming in waves across the grey rooftops and down the narrow streets and that noise punctuated by deeper roars of near misses and then bursts of tribal chanting; their own United songs they recognised, which made them hurry. Stevie looked at his mates one by one and he could see their excitement, their eagerness to be there. The look on their faces, almost ecstatic in their anticipation.

Then they saw the ground, the old stands, years of history, the hated all-white colours of Leeds United, mortal enemies, not quite as bad as the Scousers, but close. They could hear the shouts of the programme sellers and the odd ticket tout, although this was a sell-out and most of the crowd had already gone in. There were just a few stragglers, like themselves, milling about and lots of coppers on the ground, relaxed now on the outside, talking and laughing amongst themselves. Then eight coppers on horseback, more tense than their colleagues, all in a row, red-faced from the cold were still watchful for trouble, great clumps of air from the horses' nostrils, the clinking of bridles, great piles of horseshit underneath and around them, some still steaming in the cold air, some dispersed by thousands of footsteps.

Across the road wafted the sweet smell of onions from the hotdog stands and they ate two each before they went in. The beer had started to wear off and hunger was taking its place, and it would be another hour or so at least before the fighting would start properly. Couldn't fight on an empty stomach.

"You see, our kid," Stevie told me, "the football is exciting, like. We love the team and we want them to win but the real excitement is not on the pitch. It's around it on the terrace steps and in the stands. It's not in the footballers and what they can do. It's in the armies and what we can do. It's standing crushed, shoulder to shoulder, skin to skin; you can smell their ale, their sweat, their piss because they piss where they stand, you know. Right there in the away end.

Then when we sing as one voice or we shout United, sometimes it feels like ten thousand have travelled from all over the country and we sing as one. Nobody misses a word, or a beat. That sends a tingle up your spine.

You know in that film *Zulu* when they are standing on the hillside and they are yelling and then they beat those drums. That's the feeling. The power of the noise. Fair puts a lump in your throat to hear that and see them respond from the other side.

Then when we score, the whole crowd moves like a gigantic wave down the terrace steps, and I tell you, if you fall, you're crushed under thousands of legs. Then it moves back in again. That crowd, when you see it on the telly, looks still. Well, I tell you, it never stops moving. It's like a great big sea of different people with a massive joined-up strength. When you come out at the end, it's like you've played the bleeding match yourself, you're that knackered.

There's more to come though. Sometimes fighting happens on the inside but that's usually just a skirmish. Some climb the fence and there's some rucking before the coppers get to you, but not much. Most of it happens outside.

We're leaving the ground and some of the kids that are there from Manchester, some not much older than you, are hanging off the upper tiers and jumping down onto our terrace, so keen are they to get outside into the Leeds lot. I see a big old sergeant; he looks like a grandad, but a tough one, and he's got six of these lads, about fourteen or fifteen years old, standing face up against the wall and he's giving them a rollicking. Then one by one he bangs their heads against the wall, they make a sort of slapping sound and the kids all swear and rub their heads then he sends them packing. But they're alright because they're outside and they know the fighting will start.

Outside there's lads from both sides running up and down and there's little battles all over the place. The horses are clattering up the cobbles. I see one copper on horseback and he's holding a lad up by his lapels, he's got him eye to eye, with the kid's feet about four feet off the ground. It looks funny and we all laugh, although he looks like one of ours. All you can hear is swearing, and dogs barking, and sirens going, and the crowd roaring and then suddenly we're fighting too and I've punched and I'm getting punched and this older guy, about forty he is, calls over, "Stand Reds stand" and we stand toe to toe and we take them on. They back off then come back for more, and we kick one whose gone down and more come at us and I punch some Yorkshire kid smack in the mouth and blood fills his face and he looks at me with shock in his eyes and he stands for a moment, and then goes down. Then from out of nowhere come five lads at least and kick him where he's fallen. Then do you know what happens?"

Stevie paused. He seemed to be reliving the action in the telling of it and he's breathless with exertion although he is sitting across from me on his own bed.

"Well I've seen this lad go down," he continued, "and I have seen the fear in his eyes and I can hear his cries of pain as he's getting kicked. Suddenly I don't feel so sure about what's happening."

"What do you mean?" I asked, beginning to think this story would never end.

"This kid was in the wrong place. What's so good about beating up someone who can't fight back?" he reasoned, "someone who's weaker than me. That doesn't make sense. So do you know what I did?"

"Go on, Stevie, what did you do?" I said

"I protected him. I pulled my lads off him one by one then picked him up and sent him up some side street where it was quiet so he could run off out of it. You should have heard my mates. They couldn't believe what I had done. 'What are yer doing, yer mad get?' they were saying. 'Have yer gone fooking soft in the head?'

I said he was just a kid, too weak and too scared. No pleasure in seeing that. And they just looked at me like I was mad. Then the fighting started again, and there were plenty of hard lads to have a go at, so that's what we did.

Then we are all down the train station to get a train back to Manchester and there are fights all over the platforms and lads down on the tracks. One nutter even jumps on the side of a train as it's pulling out and he's punching lads through the open window. He nearly doesn't get off because the lads on the inside have grabbed him and won't let go, and it looks for a while as if they're going to take him all the way back to Manchester stuck to the side of the train; but they chuck him off just as the platform runs out and he goes for a tumble. We're creased up, we are, at that."

"Stevie," I said, "I don't understand you sometimes. You like all the fighting and getting one over on the home fans. Then you go soft and let that kid go. No wonder your mates were confused."

"I was confused myself as to why I defended him. Then later on I realised. He reminded me of you. Same dopey look. Not really a fighter. Brave enough but not mean enough. Got himself into a scrape and suddenly realised he was in trouble. That's you all over, our kid. He could have been you. He needed a bit of help, a guardian angel if you like, and luckily he had me there. Some of the others I know would have stamped him into the cobbles and left him for dead."

"Are you sure you're cut out to be a football hooligan, Stevie?" I asked, a little put out that he regarded me as no good in a fight, "if you're going to let the enemy off the hook just because they remind you of me."

"Oh yeah, we have a great time when we travel away," he assured me. "It's not like I'm really there. It's like a dream while it's all going on. I should think it's the nearest thing to being in a proper battle when it's all going off. There's fear and confusion and then elation when you get through it. Nothing like it, our kid. That feeling of invading and winning then getting away with it. Surviving. Best feeling I've ever had. I'll take you with me one day when you've toughened up a bit."

Chapter 4

THE RED INDIAN MILKMAN

So at 5.00 am the next morning Billy and I stood outside the dairy waiting for the fleet of electric milk floats to leave. It was still dark and although there was a pink glow over the hills where the sun was waiting, the late summer air was cold and our breath was coming out in great bursts, like puffs of smoke from the factory chimneys. We were jumping up and down on the pavement like mad things, the nails in our boots screeching, and we beat our crossed arms against our chests like they made us do at school when the heating broke down.

We knew the milkman we wanted to work for. His name was Ben and he was a Red Indian. He looked like one too. He looked a bit like the pictures of Sitting Bull in the 'Look and Learn,' although his face was thinner and his hair still shiny and black as coal, if not as long. Ben had that same look that Chinamen can have, when it's hard to know what they're thinking about deep down. Instead of buckskins and feathers he wore the 'Hulme Fields Dairy' standard issue fawn coat, but not the peaked cap that went with it. He didn't look stern like an Indian usually does but then we thought it wouldn't be a good idea to get on the wrong side of him either as he moved with a certain cat-like grace and would probably be handy if it came to a fight. But we had heard from other lads who helped with the rounds that Ben was one of those that would let you drive the float as well as pay you a fair wage. All strictly against dairy rules but, provided you could take your chance with an Indian, it was worth a shout and, for him, the difference between a cushy job and a hard one.

54

So down the road away from the dairy so the bosses couldn't see us, we asked the Indian to take us on. He just looked at us and said "Climb aboard" in a deep, slightly American voice, as if he was welcoming us onto a boat. So we did, wondering exactly what we were getting into.

While it was still dark, and if the road was quiet, he let us drive the milk float; the high-pitched whooshing of the electric motor as we twisted and turned the big black steering wheel, negotiating a path through orange street-lit puddles and down potholed cinder tracks, the milk bottles clinking musically in their crates at the back. The Indian just sat there between us, the three of us in a line on the bench seat, the black leather cold and sticky on our legs, sometimes me steering, sometimes Billy, and when there were more people on the pavements and more cars on the road, mostly him. He smoked his small cigars and once he had shown us all the drops he went silent, half-closed his eyes and let Billy and me crunch up gravel driveways and stone stairways carrying goldtops, silvertops and bottles of sterilised for the poorer ones.

I'm not sure if we picked him or he picked us, but it was a good arrangement.

As we got to know Ben more, we realised that he didn't like talking very much but then Billy and I understood that. On all the films and the TV programmes, like *Wagon Train*, *Cheyenne* and *Bronco Lane*, the Indians never seemed to be the chatty types. Maybe if they were holding a pow wow with the white man they would talk because they had to, but you could just tell that it was not in their nature and that they would rather get on and do things. Even in the *Lone Ranger*, Tonto talked quite a lot and the Lone Ranger always asked for his opinion but he was still a man of action and would rather be riding his horse, Scout, and catching bad men than sitting around in saloons playing cards and drinking firewater. Not that the Lone Ranger did either but some of them, Rowdy Yates in *Rawhide*, or the boys in *Laramie*, were quite happy to drink a beer and kiss girls. As for little Joe in *Bonanza*, well he was girl mad!

We often talked about the Indian when we weren't with him and we discussed the very subject of grumpy Indians one wet morning sat against the sub-station wall in Moss Street. Linton, who read a lot of books, said the reason that Indians didn't say much was because they were always pissed off, on account of the fact that they were always losing to the white man whether they were in the right or not, and that was bound to get you down after a while.

Billy then chipped in with his thoughts, saying that the Red Indian was mostly in the wrong and that if he got half a chance would murder women and children in their beds sooner than look at them and until they could be civilised the white man was duty bound to keep them under the thumb. Then I piped up. I was more on Linton's side than Billy's.

"It wasn't that simple and the films and TV didn't always get it right," I said, "and maybe we should ask Ben more about it and how he felt, as a true American Indian always being on the losing side, albeit over a hundred years later and thousands of miles away in cold wet Manchester."

Which is what we planned to do the next time we worked for him on the following Saturday. We resumed the conversation in whispers as we delivered milk in the cold half-light down Cheadle Avenue.

"So first opportunity we'll ask him then," said Billy as he went into number thirty seven and I crossed into number thirty nine, which belonged to the parents of Christine MacNeill.

It was 6.00 am and there were lights on in a few of the houses but Chrissy's house was in darkness. I looked up at her bedroom and saw her yellow curtains still drawn tightly together and I tried to imagine her curled up asleep under her blankets breathing gently, with that half-smile she always had in the day time, still on her lips even in sleep. It was a strange comforting feeling, me out in the cold delivering milk to a girl I liked who would be unaware that I had stopped to kiss each of the silver tops of the four bottles as I placed them at her front door. She couldn't guess as she poured the milk onto her breakfast cereal that I, Michael Vincent Gibson, was solely responsible for getting a healthy calcium intake to her every morning, so that her legs would grow long and her teeth stay white, at least until she had children, and they started falling out.

"How should we put it exactly?" I said as we rejoined each other at the road, my mind still half on MacNeill.

"We'll just ask if the Indians were really as savage and cruel as they are in the films," said Billy with unusual patience. "He's bound to know what really happened. It's his own history. It's like us knowing about Francis Drake and Robin Hood; that's our history."

"Alright," I said, "but we'll have to pick our moment. We don't want to upset him or get kicked off the round."

I looked across to the float, where Ben was sitting waiting for us to get back. He didn't act in a mad or excitable way. He never shouted or even raised his voice slightly and he never hurried us. He just sat patiently looking straight ahead out of the smeary windscreen, looking with sad black eyes down the Stockport Road, all the way back to America.

One early Saturday morning a few weeks after the incident with the Spills at the rope swing, Billy and I were sat in the cab alongside Ben discussing revenge. We were down the end of Queens Road, and turning into the road that runs between the clothing factories and the river we called the Ladybrook. About halfway down, Ben stopped the float for no reason. This part of the river was not running through fields but through a large cutting populated by half-dead trees and thick thorny scrub, just before it went underground into a dark sinister tunnel. There was a powerful rumour that in the waters around the entrance there lived a big eel that could bite your hand off if you weren't careful. Many had tried to fish for it but with no success because not only was the eel vicious, it was also crafty. Needless to say, nobody, not even Spills, would paddle in this part of the river. When we told Ben about the eel he said that he was an Indian from the lakes of America and that he knew some good tricks for catching eels in particular and that one day, if we worked hard for him, he would show us a few in return.

The tunnel looked like the entrance to Hell itself, but was really just the start of another piece of river called the Mickerbrook, which finally ran into the River Mersey. Don't tell those Scousers but their precious river spends almost as much time in Manchester as it does in Liverpool.

The road we had stopped on was unpaved and its potholes were full of water like black treacle and for a moment Billy and I looked at one another, suddenly and uncomfortably aware that it was early morning, completely deserted and we didn't know the Indian from Adam. There was a silence like the one I get when I sit at the top of my tree looking a hundred feet down, a sudden fleeting feeling of being where I shouldn't be. Then the Indian spoke. We didn't need to find the right moment to ask him directly about his history because he was ready to tell us anyway. It just all came pouring out.

He spoke to us about America and about the place where he came from. A state called Massachusetts on the eastern side of the country, not very far from New York. At least not far in American terms, which is a land of great distances.

Ben told us that about two or three hundred years ago in America, there were only a few white men and that most of the country was still populated by numerous tribes of Native American Indians that had been there living more or less in peace, since as long as Man had walked the Earth. Forest tribes like the Chippewa, the Cherokee, the Iroquois, the Seminole, the Mohawks. Even the real warriors, the plains Indians like the Sioux, the Cheyenne, the Pawnee, the Blackfoot and the desert tribes like the Apache and the Commanche lived reasonably peaceful happy lives, although they did fight and raid each other occasionally. He said that even though back in England they were already building big cities filled with lots of houses and factories, and people went to work and children went to school, at the time America was still a young country and the Indians were able to do pretty much what they felt like, close to nature in a land that was not built on or exploited. But even in those happy times before the white man drove the Indians ever westwards with a mixture of bribes and threats and warlike actions, the tribes did occasionally fight amongst themselves and this could be pretty bloody since the Indian braves were brutal with their knives and tomahawks, not to say their bows and arrows. In the time of his great great-grandfather, Ben's own tribe had fallen out with his neighbours. The reason for this was their argument over fishing rights in the big lake that each tribe was camped at either end of. His tribe were called the Nipmucks and one day they went and fished at the top end of the lake, where the other tribe had their camp. The other tribe didn't like this and felt that their territory was being invaded, so the very next day their canoes came right down to the Nipmuck end of the lake to fish in full view of their camp, which of course the Nipmucks didn't like. To cut a long story short, relations broke down and inevitably whenever the tribes attempted to fish the lake at the same time, instead of catching any fish they would start fighting one another. The fish must have been laughing but the villagers on each side of the lake weren't because not only were they losing good men but they were going hungry as well. Clearly something had to be done to stop all the bloodshed.

"So what did they do?" Billy and I asked almost simultaneously. The Indian knew how to hold a story, that was for sure; he had us on the edge of our seats.

"Well," he continued, after pausing to suck on his cigar and blow a blue stream of smoke out, a bit like a smoke signal, "the elders from each tribe got together and called a pow wow, a big meeting, and they all sat around and smoked a big pipe of peace. Then after days of talking on how to resolve this very difficult situation they came up with a solution."

"Yes?" we urged him, impatient for his answer. "What did they decide?"

"The chiefs decided that my tribe, the Nipmucks, could only fish on our side of the lake and the other tribe, our enemies, could fish only on their side of the lake. And nobody could fish in the middle. Cha Ga Ga Garg Man ChaGa Garg Chabuna Gunga Marg."

"What?" we asked.

"It means, in the language of Nipmuck, you fish your side of the lake, we'll fish our side, and neither of us will fish in the middle." He recited the words again. "Chagagagargmanchagagargchabunagungamarg," it rolled off his tongue like a poem, "and to this day that is the name of the lake. It's in Massacheusetts, where I come from. It's one of the longest names in the world. So they say. I've got a picture of the sign somewhere," he felt inside his breast pocket and pulled out an old battered leather wallet.

"That's a good story, Ben," I said.

"It's the truth, kid, it's what they did. It's all come down through the generations."

"I tell you," said Billy, "if it had been me, I would have done it all different."

"What do you mean?" I said.

"Well if I had been chief, I would have gathered all my men. I would have armed them to the teeth. Then I would have sailed across the lake in the middle of the night when there was no moon and it was all misty, and I would have killed the other tribe, every last one of them, as they slept. That way I would have kept all the fish."

"That's interesting what you say," said Ben, still flicking through the folds of his wallet looking for his photo, "because that would have been my instinct had I lived back then, and I think a lot of them would have wanted to. Not just for the fish, you understand, but for the revenge of those who had been killed in the disputes. A Nipmuck, like any warrior, needs to have revenge."

"Maybe they were sick of all the killing," I said. "Maybe they thought there was plenty of fish for everyone."

"No," said Ben. "It was simpler than that. They wanted to stand together against the White Man. Even then they could see that he was their biggest enemy and that anything he said or did couldn't be trusted. No offence."

"None taken," we both said quickly.

There was a grunt of satisfaction from the Indian as he finally found his photo. He passed it to us and we held it carefully because it was old and tattered and we didn't want the thing to fall apart on us.

It was a picture of Ben looking much younger, about fourteen years old, a little older than we were at the time. He was standing next to an open-top car, an old Cadillac, he told us. He had one foot on the bumper and he was wearing a very bright red and blue checked shirt, like the lumberjacks wear. Beside him, and below because she was smaller, was a much older woman, with deep lines on her face and long black hair. In fact, she looked far more Red Indian than Ben did. She would have been beautiful once but her beauty had gone and had been replaced by a look of sadness and loss and, although she smiled for the photographer, her smile was thin and tired. In the picture, Ben was wrapping one protective arm around the woman's shoulder and with the other pointing dramatically up to the sign above him: Lake Chagagagargmancharggagargchabunagungamarg. An old wooden sign painted in brown stain with the letters in white, curved in an arc so as to fit the whole name in.

"Who is that lady with you, Ben?" ventured Billy and I gasped slightly at his bluntness, mindful that the Indian came across as very private and usually not that inclined to talk much to us.

But it appeared that he was in a mood for conversation.

"That was my mother. She was a full blood Indian, as you can see. She is a long way from me now. A long time ago." His voice was distant, like his thoughts, because he was thinking about her; that was obvious, even to us.

"What happened to her?" asked Billy trying to keep Ben talking. We were both curious to know his story.

"She died." He said this in barely a whisper but we both heard him alright.

"We're sorry, Ben," I said, "we really are and we understand if you don't want to talk about it."

"She died of a broken heart," he continued seemingly oblivious to our sympathy. "Just withered away like a sick animal."

There was a long silence and then I couldn't help myself.

"Why?" I whispered, Billy now quiet beside me.

"Because my father left her," his voice louder now, and angrier. "Left her suddenly, to return to his own land. Left her behind with three young children and no money. He left her to fend for herself and she couldn't do it. I was the eldest. I did my best but I was just your age. I couldn't make a difference. She pined away because she still loved him. Everyday she looked down the road that ran past that lake to see if he was coming back to her. And every day was the same; he never came back. Eventually she got sick and gave up hope. She died ten years ago when I was just seventeen."

"But why did you come to Manchester, Ben?" asked Billy. "If I lived in America I wouldn't want to leave it to come and live in this dump with the rain and the Spills and all that shite. The only good thing is the football but that's not enough to make up for it."

"Because right here is where my father came from," replied Ben. "Right here in Manchester, England. My father is the same as you two boys. He is a white man from Manchester."

"Jesus Christ," said Billy.

"I came here a couple of months back to try and find him, but he's harder to find than one of us. They say if an Indian doesn't want to be found then you won't find him, but for a white man he's pretty hard to track down also. It's taken me longer than I thought and I ran out of money so I've had to work. As you can see."

"What if he's not here?" I asked him.

"Then I'll move on."

"What will you say to him when you find him?" asked Billy.

"I will tell him what he did to his family. What he did to the woman who loved him. What he did to the children who loved him."

"Then what?"

Ben reached inside his checked coat, which he wore on cold mornings before the sun came up, and pulled from some sort of sheath an evil-looking knife. He obviously took good care of it because its five inch steel blade gleamed in the half-light of the cab. He held the bone handle lightly in his big brown fist. Billy and I tensed in our seats beside him and I felt the hairs on my arms go up.

"He gave me this knife when I was just a kid and I carry it everywhere. For an Indian from the lakes who is always fishing this is the best knife to have for gutting and disgorging. I always keep it sharp. It is a good knife. I keep it for your eel. Maybe I keep it for my father when I find him. Or maybe I will forgive him. It's hard to say."

All I could hear then in that float was the sound of our breathing, and the distant hum of machinery from the factories nearby.

I looked out of my side at the river and the tunnel below us. I was thinking about my own dad and how unhappy he always seemed to be, and how sometimes when they both thought we were all asleep my mum and dad promised each other in quiet, measured voices, not the screams and shouts we were used to, that as soon as George and I were old enough to stand it, that one or the other would leave home. Sometimes it was hard to measure just who would get out of the door first, such was their eagerness to be gone, and sometimes, in my stronger, angrier moments, I wished both of them would just piss off and leave us all to it. That wasn't often though. Mostly there was a nagging worry deep in my gut for days on end that one of them would keep their promise to the other, and go. Then things would go quiet again and I would stop worrying.

"C'mon," said Ben, breaking the spell, "we have to go and collect some unpaid bills. I need you to ride shotgun for me while I go inside the houses." He saw us hesitate. "I'll give you extra."

"OK by us," I said, nodding at Billy, and we both put our feet up on the black metal dash of the float and sat back as we always did when we had a bit of a ride between drops. That float was so smooth, and it was still so early that we could nod off if the ride was long enough, and today we both did. We must have been asleep for only a few minutes but when he stopped, the breaks squeaked, and we woke up to find ourselves amongst unfamiliar buildings.

For a moment we were disorientated and then a sick feeling came into the bottom of my stomach as I realised that Ben had driven us right into the heart of enemy territory. He hadn't told us what he was going to do but he had driven up the end of Queens Road, taken a sharp right into Brookfield Lane then headed a mile up, as if going to Stockport. Then he had turned right into the new overspill estate and, while we had slept like babies, had driven right down into the heart of it.

Even though we had never been inside the estate, we knew straight away where we were. We had imagined it often enough and we could convert in our brains an inverse of what we had seen from across the river. We were in the middle of those white blocks of flats, parked up by a big piece of grass covered in debris from last night's fun and games, oil drums and tyres, and the Indian was merrily checking to himself at which address he was going to start collecting the dairy's money from.

"Bloody hell," whispered Billy beside me. "Do you see where he has taken us? Only right into the Spills' back yard. If they see us here, we're done for."

I didn't answer him because there was nothing to say. All we could do was press ourselves into the back of the cab, away from the open doors, and keep quiet. These floats had no doors to close so we couldn't even lock ourselves in. Already, despite only being 9.00 am, there were kids about. The decision as to whether to cut and run had been made for us. We were going to have to stay put.

"What's up with you two?" said the Indian, sucking on one of his cheroots and blowing out a long thin stream of acrid blue smoke.

"How many houses to do here, Ben?" I asked.

"Why, are you in a hurry?"

"It's not that. It's just that this is unfriendly territory for us, isn't that right, Billy?"

Billy grunted, his eyes sweeping the open ground nervously.

Ben looked around and surveyed the landscape. "Yeah I heard that from the guys at the dairy." He grinned. "That's why I'm doing the collecting today. It's a favour. Man who normally does this is off sick with an ulcer so I said I'd help out. That's why I've got you two. While I'm in the houses you can ride shotgun on the float."

"Ben we may not be the best two to guard the float. These Spills

64

hate us. These are the animals we told you about. You know. Down at the river."

"If they catch us, they'll kill us, it's as simple as that," said Billy, a little dramatically, I thought. He was concentrating on a cluster of mean-eyed lads kicking a ball on a patch of green in between a couple of three storey blocks. They hadn't seen us yet, hadn't smelt us, but we were close to them.

"Don't worry," said Ben, "if anyone comes close just tell them I'm on my way. If they steal anything, just shout for me."

"We are going to get battered, I can feel it," muttered Billy, his head sinking into the collar of his windcheater like a human tortoise.

I turned back to him. "Have you recognised any of them yet?"

"Not yet," he said. "Maybe ours come from a different side of the estate."

"It won't make a difference. If any of them see us, they'll be over here. What are we going to do?"

"Dunno," said Billy grumpily. "Sit here and pray, is probably our best bet."

"Maybe we should just run for it," I ventured. "Leave the Indian to do his own bloody collecting."

"We wouldn't get ten yards," muttered Billy.

Then to our relief the Indian reappeared but it was only to collect his big collecting ledger. He opened it, and scanned down the page.

"Turpin Street. Numbers twenty three, twenty five and thirty one. They all owe. Back in a minute. Keep your eye on that lot," he indicated the lads on the grass, as he set off across the road.

We shrank even further back into the cab, if that was possible.

"He's bloody mental, that Indian," said Billy.

"They probably all are," I reasoned. "It's in their blood. If you've faced redcoats or the seventh Cavalry in your recent history, a bunch of Spills aren't going to bother you much, are they?"

"Look, keep your voice down," he hissed at me. "If we get out of this, I'm packing this job in today. I've had it with this bloke. Oh no. Look, here they come. We're done for."

I looked out and saw a group of lads walking over towards the float. There was no point huddling any lower in our seats like Billy was trying to do, because they had seen us and were on their way.

They came as a group and stood around the cab of the float, two on the driver's side, two on the passenger's side and one standing in the front, staring in through the windscreen as if he was inspecting something interesting in a shop window.

"Who the fook are youse two?" I heard one of them say. "You're not from round here, are yer?"

"We're with the milkman," I said cursing my own posh-sounding voice. "He's back in a minute."

"Is he now," said another Spill, round-faced and with black curly hair. "He ain't here now though, is he?" And he leant to the side and pulled a silvertop from the crates behind us. He flipped the top with his thumb and started to drink from it, head back Adam's apple jumping, dribbles of white milk escaping down his chin. I thought he was going to finish the bottle but he emptied the dregs out onto the road, making a vivid white splash, almost like paint, onto the tarmac.

"You owe us for that," said Billy, bravely I thought. "A pint will cost 1s and 2d."

"Fook off!" said the milky Spill with real menace. "Make me pay."

"It's alright," I said quickly. "That one is free. Have that one on us."

The one who had been looking through the windscreen came round to the back and helped himself to a goldtop. He flipped it over and put the neck to his mouth, took one gulp and spat out the creamy contents in a rush. "Ugh," he growled, "that tastes like piss," and he poured the rest of the milk, like a white cascade, onto the tarmac. I felt my heart pounding in my chest and I wanted to run but I couldn't leave the Indian's milk to these animals.

"Look," I almost pleaded, "you've had your fun. The Indian will be back in a minute. He's going to be really upset."

"Indian? What Indian?" said the big Spill who had taken the goldtop.

"The Red Indian," said Billy. Then, seeing the Spills still looking puzzled, "the milkman. He's a Red Indian and he's not to be messed with."

All five Spills stood silently for a second then burst out laughing.

Then the silvertop Spill walked to a crate of sterilised, and pulled one out by its long neck.

"This is what I think of your Indian," he said and he flipped the bottle up into the air, and as it came down in a series of perfect turns, instead of catching it he let it fall. It hit the road with a dull clink and the glass broke, and it splattered its contents in a wide, white puddle.

"Billy," I said in a raw voice, "go and find Ben. Quick." And he leapt out of the cab and shot off in the direction of the flats.

They were all doing it now, lobbing bottles into the air and watching them fall with a cacophony of breaking glass and the whoosh of splashing milk, and the road began to resemble a river of white milk. Then they found the bottles of orange juice in the little cold box at the back and the white river developed whirlpools of pasteurised orange. I could not believe how little they cared. If anything the glass and the milk and the orange juice seemed to fascinate them and urge them on. The noise attracted more people, the older Spills stayed across the road, the younger ones ventured nearer. Then after what seemed like hours, Billy returned with Ben beside him and when eventually the Spills saw him, standing quietly as if politely waiting for them to finish their destruction, they did stop and looked him up and down with scornful, uncaring grins.

"You kids all owe me a lot of money for the fun you've had," said the Indian in a slow, deliberate, dangerous voice. "Pay up and we'll forget all about it."

The round-faced, curly-haired one called Paul sniggered. "Are you this Indian these two have been whining on about. You don't look much of an Indian to me. Where's your tomahawk then?"

"Pay up," said Ben, "or I'll call the police."

All five of them laughed again. "Coppers won't come up here," said Silvertop. The last ones that did walked home, which is what youse three are going to do."

"Pay up," said Ben again, still in a quiet voice.

"Fook off," said Goldtop, the biggest of the Spills. "Make us pay," and he turned and grinned at his mates, who grinned back at him relishing the tension of the situation. "Go on, Indian, make us pay. Make us, and see what happens."

"OK. You give me no choice," said Ben. He reached deep into his coat and pulled out the knife. The knife looked even bigger now than it had done a couple of hours earlier, no longer just a fish knife, but with a blade that looked like it could kill a bear or skin a buffalo. Only then did I think it strange that he had carried it with him all this way.

"Pay up," said Ben again in a voice that had suddenly changed, that chilled, to the very core of everyone there, and not just the Spills. "Pay up or I'll cut your hearts out, you dogs."

The atmosphere had changed again and even the Spills realised that this milkman meant business and that they may have bitten off more than they could chew.

"You," said Ben, talking directly to Goldtop, the leader and the one who did all the talking. "You pay me for this shit you caused." It was strange, the angrier Ben got, the more he started to sound like a real Indian. The Spills were nervous now and suddenly I felt a bit better.

"What with, Mister?" whined Goldtop? "We ain't got no money, have we lads," and he looked round to his four mates watching the situation unfold with flickering eyes and twitchy mouths.

"Have we, lads?" he said again.

"No we haven't," they said in chorus.

Ben looked them all slowly up and down and placed the knife back in his jacket. "Alright," he said, "we'll forget about the money," and the Spills, all five of them, relaxed. I never thought I would see it, but this lot were visibly relieved.

"But next time," said Ben, "the next time that I come into your territory, you respect me and my property and my friends. He nodded over at us when he said this. "Alright Ben," I said softly under my breath, "don't push it, let's just go shall we?"

"Do you all understand me?" he said to the Spills, and I thought any minute they would jump him, knife or no knife. I could see the big one contemplating it. He had lost face in front of his little troop and he wanted to make amends. But that crafty Indian had noticed it too and he slowly took out the blade from its sheath again and ran the cold steel just once over the palm of his hand and said, "Do you understand?"

That was enough for them and they started to wander off, not in haste, but quicker than a Spill would normally depart from a scene of conflict.

Ben then turned to us, still deadly serious, and said, "C'mon, let's go."

"What about all this mess," said Billy, indicating the river of milk and orange staining the road.

"Forget all that," said Ben sharply, we need to get off this estate. I pulled a knife on those creeps. I'm hoping they'll forget about it, but if they tell the police, I'll be in the jail, and that's a fact." Then, as we drove off that overspill estate and back to the factories and the river, feeling more relieved the further we went, Ben said "What is it with you damn white men? You're always causing trouble, always in the faces of decent folk. And guess what," his anger returning momentarily, "you cause it in other men's lands and you cause it in your own."

Back at the river we sat, the three of us together in the cab, Billy jabbering away about the revenge he was going to have on "those fookin Spills" while the Indian started to fiddle with a bit of fishing line. Then he took out a little plastic box from his dairy coat pocket and opened it. Inside there was an array of fishing hooks, all different sizes and all with different coloured feathers and floats attached. He took out the biggest, a mean-looking copper-coloured barb with a vicious-looking point on it, and attached it to the line. Then he turned to us and said out of the blue, as if the previous conversation hadn't existed.

"Right, let's go and catch that eel of yours."

"What now?" I said. "Shouldn't you be getting back to the dairy? They'll be waiting for you."

"Let them wait," growled the Indian. He sniffed the air. "Today is a good day to fish."

He said this in a voice that expected to be obeyed and neither of us dared challenge him further; for now it was best to do what he said.

We all climbed from the float, went through the hole in the fence and scrambled down the bank, over roots and leaves, to the black river below. Suddenly Billy and I were following the Indian through the undergrowth, along narrow unexplored tracks, and we struggled to keep up with him. He seemed to know where he was going, as if he had been these ways before, and he trotted along like you would expect an Indian to. He made no sound, his footfalls light on the ground, and he disturbed no branches or trees that crossed his path, unlike Billy and me, who were crashing along behind him. All around were the sharp smells of mulch, crushed, saturated leaves and green shrubs that saw only weak light at best. It was overcast, and the morning light was grey and heavy, and down to our left as we followed the path, the Ladybrook seemed to flow slowly, black soupy water, opaque and malevolent; it was hard to see how anything could live in that river, never mind something as large and as voracious as the eel but too many people had seen it and talked about it for it not to be true.

Then the path dipped down to the water, and he shushed us with a wave of his hand and squatted on his haunches on a piece of bank that jutted out like a small promontory into a shallow pool. There was still nothing to be seen under the surface. Away to our right, about twenty yards downstream, was the big black tunnel into which the river disappeared like a snake into its hole, like the entrance into Hell. It made me shudder to look at it but I knew that one day we would explore it as far as we dared. He then dangled his piece of line, with its great evil hook on the end, down into the black pool, and it broke the surface and disappeared immediately, as if sinking into tar. The other end of the line he dangled around his thick brown fingers, twisting and twisting it so as not to let it slip should he get a strike, the line, even with no pressure on it yet, digging creases into his skin. Then the three of us waited for the eel to come. It didn't take long, just a few minutes, that's all, so maybe the Indian had a feel for it, like he said.

Suddenly there was a big tug on the line and it moved through Ben's fingers, tearing the skin. "Sonovabitch," we heard him say for the first time ever. That was a good swear word, I thought, and made a mental note of it. "Sonovabitch," he said again as the line went some more. To my side I could see Billy with a big grin on his face, enjoying the spectacle of the Indian being tugged along by this monster eel. The wire was cutting in more and we could see blood oozing through his fingers and the strength of it was taking Ben along the river bank and into the tunnel.

"Ben, what shall we do?" I called as the eel pulled him along the bank of the Ladybrook.

He turned and grinned, the tree's dappled light making patterns on his broad-boned face. "Do nothing," he said, "just watch what I do. Fishing is in my blood. I am an Indian from the lakes."

"Bloody hell," said Billy, "that eel is dragging him into the tunnel. Who knows where he could end up?"

"Linton said that tunnel goes to Liverpool," I said. "He wouldn't want to end up there."

His legs strained against the pull of the fish and his arms bent backwards and forwards, as if he was chopping at a root with an axe, and still that eel wouldn't stop. He was half way into the tunnel now, a silvery shadow against the blackness, and his voice, as he disappeared into the depth of it, turned hollow, then into an echo, his curses rolling back along the old brickwork as he went deeper in. I heard the language of the Nipmuck tribe as his words turned to rumbles, then to just the occasional murmurs, and finally to silence.

Billy and I waited and waited.

"Should we go in after him?" I said.

"Have you seen the time?" said Billy. "We have to go. Anyway, I'm not going in that tunnel with a mad Indian and an even madder eel. I want to live."

"What if the eel has him or has dragged him in?" I said. "We should at least tell someone."

Billy laughed. "Look, you've heard him and seen him with those Spills. That bloody Indian can look after himself and no mistake. Who knows, maybe that thing will drag him all the way out the other side and back to America, because that's where he should be. He doesn't belong here amongst all the houses. As soon as he has found his father, and hopefully not killed him, he needs to get back over there. He needs to be out in the forests and the rivers, not doing a stupid milkround in Manchester for Christ's sake.

"I don't think we should work with him for a while," I said. "Lie low, until the heat dies down. What do you say?"

"That suits me fine," said Billy.

We went back to the brook and the tunnel the next day and the milk float had gone. We went through the hole in the fence and slid down the bank to peer from a distance into the tunnel and called for him a couple of times, I don't know why because either way we knew he wasn't there. No sign of a line or bits of eel either. We had to assume that Ben had managed to untangle the line from his fingers and release the eel and that the bloody thing was alive and well and still lurking in the depths of the Ladybrook. I was relieved. I hadn't wanted any harm to befall the Indian. He had been good to Billy and me, despite his history. But we were keen to avoid him now and every time we saw a milk float appear we would duck down and hide and look carefully in the cab to see if the Indian was driving it, but he never was. We never saw him again and neither of us was sad about that, and although I had less money saved than I had hoped for, at least Billy and I weren't at the bottom of the Ladybrook with our hearts cut out, which could have happened if we had inadvertently got on the wrong side of him.

What the Indian had done for Billy, if not so much for me, was to rekindle the desire for revenge against the Spills that had dwindled in recent weeks. Seeing them almost cowering at Ben's anger over the incident with the spilt milk had given Billy renewed confidence that a battle could be won. A battle won against the Spills would bring huge kudos to Billy, and he realised that. As we left the tunnel that day and trotted home for some food, his mind was already hatching plots for a guerrilla strike into enemy territory. The next stage would be to recruit an army.

Chapter 5

REVENGE

All year round the Spills frequented the big gravel pit about half a mile the other side of the Ladybrook, beyond the top of the hill. That summer, according to local intelligence and rumour, they could be found most days swimming in the big lake at the bottom of the pit, at least when there were no workmen around. The quarry had been used for years to supply aggregate for the huge building schemes that had transformed rural Cheshire into the urban sprawl that was now the South Manchester suburbs. A while back, before the Spills had invaded, my dad had taken me up there on the back of his motorbike to have a look at the great gaping hole that we had heard so much about, me clinging onto his waist as he throttled up and down, taking the bends in the road expertly, the two of us leaning right over. My mother would have screamed if she could have seen us riding like that, but I felt so happy that day, my cheek against his white cotton shirt, smelling his smell, cigarettes and motorcycle oil, so close to be almost part of him. The wind tore at my hair and froze my teeth to my lips and the sun glinted off the silver petrol tank, and I could hear my dad above the roar of the engine whooping and yelling in his joy at being free. We got to the top of the road overlooking the quarry and stared down into it for what seemed like ages, then we got back on the bike and he took me to the pub and we sat outside, and he had a pint and I had a glass of Tizer, and then we rode home again. I would have done that every day if we could have, just ride the bike around with no interference from anybody.

The quarry was on the Spills' side of the river and therefore, for us, in extremely dangerous territory, but to venture up there was seen by some, especially Billy, not only as a test of bravado but, more importantly, as an opportunity for a surprise attack.

The latest encounter with the Spills and the Red Indian milkman had fired him up on two counts. One, the need for revenge generally, which Billy carried with him like the rest of us carried worries and cares, and secondly, seeing the previously indomitable Spills cowering, temporarily at least, at the ferocity of the milkman and his hunting knife. This had been enough to motivate Billy Skinner again.

His plan, like all good plans, was simple. Simple but inept as it turned out, but we had liked it at the time because its basic premise had been to make a guerrilla raid against the Spills, but without having to look them directly in their mean little eyes.

We gathered on a hot Sunday afternoon in late August just down from the rope swing, at a crossing point of shallower water. There were twelve of us. We had gained some recruits because those who had heard the plan had reckoned it failsafe and an ideal opportunity to win themselves a little credibility with their mates this side of the Ladybrook.

As we crossed the river and walked single file, Indian style, up the hill through the long grass towards the quarry, some of our lads were laughing and making jokes and I had to keep shushing them to take it seriously or face being ambushed ourselves. But they didn't really go quiet until Billy himself, at the head of the line, raised his hand and yelled in a whisper for everyone to "Shut up. We're at the quarry."

When he had everybody's attention he whispered again, "We're at the quarry, I can hear the Spills down there," and it was only then that our new recruits realised that they were half a mile into Spills territory. Then I could see their legs visibly buckle as they started to sink to the ground for the final approach to the lip of the gravel pit.

As we crawled up to the edge it was like approaching an active volcano, such was the nervousness that had engulfed us all, and it was twelve pale faces that peered over the side of the abyss down onto the Spills below.

There must have been about a hundred of them down there, mainly lads but a few girls as well, and a lot of them were swimming up and down and jumping in and out of the stagnant-looking quarry lake. Others were perched around the side on boulders lobbing stones or just sitting around. It could have been a scene from a holiday camp but instead of white and blues and shimmering sunlight there were browns and greys and a sinister murky feel where the sun couldn't reach. Each and every one of those little dots, whom we knew to be dangerous Spills, seemed to be having a whale of a time, shouting and screaming and sliding, their cries distant and hollow rising up from the bowels of the earth. They were like ants suddenly revealed in a cross section of broken ground, busy in their own little world, oblivious to the people above, uncaring and uncared for.

Then Billy stood up at the edge of the hole where we all were, on the side where the deepest slope was, and he shouted – no screamed – down at them.

"Hey you, yer fookin Spills," he screeched, "look up here. Look up here, you bastards. Go on, get back to your slums," and then he lobbed a great big hunk of clay down into the pit and it clattered harmlessly against the gravel scree that gave the quarry its curved base. Then we all stood up and shouted. The worst words, the most insulting we could find, not in any order, just an incomprehensible high-pitched barrage of verbal abuse, and to accompany our evil words we lobbed all the muck and clay and rocks, that lay at our feet, down at the enemy in an arc of debris.

When we ceased our hysterical throwing to survey what effect we were having, every Spill in that quarry had stopped what they were doing and were staring up at us. There was a second of silence as each side weighed up the situation. I had been worried that we were so high up, that nobody in the quarry would have realised they were being attacked, but when I heard their roars, their growls of anger, and saw them grab discarded shirts and shoes and start to run up the sides of the quarry in mad pursuit, that particular fear lay dispelled. Other fears would soon replace it. The ants' nest had become a hornets' nest and in opening it right up, we acted accordingly. After staring initially immobile with wonder at the rage we had unleashed, Billy shouted, "Let's go," and, laughing hysterically with fear and joy, we turned and ran back down the hill towards the river.

I have to admit that none of us expected the Spills to chase as hard as they did that day. We didn't expect them to leave their quarry, but they did, scrambling up the loose sides on all fours like mad monkeys, and we didn't expect them to chase down the hill after us, but they did. We sped out of their territory, barely pausing at the river, splashing across through ice-cold water and into our own territory, still enjoying the chase, still confident.

On our side we finally stopped to catch our breath, shoulders heaving, a couple of the boys, like Pybus, bent double with exertion, red sweaty faces, laughing as we looked back up the hill behind us.

There must have been about forty of them still coming. We could hear their shouts and the swearing getting louder as they came from a safe distance into what seemed a more serious proximity. Occasionally one of them would bend down to lift a missile and hurl it uselessly in our direction but the main group didn't even bother with that. They were intent on coming after us.

About half of our number had already run for it to the four corners of the estates, maybe even up to Cheadle, and the six remaining, the five of us and a lad called Kenny from Queens Road, stood a hundred yards up from the river, on our own side but suddenly feeling far from safe.

"Look at that," said Vic, "there's hundreds of them."

"What are we going to do?" said Pybus, hardly able to get the words out. He was about done in.

"Pray," said Vic.

"They won't cross the river," said Billy, sounding confident.

"Do you want to bet on that?" said Linton. "I told you these were nutters. My dad is going to kill me if they come over here."

"That lot aren't going to let a little strip of water stop them," I said.

It seemed obvious to me, why not to Billy? I could see a pack of them chasing and strangely in the lead was a girl, a blonde-haired girl who was shouting as much as the rest of them. They were closer now and their contorted faces less of a blur, their promises of what they were going to do to us when they caught up more audible.

It sent a chill through my heart, I can tell you, and Linton's too, because it was at this point that he fled, saying as he ran, "What are you lot waiting for, for Christ's sake? They won't give up, those Spills. Not now they can see us." Then he was gone.

Kenny went too, following Linton up the hill, his freckly white legs, in baggy khaki shorts, pumping like a traction engine. I would have laughed if I hadn't been so scared. I knew we should probably have gone then as well, but we delayed. I don't know why.

Now only four, we stood as a group, shivering, wet with sweat and river water, waiting and hoping that the Spills would stay on their side as they had done at the rope swing, waiting for them to give up the chase.

This time it was different. They stopped at the bank alright but then, as they shouted and leapt up and down, and just as we were starting to relax a bit, that same girl with the mop of white hair walked from out of her gang and started slowly down the bank and into the river. As she walked she said nothing, just steadily waded through the water and up onto our side.

"What the bloody hell does she think she's doing?" spluttered Billy, in total disbelief, while the rest of us just stood open-mouthed, mute with fear.

Now on our side of the river, the girl, like some kind of Viking tribal leader, turned to her troops on the other side and raised her arm.

"C'mon then!" she yelled back at them. "It's no different over here. Let's get these posh kids."

Then she turned to us, standing, as we were, fifty yards away, like a small flock of trembling sheep waiting for the wolves, and she called out to us with real menace.

"I'd start running if I were you. If we catch you you're dead."

Then, as if in a stampede, they came running through the water, a crashing, roaring wave of about forty kids surrounded by spumes of displaced water, millions of droplets glinting in the sunshine, glorifying their charge. That image of them coming across the river would stay with me forever, to be recalled on those odd occasions when I wondered how it was to be outnumbered in a real battle, or overwhelmed by an unexpected power.

"Jesus H. Christ," I heard Vic say as he turned and legged it up Grange Avenue, followed closely by the rest of us, except Pybus. I heard his familiar whimper and I knew he would be the first of us to be swallowed up by the raging tide of Spills who were behind us, but I didn't care.

"I think we should split up," Billy said between great pants of breath, "every man for himself. Look, I might head up to Cheadle, but don't follow me."

"SHUT UP. You don't own the fooking road!" screamed Vic back to Billy. "I'll go where I please. It's you that got us into this mess, with your bloody revenge. I swear to God, if we get out of this, Skinner, you and me are finished. I swear on my mother's grave."

Vic always said this even though his mother was alive and kicking and was, God willing, a long way from meeting her maker.

"They've got Pybus!" I shouted. I could see the big lump forty yards behind us, swallowed up by the leading group. He went down under a hail of slaps from the pursuing pack, his hands over his ears and his red Man U. shirt sticking tight to his shuddering body.

"Forget Pybus," said Billy, "they don't want him, they won't bother with him much."

"Yeah I know, it's us they're after," Vic said, real scorn in his voice, "and they'll get us 'n'all thanks to you, you big dick."

"Look, shut up arguing, you two," I said, trying to think as we ran. "We've got a choice, as I see it. We either keep running up to Cheadle and further if necessary, and try and outrun them, or we swing back down some alleyways and hide up at home."

"I say we head back to our houses," said Billy.

"Are you fooking kidding?" screamed Vic. "I don't believe you. This lot don't care about older people. They're just as likely to beat up the old folks as us. They'd even go for dads."

"Not my dad," said Billy. "My dad would batter them."

"Well go home to your dad then. I'm not taking them anywhere near my house."

By this time we had gone three hundred yards up Grange Avenue and had turned into Queens Road and they were gaining all the time. All I could hear was the sound of our rasping breaths as we ran and the shouts and curses getting louder from behind. I could still see that bloody girl heading the pack. Suddenly, without warning, Billy sprinted off to the left, through the little cutting that went by the primary school. He was heading out of our area towards the railway. Some of the chasing pack peeled off and went after Billy, but the girl and her group stayed with me and Vic.

"Every man for himself!" he yelled back at us. "We'll meet up later."

"Not if we see you first!" shouted back Vic, his anger at Billy diluted now by real concern for his own fate. "God, Mike, what should we do? I never thought they'd come this far up."

As we had been running, I had also been thinking.

"Vic, I've had an idea" I told him. "I think we should head down to those new houses at the back of the old farm. I know it's a cul-de-sac, but we can lose them down there and maybe get out through a back garden."

"I can't run much further," gasped Vic. "I'll try anything. I'm so fagged out that in a minute I'll just lie down and take a kicking, just to get it over with."

"C'mon," I said, "let's try the farm," and we turned down the old cinder track that led down to the building site. For a few sweet, wonderful moments the Spills were out of sight and it was like being free again. We crunched over the cinder and into the half-finished estate, the final stages of the building work about to begin. By going down the track we were effectively cutting off our escape route to the north, but I hoped that the Spills would ignore it and keep going after Billy. With luck they would catch him too. I looked across to where the farm buildings had been and saw that new houses were going up in their place. The foundation holes, which only a few weeks ago had been a lake where I'd sailed the raft, were now covered in two storey detached buildings, bricks already laid to the second floor and unrecognisable as the wasteland it was before. They had also chopped the orchard down, every last tree, with just some of the stumps left poking over the long grass, and that made me sad because the tree I had climbed a hundred times had come down too. I imagined climbing it to escape the Spills, just hiding in the topmost branches until they went through but that was not possible now. I remember thinking, as we rushed through, that the new people coming into these houses might have liked an orchard in their back gardens, to pick the fruit which had been good for years and to climb the trees for a bit of peace and quiet.

Further down the old farm track that once led to the fields lay part of the estate that had been completed and was already half occupied. As we came off cinder and onto newly built pavement, a more civilised, safer atmosphere greeted us. There were people around, new homeowners, and their houses appeared big and expensive-looking. Already some of the gardens had been landscaped and these newcomers were doing normal Sunday afternoon suburban chores, like sweeping drives and washing cars, talking in sociable huddles while young children and toddlers cycled up and down unscarred tarmac on new bicycles. For a moment Vic and I stared at this alien scene, a different, more tranquil image, as if we had stepped into a TV advertisement for modern-day living.

Then from behind us a yell and we got ready to start running again, but this time the sound was familiar and with real dismay we turned and saw Billy running down the track from the site. "Wait," he was yelling "wait for me."

"He's only bloody led them down here," said Vic in disgust. "I don't believe him. He has the brains of a maggot."

Red in the face, Billy ran to us, shoulders heaving, snot running from his nose.

"We thought it was every man for himself," I said.

"I couldn't leave you on your own," he replied, with a grin.

"Crap," said Vic matter-of-factly.

"Besides," said Billy, ignoring our hostile reception as best he could, "all the Spills were chasing me. It's a bit much is that. Anyway, I think I lost them. It helps to know your area; they'll never think to come down here."

"I think we should go home," I said. "I've had enough for one day."

"Yeah," said Vic. "We don't appear to be too welcome round here, do we?"

As we had contemplated our fate on the edge of this new world, all the animated chatter had turned to low uneasy murmurs, sponges and hoses suspended in mid-air over the Zephyrs and the Zodiacs as the residents became aware of our presence. Breathless and sweating, we kept our arms by our sides and our heads down as we carried on through. We just wanted, quickly and without fuss, to get past their precious houses and get out the other end out onto Brookfield road. That's all.

Then from behind us, came another barrage of familiar noise. It was the Spills again. Behind us, back up the cinder track, came their unmistakable sound. They must have seen Billy following us down. Why else would they come down here? I could hear the echoes of their shouts and the crashing of foliage, sticks smashing nettles and the pop pop of stones hitting tree bark. They were like a swarm of locusts engulfing the land as they passed through, and all of a sudden they were only minutes behind us. We needed to act quickly and get out of sight and hope they would not search too rigorously for us. So the three of us sped across the front lawn of the nearest house, down the side path and around into the back yard and hid. We just hoped for the best, that the people would not be in. From the wall at the back we put our heads around and saw the Spills walking down the new estate, over the lawns and the driveways, ignoring loud requests to get off, knots of them, four or five lads, scanning either side, looking for us and ignoring the residents. They just didn't care what these people thought of them.

Then one of them glanced down the side of the house towards us and I moved my head back just in time. It was at least a minute before I dared to put my head back around and have another look, and it was with the beginning of that delicious feeling of having survived, of having got away with it, that I finally moved my eyes along the rough new red house bricks, along their dead straight lines of mortar, to check the scene outside.

With the semblance of a smile, not really triumphant, almost friendly, the girl who had crossed the river first, at the head of the Spills, was staring straight back at me. All the way from where she stood in the road, down the driveway, alongside the newly built house, past the hallway window right into my own panting chest she stared with bright blue eyes and straight white hair. And that smile. She was loving every minute of the chase.

I put my head back round and looked at my two comrades, both of whom had visibly cheered up. Billy squatted on his haunches against the back wall humming to himself and Vic was standing up, staring in through the kitchen window looking for life inside.

"Have they gone?" said Billy, expecting me to say yes.

"Not quite," I said

"What do you mean not quite?" His red face looked up at me sharply.

"She's out there. That girl with the blonde hair. The one that leads them."

"She doesn't lead them, you soft get."

"Well, she was first across the river. In my book that's leading. Anyway, she's there outside. Waiting for us."

"I'm not getting battered by a girl even if she is a Spill," Billy declared. "No bleedin' way!"

Vic gave up peering through the kitchen window and squatted down alongside us. He wasn't happy.

"We are in deep shite," he pronounced. Then continued, getting ever more hysterical. "We can't get over that fence behind us. We've got hundred foot walls all around. We'll have to go through them. This is all your bloody fault, Billy. You and your crazy ideas. Revenge for Pybus getting a couple of rocks on the arse. You don't even like Pybus, he's nothing to you. It's any excuse with you. You drag us in and we listen and then kerpow, before we know it we are in our own territory about to get beaten up by women. I can't believe that time after time we fall for your stupid bloody ideas. Well this is the last time…"

"Have you bloody finished moaning?" Billy shouted back at him. "You had better shut up Vic, or I swear to God I'll kill you before the Spills do."

"I've had enough of this," I said, "You two arguing all the time. I'm going through them."

"You go through them," said Billy, "I'm staying here; they'll have to drag me out."

"Oh they'll drag you out alright," said Vic, now resigned to the inevitable. "They don't care about anyone or anything. They'll go right through the house if they have to. I'm with you, Mike."

"You're mad, you two," said Billy, getting to his feet.

"Let's go," I said to Vic.

"Wait, wait," said Billy.

"WHAT?" Vic and I yelled at him in unison, angry and scared and past caring.

"I'm coming with you," he said as timidly as I'd ever heard him. Even Billy, big bluff bullshitting Billy, had finally realised that we were going to get a battering. There was no escape from these bloody Spills.

"Alright," I said, "we'll run for it. Follow me. One, two, three, let's go," and I screamed at the top of my voice, "AAAARRRGGGHHH!"

And we ran out into the heart of our enemy.

There were three of us left and still at least twenty of them, including this girl, and as bemused and outraged residents looked on, we ran through newly designed flower beds, skidded across fresh green lawns and then, finally surrounded, we fell under the blows and kicks of our mortal enemies onto suburban tarmac, warm from the sun and smelling of paraffin. Our heads buried into it as the kicks and the punches came in slow motion, the shouts and insults merging into one drone of noise, like the low growl of a huge animal. Even that noise seemed slower. I could feel rough hands grabbing my shirt, trying to get me back off the ground and standing up, not to help me, but just to knock me down again. I dared to open my eyes and I saw them all, their short sticky hair and pockmarked faces and their narrow, slitty eyes and the tough, cruel, feral look of lads who had it hard, and were used to whacking and getting whacked. Then I felt oblivion coming and my fear starting to go because all doubt had gone, and for me fear is not knowing; but now I knew for sure that I was going to get a hiding and I just wanted it over with. I was so engulfed by bodies I couldn't even hit back. Then as I felt them pushing me to my feet, I felt somebody else pushing me down again. Somebody, who was strong in will as well as in body, because they were able to overcome the clamour from the crowd to hurt me more and push me back, onto the ground.

It was the girl with the white hair. She sat astride me, her arse on my stomach, her knees gripped into my sides like I was a horse, and she was riding me. With her arms and elbows she fended off the other Spills who were still trying to pick me up.

"No, no," she said, "leave this one to me, you lot get the others. I can deal with this one on my own, and she looked down into my face from above. I saw blue oval eyes with a mean glint in them, framed by the white hair that then fell forward over her face. I saw the sun shining brightly behind it, so it seemed almost like a halo, which I thought was funny because everyone knew that Spills never washed because they were slum kids at heart. Yet her hair looked so clean it could have been golden.

Then she pursed her lips, and ever so slowly she let a stream of spit dangle down onto my face, a long stringy piece of saliva that hit my own lips, and she laughed as I tried and failed to avoid it.

She wore jeans, a sort of light blue colour but darker in places, where they were wet from the river water. I could feel the hardness of her bones in her legs and arse against my ribs. She was leaning so hard down on me that it hurt. I could tell she was as tough as any lad.

"I can deal with you can't I, you little posh boy?" she said. "I could beat you easy."

I didn't reply.

"Go on," she said, more anger in her voice, "admit it or I'll get them back," and she nodded her head over in the direction where her friends were beating up mine.

"Yes," I said.

"YES WHAT?" she persisted.

"Yes. You could beat me up." I didn't really believe it but it seemed like a good idea to say it anyway. It seemed to satisfy the girl at least.

"Good," she said and stood up, her feet, in old black pumps, either side of my torso. "Remember this, kid," she said, "I saved you from a beating today. Our lot are really pissed off with you and your soft mates, as I'm sure they'll tell you."

I looked over across the gardens where both Billy and Vic lay on the ground. I could see a stream of blood coming from Billy's nose. Their attackers were already bored with them and were starting to move away. Some of the braver house owners, those who weren't hiding behind their curtains, were berating them, but they couldn't have cared less. They laughed and joked as they sauntered out of the estate. One of them shouted back to the girl, who stood above me, still smiling.

"Come on. They've phoned for the coppers. Time we went."

"Why did you save me," I called out to her as she started to walk away. There were tiny little rivulets of water still running from her jeans and her shirt and falling onto the ground. I could see them clearly from where I lay. I made no effort to get up. I still didn't trust her, not to give me a clout, even at this late stage, if I made a move.

"I don't know," she said, looking back down at me. Maybe I felt sorry for you."

"Yeah, but why me and not the other two?"

"Maybe because you're so skinny. I was worried they would break you in half. Anyway, don't worry about it. You don't owe me and I don't fancy you. So don't get any ideas." She turned to walk up the road to catch up with her gang but turned as she went.

"But if you and your lot cross the river again, well next time I'll let them kill you."

Then she smiled at me. A tough girl smile, not like the ugly Spill that she was. A smile that I've never forgotten although the sight of her sauntering off round the corner that day, dripping wet and victorious, was the cause of many a piss take, by Billy and Vic who through their own beatings had seen me battered by a girl. I didn't mind so much though. Part of me in a strange way felt quite close to her and I thought that one day I would go looking for her and talk to her properly and calmly, not in the middle of a battle like we were that day when everybody was trying to knock everybody else into the middle of next week.

Chapter 6

THE SEVEN ARCHES

After that last battle against the Spills, we retreated back into home territory for a while. We moved upstream, past the recreation ground towards the railway viaduct that was known to all as the 'Seven Arches.' The Spills never came up this far. They weren't natural explorers like we were and they rarely left their own territory unless they were provoked, which of course we now knew, to our cost. But up by the arches we were far enough away to feel safe.

It was so called because, as the name suggests, from one end to the other, there curved in magnificent exactitude, and on truly astonishing scale, eight brick-built columns incorporating seven arches as one complete, continuous structure.

To us twelve and thirteen year olds, it looked impressive, but even our dads all professed mild respect for the craftsmanship and its size, and they hadn't even seen it close to like we had. Up close to the arches it became awe-inspiring.

The first time we got underneath them, we had crossed the fences from the recreation ground to explore what lay beyond our regular domain. Crossing the two fields on the approach, whilst all the time hugging close to the familiar, albeit relatively unexplored sanctuary of the Ladybrook, we walked towards the unknown lands of Bramhall and Hazel Grove just to stand under that big central arch.

The first time we did it, Billy, Vic, Linton, Pybus and me made the journey and just as we got to stand underneath, a train went overhead, probably on its way from Cheadle Hulme to Stockport. There was such an almighty blast of sound, a mixture of clanking and roaring, we thought the world had come to an end. We turned tail and ran for our lives, skipping over long tufts of grass like African gazelle, Pybus, as ever, bringing up the rear like some old hippopotamus. We had gone about a hundred yards before we realised it was just a train and we came to a stop with self-conscious, but relieved bursts of laughter escaping through our breathlessness in wheezy, high-pitched squeals.

"Bloody hell," shouted Billy above the noise of the train now fading, "I thought the bloody thing was coming down on us."

"So did I," I agreed, "I thought we'd had it." My head was down on my knees catching my breath.

Pybus stood there, red as fire, sucking in air. He tried to speak but thought better of it.

We turned around and looked at the viaduct again. We stood knee deep in wild grass and cow parsley and looked up at what, to us, was the biggest man-made structure we had ever seen close to. They were building skyscrapers in Manchester now and to stand under one of those and look up made you want to fall over at the sheer height of it, but still, for some strange reason the arches impressed us more. This huge industrial edifice had been constructed by hundreds of men not much bigger than we were now, perched precariously off the sides, probably on wooden scaffolding, often falling to their deaths in the process, laying each individual brick, one on top of the other, day after day, right up to the clouds. That is what truly impressed us. That men, now dead, had built such a wonderful thing.

On that first visit, when we regained our courage after the first train had gone over, we crept back under that great cavernous central arch and lay down in the grass beneath it to stare up at the intricacies of the brickwork, like others might look at the roof of a church or a temple. We studied the lines of the mortar and attempted to count the bricks, but there were just too many.

The next train that came over the arches, we were ready for it, for although the volume of the clacketty-clacking had our hands over our ears, it didn't send us running like last time. We lay down on our backs again and dozed in the afternoon sun. It was unusual for there to be so much peace around us. Usually there was some kind of banter going on, if not outright horseplay, but not today. The air was heavy and silent. Even the pigs in the next field, who had been making a racket all morning, had quietened down. Once that last train had gone over and the air had recovered, no sound intruded. Not for a while at least.

I think I heard it first because I had one ear to the ground listening for another train. Instead I could hear footsteps, rapid paced, soles of heavy boots hitting the same hollow path that we had followed from the rec an hour before. I looked up quickly from my place in the long grass and strained my eyes but I couldn't see who it was. There was too much scrub, too many bushes in the way. I put my ear to the ground and strained to hear. The sound was unmistakable. The thump, thump, thump like a distant drum of approaching feet.

"Somebody's coming," I hissed as loudly as I dared to the knot of boys scattered on the ground. "Somebody's coming," I hissed again and then finally a response. I could see that their thoughts were as mine. SPILLS. Their features froze into white clay.

The five of us collectively, as well-drilled as infantry soldiers, made for cover, sliding from the short grass under the arch down into the longer stuff along the bank of the river, beyond and below the path. We huddled amid the bushes and the bracken, feet almost in the brook, eyes peering through foliage up at the path, completely hidden from anybody walking along it. At least that is what we were hoping. We waited and we waited, hearts pounding.

I could hear a whistle, a tune I recognised but couldn't recall, a jaunty old war song maybe, and the sound of feet. Only one pair of feet though, no more than that, and then around the corner came old Nelson, sleeve pinned to his breast pocket, tall and one-eyed, his other eye covered by a black patch just like the one our great admiral wore in his later years. This modern-day Nelson was the local hermit, an outcast, and every day, so it was said, he made his way off the estate and across the fields to watch the trains. He lived in a little terraced house in Balmoral Avenue where he kept himself to himself; never bothering anyone, and never letting anyone bother him. He was a complete loner.

The adults ignored him and even those kids who called him names did it from a safe distance. Something told them it was best not to get too close.

From our position in the undergrowth we watched as Nelson, surprisingly tall close up and agile too, climbed up the steep embankment alongside the arches and hopped over the track without a care in the world, although we all knew that to do that was definitely not allowed. He acted as if he didn't know we were there, but something told me, call it intuition, that he knew all right, but chose to keep it to himself. We watched him go up and out of sight, breathing huge sighs of relief that it hadn't been the Spills, and glad that he hadn't hung around either.

We used the arches off and on for the next few weeks and most days we would see Nelson, and although we wouldn't leap into the undergrowth every time he came by, we kept our distance and thankfully he kept his.

The day Vic brought his dog, we had planned to cross the river, climb up to the railway line from the other side, and in so doing hopefully avoid Nelson, and then try and walk back along the seven arches, which we knew was both dangerous and against the law. So on yet another warm day, with just our shorts on and socks and shoes tied together and hung around our necks, we started to paddle across.

Vic had his dog, Hazel, on a makeshift lead of baler twine that he had found, but it was obvious to everyone that the dog didn't fancy the water much because it dug its paws into the sandy bank and snarled at Vic as he pulled on its string.

"She doesn't seem to like you much," said Pybus, "that faithful old dog of yours."

Vic was tugging on the string, getting redder in the face and swearing at Hazel.

"C'mon you stupid dog, get in the bloody river."

Billy had already crossed and he shouted back from twenty yards away, "Put the animal on your shoulders like the poachers do and carry it over."

"She's not bloody dead," shouted back Vic, who was now in the shallows himself but below the level of his dog, who was firmly dug in on the bank above.

"Far from it," I said.

Vic was getting exasperated. "I'm going to have to take her home. She's not interested."

There was a chorus of scorn from all of us.

"Just chuck it in," said Billy, "it'll bloody well have to swim then."

"Are you kidding?" said Vic. "If my mum finds out that I've upset her precious bloody dog, she'll kill me. She loves that dog!"

"How will your mum know?" Billy was getting impatient, we could tell. "What's the dog going to do, tell on you, yer soft get?"

"She'll know alright," said Vic. "Besides, I'm not meant to have her down here, she only ever goes to the park."

"What?" exclaimed Pybus. "You've kidnapped your own dog?"

"I felt sorry for her," said Vic. "She never does anything. Never gets any fresh air. We all run around more than she does."

"No wonder it's so fat," I said.

"No wonder it's so bleeding stupid," said Billy, wading back in from the other side.

"Alright," Vic finally conceded. "Alright, I'll try carrying her." He went back up the bank to where the dog stood, fat and furry and with a grin on its face as if it knew it was annoying us. Vic looked at her for a moment and I could hear a low growl in its throat. It sounded like a warning.

Vic whispered to me out of the corner of his mouth, so the dog wouldn't realise we were making a plan concerning her, "Mike, I'm going to grab Hazel and take her over. You hold onto the string just for insurance. If I go under, whatever you do, don't let go of the dog. Once she's in the water she should be fine."

"I don't like this," said Pybus. "That dog seems mean enough to drown you both."

"Shut up, Pybus," said Billy back on the far bank. "It's either that or Vic goes home. It's alright, Vic, if you lose the dog, I'll grab it from this side."

"Yeah thanks, Billy," said Vic, "very reassuring," and I heard him mouth "soft get" under his breath, before turning to me.

"C'mon," he said, "I'm going to ambush her." With that, he leapt at the dog, and before it could react he had scooped it up in his arms, turned and started across the Ladybrook. Hazel yelped with surprise but could do little else, at least not initially, because Vic held her tight. I made a grab for the piece of string and followed right behind them into the water.

All went well for the first few yards then about halfway across Vic stumbled and lost his balance.

"Mike, this dog is too bloody heavy." I could hear Vic's voice straining with the weight of her and then he stumbled again.

"Hold on, Vic," I said, "we're nearly there."

"I'm going to have to put her down. Hold onto the string, whatever you do."

From the other side, Billy, who had been joined by Pybus, was shouting directions.

"Follow my directions. Go left, go right," he was yelling, as if he was Captain Ahab and he knew all the channels and the shallows.

Like idiots, we stopped and listened to him.

"Vic," I said, "hold on we're nearly across."

"I can't. The dog's too heavy. My arms are killing me. You'll be alright. Just hold the lead and the dog will swim across," and he lowered Hazel as gently as he could into the two and a half feet of water that we were paddling across. The dog's eyes nearly popped out of her head. She was obviously not used to water, not cold river water anyway, and it took her a while to get her stumpy little legs moving so she could float, let alone swim. Suddenly her smile had gone and she looked quite pissed off.

"Here you are, Vic," I said, eager to be rid of her. "Have the string."

"Hold on, will you, while I get some feeling back." Vic was rubbing his arms vigorously. "Thank God for that," he said. "That dog is like a bag of cement to carry."

The water was only up to my knees at this point and the river-bed was solid but as soon as I had hold of the string with Vic's stupid dog on the end of it, I began to feel a bit unsteady. By luck more than judgement Billy and Pybus had crossed along a shallow channel, but either side of me the water changed colour and seemingly texture too, and I could see darker and deeper pools. Not for the first time, or the last time, did I think that this river was full of surprises.

In my head, just for a split second, everything seemed to go quiet, that same quiet as when the Spills appeared at the rope swing weeks before. There was a dry taste in my mouth, not very nice. I could see Billy shouting, his mouth moving and laughing but I couldn't hear the sound. Vic was ahead of me almost across. I think Pybus was with Billy. Then away to my left, ten yards downstream, there came a sudden flapping sound of ducks or coots or some kind of river bird.

At this, Vic's dog was off, her dread of the water forgotten. She fair skimmed over the surface, such was her eagerness to get to the ducks, and there was me right behind it, clinging on to the piece of string for dear life. For a few yards, until I could haul the brute back, she took me with her and, in so doing, took me out of two and a half feet of water and put me into six feet of water. She had caught me completely by surprise and in a split second the dog and I were in one of the deep pools. I went well and truly under, I might as well have dived in. I went crashing through the dark brown surface into another world, but almost immediately I came up to the surface again coughing, spluttering and spitting out river water, still holding the piece of string with this stupid thrashing dog on the other end. I could see Billy and Vic's mouths hideously open, laughing, before I tried to put my feet on the river-bed and found nothing there. There was a huge void. I just had time to shout help and I went in again my open mouth filling up with slime and what felt like the whole river washing over my head. This time I let go of the string but I was still underneath the water and all I could see was bubbles and dust and little molecules fizzing and popping as if I was stuck in a bottle of dirty brown lemonade. Just when I thought I was really stuck and wouldn't get out, I broke the surface again and outside the river was silent and the expressions on my friends' faces had changed. They were no longer laughing. In fact they looked scared and their looks made me scared. I was scrabbling away with my legs like some demented swan trying to get to solid ground but no matter where I tried I couldn't find it. My arms started to flap, trying instinctively to swim, but I had never been taught and all I did was make more splashing noises. Time after time I sought firm ground, only to fail miserably, and I finally plunged from fear headlong into panic. Previously it had been a bit of a joke but not anymore. Now this was out of control and I began to beg for my life, my tears mixing with the river water and my cries merging with those of my friends, who were trying, through their own fear, to get to me. Above me the clouds looked away. I liked clouds normally but now they didn't want to know me. Then I thought of my mum at home doing the housework, tidying up after everybody, working one handed because there was usually a cigarette in the other, oblivious to what was happening to me. Hell I was angry, but not as angry as my mum would be if she found out that I had drowned. I waited for my life to flash by like they say, but nothing happened. Maybe my little life had nothing in it worth flashbacking to. Then finally I did see something. Mum, and our Stevie, and our Sandra, and our George all in a row, all looking down and crying as if they were looking at me floating in the river, like one of those bodies you see on the films. But there was no sign of my dad and I thought where the bloody hell was he when I needed him, and then I thought, thank God, he's come to rescue me, because all of a sudden and just in time, a great power lifted me up, up, up through the brown, reedy, frog-spawny water, out of this hole that I was in.

This unseen hand with huge strength, fingers gripping my wet clothes in a vice-like grip, lifted me out and clear of the frothing pool, and the air on my face was cold, and although I was coughing and puking, at last my breath came back.

At first I thought that my dad really had pulled me out but then I saw the one-armed man from Balmoral Drive, the one we called Nelson, who went to the railway every day, and it dawned on me that Nelson had saved my life.

In my watery dream I could hear them all gabbling at me. Old Nelson was giving them all directions in a short sharp voice. "Pull him clear" and "Get him on his side" and surprisingly the others were doing what he was saying. He had taken complete control and there was something in his voice that expected nothing else than to be obeyed, and quickly.

I could feel water oozing out of the side of my mouth and down my cheek. Snot was coming out of my nose but I didn't care. At least my lungs had stopped burning.

I heard Vic ask, "Shall we pump his arms to get more water out?" and Billy reply scornfully, "This is not bleeding Yogi Bear and Boo Boo. This is real."

Finally I opened my eyes and the first thing I was able to focus on was Vic's dog, Hazel, her tongue distended grotesquely in the forefront of my vision as it sat panting with concern at my predicament.

"Take your dog home, Vic, will you please," I said and there was an immediate chorus of relief from my audience.

"Are you alright, you daft get?" said Billy, as near as he could get to tender concern.

"God, Mike. We thought you were a gonner for a minute," said Pybus. "It was all that bloody dog's fault. I told you it was a menace."

"Shut up, Pybus," said Vic. "Hazel didn't mean it, you know that, don't you, Mike? You saved her life I swear. My mum would be really grateful. She loves that dog like a child. Unfortunately I don't think I can explain all this to her. It would be too much for her to take, if you know what I mean. She's on tranquillisers as it is."

"No, Vic. It's alright," I reassured him. "Don't tell your mum, just leave your dog at home in the future. That's all I ask."

Then I saw Nelson standing at the back of this huddle quiet and concerned. I raised myself up on one elbow.

"How are you feeling?" he asked.

"Much better than a minute ago," I replied, my voice croaky and sore.

He was silent as he looked down at me and I could see the greyness of his skin and the sparseness of his hair. I saw little wrinkles around his unpatched eye and again at the corner of his mouth, which made his lips droop downwards and gave him a look of sadness. Maybe he was sad for a good reason or maybe he was just a miserable old sod. It was hard to tell how old he was – some would say sixty but he could have been much younger.

But most of all I saw his empty sleeve. He wore a white shirt with thin blue vertical stripes, no tie and his empty left sleeve was folded neatly across his breast pocket and pinned there by a safety pin.

I thought, as I lay there in the long grass of the river bank, at last starting to shiver, that it was a strange thing to do. Pin an empty sleeve to a shirt. Why? It wasn't as if the arm was going to grow back. All pinning the sleeve achieved, besides looking stupid, was to announce the fact that you were minus an arm. *Look at me I've only got one arm. I lost the other bastard fighting in the war for you ungrateful lot.* For some reason Nelson's sleeve was annoying me.

Then slowly, as I recovered from my near drowning, everything started to make sense. Of course if you cut the sleeve off, well that would be like admitting defeat. Maybe he was waiting for a false arm. Maybe he already had one but didn't like wearing it because it was heavy or itchy. Or he had sent off for one ages ago, and he was still waiting for it. Everyday the postman came, still no arm. Poor old Nelson, no wonder he looked so miserable. That would piss anyone off.

Finally Pybus broke the silence.

"He pulled you out. He saved you," said Pybus.

"Yeah," agreed Billy. "He pulled you out with his one good arm."

"You're pretty strong, Mister, I'll give you that." This from Vic, who at least had the grace to sound grateful, seeing as how he and his stupid dog had caused it all.

Old Nelson stood there looking at me. "You need to get warm," he said. "Either your mates should get you home or you should strip off and go and lie in the sunshine. Either way you've had a bit of a shock. You don't want to catch cold as well. Me, I've got to be going."

"Thanks for saving me," I said, finally remembering my manners.

For the first time he smiled, a thin, almost sad, smile.

"You didn't need me kid. You would've got out on your own. I just gave you a bit of help, that's all."

Then he went, and we all watched him walk towards the seven arches and climb up the side of the embankment to go and watch the trains like he always did, or did every time we were there at least.

A few days had gone by since Nelson had pulled me from the Ladybrook and I hadn't seen him about since then. Usually he wasn't hard to find because he walked to the arches every day and you could usually hear accompanying cat calls from the kids as he walked by. "Oy mate where's yer parrot?" or "Splice the mainbrace Captain," that sort of thing. A lot of them seemed to think that he was Long John Silver although he had two good legs as far as I knew. These kids never got too close to him with their cat-calling because there was something about him, even though he ignored them completely, that suggested that underneath his indifference there was a darker side. That he could turn if pressed too hard. Since the day that he had rescued me, he had gone up in our estimation and our days of calling him names had gone.

But I was nagged by the fact that I hadn't thanked him properly for saving me, not for reasons of politeness but because I kept having nightmares about that day and I got it into my head that only he could get rid of them. Just one visit, that was all it would take. I waited days for him to appear on the street but he never came so finally, almost out of desperation, I knocked on his door. Number twenty five Balmoral Avenue.

I knocked for ages and I was on the verge of giving up when finally the door opened and peering at me out of a gloomy hallway was an unshaven, pale, wasted old man. It was only that he wore an eye patch that he had any resemblance to the sad, lonely but impeccably turned out old man that we saw most days walking to the arches. Then a second behind him, wafting out of the house into the cool morning air around me, was the unmistakable smell of alcohol, sharp and sickly, distinctive within an amalgam of other odours emanating from inside, of sweat and hair oil and burnt food. Involuntarily I gagged as it hit me.

Yet Nelson's house was humming, not just with all this, but with something else as well, something that I couldn't have identified at the time but which I can now. His house smelt of sickness and despair and the onrush of death. On the doorstep he blinked down at me with his one good eye, moist and red veined, initially not recognising me.

I felt I had to speak but already I was feeling that this was not one of my better ideas, to go calling on a strange and lonely old man like I was the district nurse or something.

"Hello there," I said, like some posh kid. "I just thought I would come and see you and say thank you properly." Then still not getting a response I elaborated, "you helped me at the river the other week. You know, when I fell in."

Finally he gave a look of recognition. He stood there, one hand on the door, holding it around him protectively like a cloak, and for a moment I thought he was going to shut it in my face. But he didn't. Still not saying a word, he opened the door wide and then turned on his heel and walked back into the black hole that was the rest of his house. For seconds I stood on his doorstep at a bit of a loss as to what to do. He had not formally invited me in, merely left the door open. I suppose that would have to do. Against my better judgement, and swearing that it would be the one and only time, I stepped over his threshold. As I did, I wondered to myself what my mother would say to me if she knew, that within a radius of just a few miles from where at least four children had disappeared in the last twelve months, without warning and without trace, her precious son was going alone and unprotected into the house of an unknown man. She would not have been impressed.

The house was in a mess. It was obvious that nobody ever cleaned it and probable that nobody else even visited. The main room, the lounge I suppose you would call it, was full of papers and photographs and all sorts of paraphernalia, all spread out on every available flat surface. In the corner a small wooden dining table was again covered in papers and newspaper clippings, except for one part of it and that was occupied by quite a substantial-looking old typewriter with a sheaf of paper sticking out of the top of it. There were a few lines of black type at the top of the page and I realised that I had interrupted old Nelson in his work, and his work seemed to be writing a book or pamphlet of some kind. I gathered quickly from all the information lying about that it was about the war, not that one against the Germans that we were always talking about in history at school, but the one against the Japanese in the Far East that sometimes my dad talked about because he was right there at the end of it with the engineers, building bridges and roads for the allied push. I always remember what he used to say about the atomic bombs. "If it hadn't been for those bombs, kid, those Japs never would have given up and I would have bought it in the next push in Malaya. A week away we were from going in and I tell you son, you wouldn't have been here, that's a fact." He would tell me that from time to time.

Then here I was in Nelson's house and he's also got a thing about the Japanese, judging by all the pictures and newspapers around the place. There were lots of pictures of a railway pasted up on the walls or just lying about. Well we knew he liked the railway. He was up there every day. Although in the photos this was no Cheadle to Stockport line, this was a railway line in the jungle, and all the way along it, standing in various positions, were long lines of emaciated white men that I took to be English soldiers. They were dressed in just shorts and they looked like skeletons, their ribs and their leg bones protruding from their tight white skin as if they would break through and splinter, and strangely most of them still managed to smile at the camera. I had seen this railway reproduced in a Hollywood film with well-known actors only recently, but it looked like old Nelson was interested in the real story. If he had been one of those men in the picture alongside the railway line, it might explain why he was so thin now. I took in this whole scenario, in just a few seconds, and I apologised again for interrupting him.

"Don't apologise," said Nelson, "I've waited twenty years to get the book finished. A visit from you won't change anything. Nobody's interested anyway. We're all forgotten. Forgotten but not quite gone." He said that last bit with real bitterness in his voice but already my attention had been diverted elsewhere. I hadn't seen it before amongst all the other clutter but placed carelessly against the upright of his mantelpiece was a sword, or at least a scabbard containing a sword. However, I had not seen anything like this before.

It was about three feet in total length and with what I presumed to be the blade encased within was a basic scabbard of brown leather. The handle of the sword extended beyond a hexagonally-shaped hand guard or hilt, the handle itself a continuation of the arc of the blade, not straight like you would expect. The covering on the handle, now shiny with age, looked like nylon or leather strands that had been tightly interwoven to form another covering, but within that binding there were diamond-shaped indents that had possibly once contained precious stones, which ran horizontally at intervals to the top. Right at the top of the sword there was an ornate metal casing an inch in depth which would have prevented the hands from slipping off when whirling the thing around your head. It was a wonderful-looking sword and I couldn't take my eyes from it, and Nelson soon spotted my interest.

"That sword you're looking at has a bloody history and no mistake," he said enigmatically.

"Why, what happened with it?" I asked.

"It killed a man," Nelson paused then added, "a friend of mine in fact."

"Bloody hell," I replied, genuinely taken aback. "Sorry," I added at having sworn.

But he ignored me and carried on, his mouth twisting in and out of shape as he told his story.

"I took that same sword off a Japanese officer when they eventually surrendered at the end of the war in the Far East, but not before he had killed my friend and several more afterwards. Those Japanese were cruel to us," he said, "cruellest bastards you could ever wish to meet, they were."

"Why were you all so thin?" I asked, nodding with my head to the pictures on his wall. "Did those Japs starve you?"

"Starving was the least of it," said Nelson and he took another big slug of whiskey from his glass. His one eye grew ever more red and weepy and I noticed the words, in his strong Lancashire accent, were starting to slur.

"They beat you, they slapped you, they wrapped you in barbed wire. Then they filled you full of water, and jumped up and down on top of you until your stomach burst open."

His tone, low at first, grew ever higher as he recounted each separate torture until he started to sound almost hysterical and I wished that he would stop. Such was his intensity that I cursed myself for provoking him with all my questions but it was too late.

"They put bamboo shoots up under your fingernails, which would make even the toughest of men scream with the sheer agony of it. Then when you were really bad, when you stole medication to prevent a comrade with blood poisoning from dying, when you stole from them... well then the bastards chopped your fucking head off."

He was almost screeching now and I thought somebody must surely hear from outside. It was like watching a mad man.

"Look, I'll show you," he gibbered at me. "Here, I'll show you how they killed my mate. Do you want to see?"

I don't know if it was the whiskey or if Nelson had gone mental like everyone always suspected but I began to curse my own misjudgement in entering the house. I really began to wonder if I would get out alive and I could hear myself start to whimper, pleading to be allowed to leave. Then his power and strength of will began to overcome me and I could feel myself wanting to capitulate to him and go to my death without protest. Such was that power, of his madness and his bitterness, that I was losing the will to resist him or fight back.

I honestly thought that he was losing his mind and that I would lose mine. My whole body shook from within and I could feel the tears come.

"Kneel on the floor," he ordered.

"Please," I begged him, "I have to go. I'll get killed if I'm late for my tea."

"KNEEL!" he yelled, and frightened out of my wits I kneeled before him, while he waved the sword above me.

Then he spoke more reassuringly and I clutched at straws, wanting to believe that his reason had returned. That if it could leave him so suddenly, then so it could return, and that his madness might still be fleeting enough to spare me.

"It's alright," he said, "I'm not going to hurt you. Just kneel on the floor and I'll show you what they did to old Mac."

I wanted to believe him, and I tried my hardest to, but the fact remained that I was still playing victim in a mock execution. Even if he didn't want to kill me, he was drunk enough to make a mistake. That bloody sword could slip. It was not like he had a two-handed grip.

I wondered who Mac had been. Certainly, as I knelt down on Nelson's rug amongst the dust and the papers of his lifetime's work, I trembled as much as Mac would have been trembling twenty years before. My eyes started to itch too so I knew there was probably a cat around, one of my allergies was to cat hair and Nelson's rug was covered in it. I bet myself that the cat was thin and vicious and grey, a feline version of a drunken Nelson.

I remember wishing that I had found out Nelson's real name. I had to keep him talking, say anything to keep him from lifting that sword above my head.

"My friends and I were wondering why you always go up to the railway line, Sir?" I asked him, my voice crackling with dread at his unpredictability but desperate to appear calm and trusting of him. It wasn't easy to do but it did distract him for a moment because he was only too willing to tell me.

"Have you ever been onto a railway line?" he asked, finally lowering the sword and pausing to reflect on what I had asked him. I was still kneeling but had managed to turn my head to face him, to look him in the eye. I thought of that old Bible story where Abraham is asked to kill his own son as proof of his faith in God and I now had a pretty good idea of how the lad must have felt.

"Yes," I replied. Billy, Vic and I had climbed the embankment and just briefly stepped on the track as a sort of dare, about a week after I had fallen in the river. There were no trains in sight, but we didn't hang around to wait for one either. "I liked it up there," I told him, "it was peaceful and I liked the way the track disappeared into a tiny little point like it was taking us a long way away. It was like being somewhere else, maybe in another country."

"I think you understand, boy," said Nelson. "A railway has its own peace, its own silence. But for me a railway line is something more. Yes, a hell of a lot more. A line, any railway line anywhere, not just in the jungle like you see in the photographs where I spent so much time, is an escape, a road to freedom.

But more than that, for me it is redemption as well as peace; from that space and that strange silence I get clarity and forgiveness. But I wouldn't expect you to understand all of that because thankfully you haven't been to war. Hopefully you never will."

As he explained this, his voice had lowered and he had drifted away momentarily, probably remembering all that he had been through, but all too soon and unfortunately for me he suddenly snapped back into the present again.

"Right," said Nelson resuming his demonstration. "This is what happened. We were all stood on the parade ground in the middle of the jungle and it was a hundred and five degrees Fahrenheit. Everybody was there, the sick, the dying, as well as those that were reasonably well. There must have been about a hundred and twenty of us in three lines, all stood to attention. Like this," and he snapped himself to attention, although, even from my crouched position on the floor, I could see him wobble on his feet as he did so.

"Then this little Japanese officer walked out with Lieutenant Macallister, who himself was flanked by two guards. Together they stood in front of us, at first with their backs to us, but then on a command they all turned around to face us. They were about twenty feet away from the first line of prisoners of war. It was obvious to everybody there that Macallister was in a bad way and had probably been tortured almost to the point of death. We all knew what they had got him for. Single-handedly in the last six months he had saved at least twelve people from certain death, me included, by stealing medication from the Japanese. They were the craftiest enemy too and it took real guile as well as daring to get away with it for so long and Mac had known that they would get him eventually. When they took my arm off he was the one who stole the morphine for the pain and then the antibiotics when it became infected. I would have died were it not for him. That's a simple truth. He was the best of all men and they had him here in front of us, treating him like you wouldn't treat a fucking dog. And not one of us in those three lines would have swapped places with him, for anything. And every day that I'm alive now, I think of that day.

Nelson continued. "Then this Japanese officer, Imimoto was his name, spoke in Japanese for about a full minute. It felt like ten. Then his translator spoke in English.

'This man has been caught stealing from the glorious Japanese army, blah blah blah.' We had often heard them rant. They were good ranters. Then more charges. Then: "We sentence this man to die."

There was a pause, a long silence around the parade ground, as we absorbed what had been said. The Japanese officer spoke again, only little bits of which we understood. Then the translator spoke again for our benefit so that we would know what was to happen.

'Lieutenant Macallister is sentenced to death. He will die now on this parade ground in front of everybody and everybody is to witness the punishment. Any man who closes their eyes or looks away from this retribution and is seen to do so will receive the same punishment immediately afterwards. Is that clear?'

I was in the third row of prisoners, too weak almost to stand and at least sixty feet from Macallister, but I could see every line on his face, every tear in his eye, every piece of fear on his skin as the guard on each side of him forced him to his knees. Then I saw that devil Imimoto take his sword from its scabbard and hold it still, an inch above Macallister's neck. He had a big strong neck. He had played rugby at university. He had been a prop forward, a strong man.

Then Nelson spoke directly to me on the floor. "Like this," he said, "like I'm showing you now," and he raised the sword above me with his one hand. I couldn't see it because my eyes were on the floor, but I could feel the blade in the air above me and I could hear it whoosh. I thought what it must be like to die, to know with fair certainty that these were your last seconds. Then, strangely, I didn't think of myself. For a time at least I considered the lost children. Had they been murdered like everybody said, especially all the mothers, and they themselves begun to realise at any point that they were not going to escape the evil people that they had become entangled with? Did those kids know, like Macallister knew, that this was real and that their final moment had come? That they weren't going home to their mothers?

Because Nelson finished his story then and he said as much.

"For one second, then two while we all looked. I tried to look into his eyes then, to give him courage to say that I was sorry for him, that I was grateful to him for saving my life but he couldn't look up. I could see the top of his head that's all, thinning red hair wet with perspiration. Maybe he went into a world of his own. I hope he did. I can't bear to think that he would have been even far more terrified than I was, than we all were. We heard him praying, a gabble of words in a broad Glasgow accent, begging forgiveness from God, but not from his captors, then one last cry for his mother. A shrill, strangulated childlike cry of "MUM" reverberated around that parade ground and it went into the very heart and soul of every allied man there, never to be forgotten by any of us, certainly not by me. Then the sword fell with a swish and a thump as it hit his neck, his big strong neck, and his head rolled onto the dust of the parade ground. There was a gush of blood from the body but that soon slowed to a flow no heavier than a summer shower of rain."

Strangely by this time my own fear had gone. By the tone of Nelson's voice, by the sadness and despair in it, I knew that he was not going to hurt me, as drunk as he was. In a clumsy and wholly misjudged way through drunkenness and solitude he had tried to show me graphically what had happened to his friend and I had fallen for it and strangely I felt almost embarrassed that I had first put myself in that situation and then secondly been so scared by it. I was angry as well though and I wanted to leave now and quickly. I knew I would never visit him again, no matter how remorseful he would be. When I got to my feet Nelson sat in his armchair, his head in his hands, and the sword stood propped against his mantelpiece where it had been when I came in, as if nothing had happened. I sneezed suddenly but he didn't even stir, just carried on staring into space.

I turned and walked down the hall and opened the front door. Then after first checking to see that nobody I knew was out in the street, I closed the door quietly behind me and went back out into the warm sunshine.

We were at the arches the next day and Nelson walked past like he always did, but this time he stopped. He was back to his immaculate best, a different man to the washed-out drunk that I had encountered the day before. I hadn't told any of the others yet; there would be too many awkward questions, too much piss-taking if they knew I had gone to visit him. So I kept quiet, although when Nelson appeared, I found myself recoiling and ready to run. He had pulled me from the river but I would never trust him again and I went to my haunches when he stopped on the path below the slight bank where we were.

He ignored the others and spoke directly to me.

"I left the sword for you," he said. "The back door is open. Reach inside and it's there in the corner. When you next go by take it, it's yours."

"I can't take it," I protested. "It wouldn't be right." But he cut me short in that same voice he had used at the river when he was giving orders to the others.

"Take it," he barked, "you want it and it's no good to me. Not now. I can't forget with that damn thing around me." Then he peered at me closely with his wrinkled red eyes and said. "Keep it if you wish kid but remember. There are bad people who have owned it," and he turned and walked up the embankment to the track as he always did.

The others had all been sitting quietly while this conversation took place but now they were curious.

"What was all that about?" said Billy. "What's that about a sword?"

"Oh it's just an old sword he owns," I replied trying to act casual. "Old Japanese thing."

"How come you know about it?" said Vic, straight to the point as usual. "Been round there have you?"

"What if I have?" I was sick of Vic's snide comments. "What's it to you?"

"You want to be careful of him," said Pybus. "He looks close to the edge to me. Did you see his eyes? Bloodshot they were."

"He's a nutter" said Billy. "Pure and simple."

"You shouldn't go round there," said Linton. "You don't know what he could do. Even if he did save you from Vic's dog."

They all laughed and the mood lightened a little.

"I don't intend to go round there," I reassured them. Why would I?"

"To get that sword of course," said Pybus. "I'll expect you'll do that".

Then a train went over the arches above us and killed the conversation which I was relieved about. It was a long train because it went on for ages, clacketty clacking above our heads, bombarding our thoughts, and we lay on our backs inside and outside the cover of the arch, eyes closed and quiet waiting for the peace to return.

Then Billy disturbed the peace as he often did by moaning about something.

"Aarghh!" He yelled. "I felt something. It got me smack in the eye." He was rubbing his big meaty fist into his socket like a child does when he wakes up.

"Probably a raindrop," I said.

"Well it's not raining over here," said Vic, out of sight in the long grass.

"It's probably cuckoo spit," said Pybus.

We all laughed.

Then Billy jumped to his feet. "Do you think it's lads on top of the arches? It's not the Spills is it?"

We all stood up.

"No," I said. "It's too far down for the Spills. They don't come down this far."

"It might be that Bramhall lot though," said Vic. We screwed up our eyes and scanned the parapet of the viaduct for any sign of hostile life but it was a silhouette against the silvery sky and there were no signs.

"No one would be mad enough to go up there would they?" I said to no one in particular. Then I looked at Billy and his eye was a red smudge.

"Give me your hand," I said to him.

"What for?" he said stepping back a little.

"Just give it to me." Sure enough there was a red smudge where he had wiped his face with his sleeve.

"Let me look at your head," I persisted.

I took his big hairy head in my two hands and searched for any sign of a cut. There was no sign.

The others were looking at me with baffled looks and Billy tried to protest but I cut him short.

"Where were you lying?" I asked him.

"What?"

"Where were you lying?"

"Why?"

"Just show me."

"About there," Billy indicated his place in the long grass, just out from the middle arch. "Now tell me why you want to know," he asked, annoyed.

I put my finger in the grass where Billy's head had been and patted the area around. Then I raised my finger to the rest of them.

"Blood," I declared almost triumphantly.

"Oh God!" wailed Billy. "I'm bleeding and I don't even know it. Where am I bleeding?" he squealed patting his face and head, searching for the source of it.

"Calm down, Billy," I had to almost yell at him. "It's not your blood."

He finally stopped dancing around and returned to his normal, confident self. "Well," he said, turning to the others, still watching the proceedings with confusion, like passers-by at an accident.

"Whose blood is it then, if it's not mine?"

"Lie down where you were, Billy," I said.

"Have you gone mad?"

"Just lie down."

The others were looking at me strangely.

"What's going on, what's wrong with him?" I heard Pybus say.

"He's trying to find out where the blood is coming from," said Linton.

"Lie down there just as you were, with your head dead still. That's it, like that. Now close your eyes I would. Now stand back, lads, and watch his ugly mug."

The four of us squatted at various points a couple of yards distant round the prone figure of Billy, waiting for a sign. And, sure enough, it came. We didn't have to wait long. After about ten seconds, a drop of red stuff fell with an audible plop from somewhere high up on the railway arches and landed right in the middle of Billy Skinner's forehead. It stayed the size of a large pimple for a few seconds and then, like a red ink stain, started to run down the contours of his face. Then another one, and then another. The four of us watched Billy's face turn ever more speckled red, then slowly we turned our heads upwards to the top of the arches, to the parapet that ran alongside the railway track, from where the blood had now started to flow more freely.

We didn't get up to the line. We would have done had we got the chance but the police and the fire engines and ambulances got there first. It was probably as well they did. I don't know how much of old Nelson was left bloody and broken on that parapet where the 5:15 from Birmingham via Crewe had tore into him at sixty five mph. but we do know that his head ended up in Stockport wedged onto the front of the train like some grisly barbarian trophy. We know because Linton's dad, yes him again who knew everything because he was the nosiest copper in Manchester Central, told Linton in strictest confidence. Linton, a couple of days later, related it to us, including the bit, apparently true, about the old copper whose job it was to carry the head away and the nearest thing to hand was a carrier bag. When some old woman complained to him about the delays to the trains and what was the reason for it, apparently this copper opened his carrier bag, let the woman peer inside and told her that it was all the fault of the man in the bag. She passed out and he got suspended on full pay pending a disciplinary.

I was sad about old Nelson but that bit about the carrier bag gave us all a laugh. Especially when we thought how shocking old Nelson's head, which had been frightening enough when attached to his body, would have looked, lying decapitated at the bottom of a Woolworths bag. Linton also told us that they spent longer than they should have done looking for the rest of him because nobody told them that he was already missing an arm. We could have told them that but the coppers never asked us.

A couple of days later, when it had all died down, I went round to Nelson's house, to the back door where he had told me to go. I knew I was taking a big risk snooping round a dead man's house, but I had to have that sword.

Besides, Nelson said I could have it. He virtually forced it on me and the other lot were witnesses, so I was only claiming what was rightfully mine. In fact, when I thought about it, telling me to take his sword would have been the last words he ever uttered on this earth. Unless you count the "Oh shit" he would have squeezed out before the train got him. That's if he saw it at all, or if being hit by the train was an accident or deliberate on his part. If the latter were true then maybe he said something else like the name of a sweetheart or "Take me unto Jesus" or something. It wouldn't have been that great for the train driver either. Rolling along happily like Casey Jones, and suddenly there's a bald man with an eye patch and one arm missing standing in front of your train like the grim reaper. It's enough to put you off train driving for life.

I was thinking these things as I crept down his garden path to the back door and pushed it gently open. I didn't go in but reached around it to the dark recess behind, my hand groping the wall for something to take hold of. If I had been in a horror film something would have grabbed me, but I wasn't, thank God, and finally my hand settled on the hilt of that sword. I grabbed it and ran, holding the long sword flat against the length of my body. When I got to the pavement outside I walked quickly along Queens Road, back into Grange Avenue and then cut through Moss Road towards home, keeping my head down and looking for nobody. I wasn't for stopping. After an age I reached the house and checked it out. There was nobody around, not even mum. I ran straight past the back door and into the garden to the shed to finally squeeze that sword into a little space behind all the tools that we had, in amongst the spades and the hoes and the forks that my dad never used. I knew my sword would be safe there until I could think what to do with it.

After all this adventure I could have done with a quiet time for a few days or so, but that same evening that I hid the sword in the shed was my last few hours of freedom. The next day I was going back to school, and the nervous anticipation that had started to creep into my waking moments in the last week of the holiday came in a fearful rush as I tried to sleep. Outside the hot day had become a humid night, until in the early hours, finally the weather broke, welcome rain, heavy splashes against my window pane, the air suddenly cooler giving relief from the closeness. I still couldn't sleep though so I wandered downstairs to get a drink of water. The house was quiet and in darkness as I tiptoed down to the kitchen, and when I turned on the light what I saw made me cry out.

My dad was just sitting there at the kitchen table, in the dark, alone, just staring into the blackness. He was still wearing his coat, as if he had forgotten to take it off when he had come in from work and he sat there, not drinking, not eating, not even smoking; just staring into empty space. I nearly jumped out of my skin with fright and I couldn't help swearing at him, which luckily he took no notice of. I don't think he was drunk or even that tired, he just had things on his mind.

"Bloody hell, Dad," I said to him, "you scared me. What are you doing sat here in the dark?"

He was blinking at the sudden burst of light and for a moment seemed to be getting his bearings, then he turned to me, slowly and deliberately, as if he had a pain in his side, and looked at me with red-rimmed eyes, the same eyes I get when I get mixed up with cat fur.

"Just thinking," he said. "Trying to get some peace and quiet, that's all."

"Are you coming or going?" I asked, nodding at his coat. I thought you had finished nights for a while."

He didn't answer me, but changed the subject.

"You got school tomorrow?"

"Yeah," I replied, none too enthusiastically.

"It'll be alright," he said unconvincingly.

"I'd rather be outside and free. Not stuck inside doing lessons."

"Can't do that now, that's for sure," said my dad. "These days you need to do your lessons, the best you can."

"I've got another three years of school," I muttered in despair. "How am I going to stick that out?"

"You need to go to school and get some qualifications." He saw my look and his tone changed. His voice became sharper and his words more urgent. "You're grinning at me, son, but I'm right and you'll find that out. If you do well at school, you may get lucky and one day work for yourself and not get paid low wages by somebody else who couldn't care less about you or your family. On the other hand, if you don't, you'll always be broke, and tired and used. Not to say trapped. You mark my words. It's a dog-eat-dog world out there and people will always take advantage of you. It's better to be the one giving the orders than the one taking them."

"I'm just a kid," I said. "Work is a long way off. Work like you do, anyway."

"It catches up on you, that's all I'm saying. I'm giving you free advice Michael. It's up to you whether you take it or not."

I looked at him again, sitting at the table, and I was conscious of how serious he looked. He meant what he said, I could see that. I had poured myself a glass of water at the sink and I turned round to face him again and pressed the cold glass against my forehead and rolled it across my skin like a small barrel, cooling me down. The truth was that my dad didn't normally give out advice like this, not considered advice anyway, and I was pretty flattered that he was doing it now, just to me. Like he was really interested in what I did, for a change.

"Alright," I said because I wanted to please him.

"Alright, what?" said my dad.

"Alright I'm going to work hard at school. Try my best."

"You're serious?"

"I promise Dad. I want to get somewhere in life." Now he looked pleased.

"Well, kid, you want freedom, real freedom in the future to do what you please, going to school is a good place to start." He pushed back his chair and it made a scraping sound on the floor. Then he stood up from the table and walked towards the back door. Casually, almost as an afterthought, he justified his exit with a faint smile.

"Or you'll end up like me," he said. "Taking long walks at midnight just to get rid of the boredom of it all." Then he opened the back door and walked out into the blackness.

Chapter 7

THE SCHOOL

The smell of school, disinfectant, floor polish and something like cabbage boiling in the kitchens all filled my senses as I rolled in on a wave of rowdy boys and chattering girls, through the glass doors of the main entrance to Kingswood Secondary Modern School. It was the first day of the autumn term and in those first moments of acclimatisation, in that melee of flesh and bone and hair that was all around me, so the freedom of summer was forgotten and I breathed the unfamiliar air of rules, restraint, uniform and order and my heart sank at the thought of the long weeks ahead.

The crowd was a real mix of older, tougher-looking lads with longer hair and some badly needing to shave, wearing very basic school uniform, trousers and a white shirt and maybe a bedraggled tie hanging loosely knotted around their necks. Some of them, maybe the real poor ones, didn't have school regulation black shoes on and just wore a pair of white pumps. I saw Joe Fenners, who I had last seen at the building site driving a dumper truck, being admonished by a teacher for being improperly dressed, but Fenners just smirked. He hadn't worried much about 'borrowing' the dumper so I doubted whether he cared particularly about school uniform, especially in his last few months of school.

I looked around for familiar friendly faces and was relieved to see Billy and Vic talking within a bigger group of lads across the hall, but before I had a chance to join them several teachers appeared as if from nowhere and started to bellow directions at the crowd.

"INTO THE HALL ALL OF YOU, NOW!" yelled a bald-headed man in a broad Scottish accent. He wore glasses and a tweed jacket and although he was only small, smaller than a lot of the older boys, he had a voice like a foghorn. He looked like a weed to me, but everybody, young and old alike, jumped to attention and filed obediently into the hall. I found out later he was Mr McGrain, the chemistry teacher and I would be meeting him later in a double lesson. He was shouting short sharp commands, like some mad shepherd, and the new ones who were still unfamiliar with the drill, were, just like sheep in a crowded space, getting into a bit of a panic. They were dashing around in all directions, their new blazers done up, their hair slicked down and their new satchels, placed lovingly on the young shoulders that morning by bereft mums, crashing into walls and notice boards as they spun around in a haze of confused terror. I somehow managed to keep my cool although I was nervous.

"COME ON, WE HAVE'NAE GOT ALL DAY," shouted McGrain. "MOVE, STEVENS, AND YOU, FENNERS, YOU MORON, GO THROUGH THE DOOR," and then, as if by magic, everybody started to follow the instructions and, in reasonably orderly lines, year by year, from first form up to fifth form, started to walk into the assembly hall. The young ones moved up to the front, under the watchful gaze of a long line of grumpy-looking teachers, the older ones, and those that had been on the receiving end of McGrain's sarcastic tirade, at the back of the hall almost out of sight.

Then when everybody had finally settled on the benches and wooden chairs and the cacophony of noise had died to just a low murmur, the headmaster, dressed more smartly than all his teachers, in a new blue suit, came striding down the central aisle.

He passed through thirty rows of ten children each side, all looking out of narrow, nervous eyes as tall, and full of purpose, he took to the stage. After acknowledging with a short sweeping smile his trusted colleagues, sat grimfaced on their platform behind his lectern, he turned and gazed fondly over his assembled pupils. I glanced down my row and saw

Pybus sitting next to Billy and I gave him a quick wink. He grinned back at me and I felt better, less alone. The whole room was hushed, the expectant faces of the new boys and girls washed in the sunlight streaming in through the high windows, the faces of the boys in the back furrowed in boredom and gloom, resigned to the impending speech, needing to smoke or play football or at least be elsewhere.

"My name is Mr Catchpole," he bellowed across the rows all the way to the back of the hall, "and I am your headmaster and all of you, yes, all of you are privileged to be in this school."

He looked around, scanning the throng for any signs of cynicism or even downright objection to his bold statement, and, seeing none, continued.

"Forget all that nonsense about the grammar school and the elite and how all those who fail the '11 plus' are for evermore confined to the scrapheap. Forget it I say."

He was starting to sound like a politician and his voice had definitely deepened to a sort of Churchillian slur but he ploughed on nevertheless, the attention of the pupils still engaged, if not all of the teachers behind him. He was saying it, not just for the benefit of the new pupils, but as a reminder to the older, more cynical pupils behind them who had heard it all before. McGrain and one or two others were stifling yawns and glancing covertly at watches, no doubt anticipating the classes ahead when they could dispense with the goodwill and get back to the business of teaching by intimidation. However, our young, progressive headmaster had not quite finished. As he ranted on I thought of Linton, sitting a couple of miles away from us, and wondered if he was going through the same old stuff at his grammar school, spouted by his own headmaster in the first assembly of the new academic year. Maybe all the kids down there, Linton included, believed it.

"I have told all your predecessors the same," Catchpole continued, indicating now with an extravagant sweep of his arm the older kids behind us "and now I tell you." At this juncture he leant right over the front of the stage, to the point where I thought he might fall on top of us, and looked down at all the new kids sitting open-mouthed below who stared intently right back up at him as if they were watching a pantomine in the City Hall.

"We will give you the skills," he continued, "that you need in an ever changing world, to make a valid contribution to society as a whole and, more specifically, your own community. Not everyone can go down the road to academia, not everyone can go to university but all of you, every single one," he beamed at us, bent at the waist and head moving from side to side like a toy animal, "will find their place in life. You will achieve. I promise you that. What is more, this school will help you find that place in life, and with the help of these ladies and gentleman behind me," he indicated his cabinet of staff, grim-faced behind him, "you can achieve what your hearts desire."

"What a load of shite," I heard one kid next to me whisper to his mate on the other side of him, but beyond that all I heard was a stony silence. A shuffling of feet, a few coughs and mutters, but mainly not a word.

"What your hearts desire," the headmaster repeated, as if trying to convince himself of this promise.

Finally he stood up straight, looked around almost as if he expected a round of applause to break out and then, when no such sound came, indicated to a teacher sitting to one side by a beaten-up old piano.

"Right," he said. "First hymn of the new term, hymn number four hundred and twenty three. 'Guide Me Now Thy Great Redeemer.' Take it away, Mr Dawson."

I knew that I was in the same class as Vic, Billy and Pybus, but after assembly I lost them in the melee of disorientated pupils, so I was unsure as to where to go. I asked a couple of older kids, a boy and a girl but they just looked at me like I was a Martian or something so I headed off down the main corridor. Then I asked a female teacher with a thin face and horn-rimmed glasses and she just sent me down another corridor with a vigorous point of her finger, without talking and without breaking stride. Everything looked vaguely familiar from the end of last term but I still wasn't sure where I should be going. It was alright at first while there were still lots of kids milling about, but as bells rang and doors slammed those kids all disappeared into their own classrooms leaving me alone to walk up empty corridors. There was a slight panic rising in my stomach and it made me slightly breathless. I was looking for room number twenty four but there were no numbers on these doors because the stupid caretaker hadn't replaced them from last term when the leavers nicked them as souvenirs, so I now zigzagged across the corridor like a hungry insect, looking through the small windows in classroom doors for a sign of familiar faces. All I got back was laughter and V signs and the odd scowl from a distracted teacher who was trying to take registration.

Finally I turned a corner and there was a row of three doors all with their numbers intact; twenty six, twenty five, and finally twenty four. I had never been so pleased to see a classroom and doubted that I would again. I peeked through the little window and immediately saw Billy's red face grinning back at me. They were all sat in rows behind desks and most seemed to be listening to the teacher. They had started without me.

Feeling nervous I knocked once.

No answer.

I knocked again and waited, my ear to the door. A few seconds went by and still no answer. Was the teacher deaf or was he ignoring me? I was getting worried by now.

I knocked again, this time louder.

"COME IN. Come in for goodness' sake." This in a loud impatient voice.

I opened the door and I could see all the kids were smiling, big grins plastered across their faces, boys and girls alike and probably at my expense. The teacher, another bald head and yet another tweed jacket, was bending over a desk painstakingly ticking off his register.

"Are you deaf, boy?" said the teacher, still not looking at me, or are you trying to break down my door?" The class laughed.

"Alright, alright. Quiet, you lot." Finally he looked up and I could see, to my surprise, that he had a kindly face, unlike so many of his colleagues. Handsome in spite of his bald pate with its silly fringe of fuzz around it, a bit like Friar Tuck's. But he had a friendly smile at least.

"Who are you?" he asked.

"Gibson Sir. Michael Gibson."

"You're late Gibson".

"I know, sir, I'm sorry, I got lost."

"Lost or having a quick smoke before morning lessons?"

"I don't smoke, Sir," I said with feeling. I resented his accusation.

"I'm only joking with you, boy," he said, "although if you hang around with these reprobates," he made a sweeping gesture with his arm to the rows of faces enjoying my delayed entrance, "it will only be a matter of time."

"Anyway." He stood and thought for a moment. "I'll mark you present, shall I?"

"Yes please, Sir."

"Good. Go and sit down then. There's a desk behind Skinner. It's better that he's in front of you, where you can keep an eye on him." There was another laugh from the class, even from Billy.

"Now you weren't here for introductions were you, Gibson? My name is Mr Sutton and I will be your form teacher. Every morning after prayers you come to this classroom and we spend the first part of the morning together, before you go onto your other lessons. Now today, on the first day of the new term, I thought it may be helpful to you all if we discussed our hopes and our fears. How we are feeling on this momentous day in our second year of main school, in this strange new world that we are plunged into, for what seems an inordinately large part of the year."

A hand shot up at the back.

"Yes. Thackeray, is it? Go on then, your hopes and fears."

"Sir?" said Thackeray. A spotty-faced youth with a crew cut.

"Yes, Thackeray."

"Do you mean our hopes and fears just for school or for life in general?"

"It could be either I suppose. Why, do you have any ideas? You could start the discussion if you like."

"Give me a chance, Sir," said Thackeray, "I'm still thinking."

Mr Sutton surveyed the blank faces in front of him and sighed.

"Come on, you lot. Think about how we feel as we are forced away from the bosom of our lovely families for hours every day into this hell hole of a school. Hopes and fears for our futures. What scares us, what inspires us in this wonderful life that we lead? Come on, who wants to be first?"

One of the girls from the group at the other end of the class to Billy and I put her hand up. I remembered her from my few weeks at the end of last term. It was Lorna Rogers, always well-dressed, pretty but with a hard face and she thought herself a little posh although she came off the council estate. She had her little band of followers but most stayed clear of her because she had a way with words. The others had warned me about her. She could be a 'sarky' cow when she had a mind to.

"I have a hope, Sir," said Lorna.

"Yes, Lorna," said Mr Sutton, encouraged.

"My hope is that William Skinner and Victor Roberts move to another school, so my friends and I don't have to listen to their bad mannered comments all the time."

All the boys broke out in laughter.

"What comments?" blurted out Billy in amused indignation. "We aven't said owt. Sir, that's not fair."

"Alright, Skinner, alright," soothed Mr Sutton.

"All last year you did," said Monica O'Hagan, one of Lorna's friends. "It got tedious."

"We've grown up since then," said Vic with a big grin. "We're big boys now."

"Big Jessies more like," said Lorna.

"That's enough!" shouted Mr Sutton, rapidly losing patience. He got up from his desk and stood at the head of the front row.

"And my fear is that they will stay here right up to the fifth form," said Lorna in a quieter voice, trying to get the last word in, as I suspect was usual.

"That's not quite what I had in mind, Lorna," said the teacher, "although at least we've got some dialogue going. Is there anybody else? Hopes and fears. Serious comment please. What about you, Skinner?"

"Alright Sir," replied Billy. "My hope is to make the football team."

"Good!"

"Then score lots of goals and get looked at by Man United. City even. Or anybody really but not Liverpool."

"Good. Good. That's better. Real hopes, real aspirations there by Skinner. Something to strive for. Any fears, Skinner?"

"Eh?"

"Any fears, any forebodings?"

Billy thought for a moment then shook his big fair head.

"No, Sir. No fears."

"Good, good." The discussion was growing and Mr Sutton was more encouraged. "Right, anybody else?" he continued. "Maybe some academic aspirations. Some ambitions. Yes you, Christine."

Christine McNeill, sitting next to her friend Lorna Rogers, had raised her right hand speculatively, then lowered it as if in doubt, then finally raised it again.

"I would like to go to university," said McNeill in an unsure voice. There was a big burst of incredulous laughter from most of those in the room, although not from me or from Mr Sutton. Some of the girls kept straight-faced in support, although Lorna was trying not to smirk.

Then McNeill continued, this time more defensively, "I would like to be a housing officer, Sir," she said, "so I could get my mum a nice house to live in, and our Julie and our Robbie. It's too crowded where we are."

I knew how she felt but the others, especially the boys, those not still giggling, looked open-mouthed at McNeill, unsure as to whether she was being serious or not. But she was.

"Give over with you woman," said Lenny King from his place

next to Vic in the back row. "You won't be going to no fancy college through this place, that's a fact."

"You'll be lucky if you get into Woolworths," added Vic.

"Mind your own business, Victor Roberts," said McNeill. "What do you know about anything?"

"Hold on, hold on," jumped in Mr. Sutton sensing his discussion was heading too close to insult and anarchy. "There is absolutely no reason why Christine can't go to university."

"You need the proper exams for university," said Vic.

"I can do proper exams if I want," said Christine, bolstered by the teacher's faith in her.

"Not in this school you can't," said Billy, joining in. "We only go up to fifteen or sixteen then we're out to work. You'll be down the factory or in the shops with the rest of us."

"I'm going to be a typist," said Monica. "Our Pamela is a typist and she makes eleven pounds a week. You could be a typist, Chrissie."

"I don't want to be a bloody typist," she countered, getting annoyed. Monica looked hurt and crossed her arms.

"Anybody can be anything they want if they set their mind to it," said Mr Sutton, pointedly glossing over McNeill's use of the word 'bloody'. Billy can be a footballer, Monica a typist and Christine can go to university and be a, what was it, a housing officer. Yes thank you, a housing officer. You just have to work hard and apply yourself.

Right. Good. Anybody else? Yes Monica?" All the boys groaned. She was not the most popular girl in the class.

"I have a fear," she said, "in fact it's more than a fear. My doctor says it's a phobia and I'm incurable." Suddenly the class went quiet and the boys especially started to show a keen interest.

"Tell the class, Monica," said Mr Sutton in a voice that sounded tired all of a sudden.

"Worms," declared Monica with real feeling.

"Worms?" enquired Mr Sutton.

"Short ones, long ones, fat ones, thin ones," said Monica. "It doesn't matter. I can't stand them. If I see one, I faint."

"Wow," said Vic. "You wouldn't want to be buried then. That's how bodies go. In the cemetery like. The worms eat the flesh then the bones turn to dust."

"Yeuck!" said the girls.

"Says who?" said Billy. "How can you know if they're underground?"

"My dad told me," countered Vic, "he used to dig graves over at the Stockport cemetery. That's what happens. It's science, isn't it, Sir?"

"Yes it is, although you can't accuse the common or garden worm of being solely responsible for the disposal of the dead, I shouldn't think. There are other factors, I'm sure."

"Maggots for a start," said Lenny King.

"Yes maggots too."

"Rats," said Billy. "Rats will eat anything."

There were yet more squeals of horror from the girls and shrieks of laughter from the boys. Mr Sutton clapped his hands and shouted to regain order.

"Alright. Alright. That's enough. Let's change the subject."

"Anyway, I can't stand worms," said Monica. "I don't care about the other stuff."

It wasn't hard to tell that Mr Sutton had had enough of the discussion but I put my hand up anyway.

"OK," he said, pointing to me. "You, the new boy. Have the last word before I send you all on your way."

"Sir, you know those kids that have disappeared?" I asked him.

"Which kids, Gibson?" he said cagily, but I knew that he knew who I meant. "Kids are always disappearing, aren't they? Except you lot, more's the pity."

But I pressed him. The class had gone quiet, waiting to hear what I had to say.

"You know Sir, the kids from all over Manchester. That kid with the specs. That little girl, whose pictures are all over the place. There are loads of them. The ones on the news."

"I know the ones," he finally acknowledged. "What about them?"

"Do you think they're dead?"

"I don't know. I hope not, but some have been lost for quite some time now. What about you? What do you think?"

"I hope they're safe, but deep down I don't think so," I said. "There's been no ransom notes or anything and they would have come home by now if they had a choice."

"I hope you are wrong, Gibson," said Mr Sutton.

"So do I, Sir. It would be horrible never to see your parents again, no matter how much they mither us. And for them too. If I disappeared off the face of the Earth, it would kill my mum. I know that for a fact. That would be my fear. That somebody got me and my mum didn't ever see me again."

"Have you seen any Spills about?" enquired Billy Skinner that lunchtime on the first day, as we scrabbled about on our knees at the far end of the playing field. We must have looked like coppers looking for discarded clues, but we weren't just peering intently at the ground, we were digging it up as well. We were on the hunt for worms, as many as we could find in the forty minutes left of free time given to us, to somehow digest the Irish stew and semolina pudding they had force-fed us at dinnertime. We were doing pretty well; so far we had about twenty of all shapes and sizes, including a giant one Vic had caught that was almost as big as a grass snake.

"I've seen a couple of the bigger Spills," I replied, "but they didn't see me."

"I've seen that ginger one from the swing," said Vic, delicately pulling a big juicy worm from the earth with his thumb and forefinger. "He's in the third year and really hard. I heard that he had already beaten up a fourth year kid on the way in this morning, and got the cane for it, but apparently he just grinned at the teacher, who whacked him even harder. It didn't do any good though. Those Spills don't feel any pain."

"They don't seem so bad when you can see them," said Pybus. "You can keep your distance then. It's when they're creeping about in the trees or chasing us, that's when they're really scary."

"I think we've got enough," said Vic changing the subject. "All these worms should shut that Monica up for the rest of the day. We need to get them in her desk quick before those girls get back from lunch. C'mon then."

First lesson that afternoon was geography with Mr Sutton again and the whole class were back at their desks on time waiting expectantly for him to arrive, some of us more expectant than others. We couldn't help ourselves, but the four of us kept glancing over to where Monica and her friends were all giggling and chattering amongst themselves, totally oblivious to what lay lurking inside her desk amongst her exercise books and pens. We must have been grinning like idiots, in anticipationof the moment when she would open the lid of her desk and find her worst nightmare lying within. We heard the footsteps of the teacher approaching and everyone stopped talking and sat up in their seats ready to stand and greet him as he entered the room. The door opened but instead of Mr Sutton, in walked Mr McGrain, the mad Scotsman from this morning's assembly, small and bald and shabbily dressed like Mr Sutton but not nice and kind like him. Sure enough, on his face there was an unfriendly scowl and his voice, rasping with annoyance, explained his unexpected appearance. In front and around me I could see the complexions of my fellow diggers changing colour, like chamaeleons, as they realised the implications of this turnaround.

"Mr Sutton has been called away, so it has fallen upon me to stand in for him," said McGrain in his broad Scottish accent, looking at his despairing audience with contempt in his eyes. I felt my stomach churn and my knees begin to shake, and I tried in vain to attract Billy's attention so we could at least try to rescue this situation, which was rapidly getting out of control. Pybus had his head in his hands and Vic had a sickly grin on his face. He was looking across at Monica and she glanced back confused at his interest, not yet understanding that he was telepathically trying to prevent her from opening her desk. She was not to know.

"Geography books out," barked McGrain. "Page twenty two, The Cave Systems in the Pennine Chain. Quickly now."

The rest of the class and I opened our desks and I thought how nice it would be just to be able to bury my head inside it and not come out until 4.00 pm. I rummaged about looking for my geography book, waiting for the scream that would surely come from Monica's corner. Now. Any second. Surely it would happen. Yet nothing happened. Not at first. There was the noise of scrabbling inside desks and the slamming of the lids down again, but no scream. I peeked out from over the lid of my desk, like Davy Crockett peering over the top of the Alamo, and tentatively looked across the rows to where Monica was sitting.

The reason she hadn't screamed yet was because she hadn't opened her desk yet. While I had my own head buried, she had walked all the way to the front of the class and handed a note to Mr McGrain. When I surfaced I saw him look at the note, nod and give it back to her. It was a doctor's note and she had permission to leave the class early. Not early enough though for the four of us. She walked back down the aisle past Vic and Billy, who both tried to warn her but who were both studiously ignored, past Pybus, who opened his mouth and couldn't say anything, then past me.

"Don't open your desk," I whispered desperately to her but she just looked at me with that mixture of confusion and defensiveness that you always saw in kids who got picked on a lot, and walked on back to her desk.

"SILENCE!" bellowed McGrain, who could, like a shark, pick up the minutest of noises and who could hear the urgent whispering going on. Monica O'Hagan sat down again, opened the lid of her desk, looked inside and then, like the most tragic of heroines, fell soundlessly out of her seat to the floor, all in one movement and in a genuine dead faint.

Monica didn't scream but all her friends did, and they jumped up and down and got into a right state as she lay prone on the floor. We all craned our necks from where we sat in an effort to gauge the

128

damage, as Mr McGrain walked purposefully down the aisle, scattering overhanging heads with the flat of his hand and shouting in an accent that had become even more Scottish in its effort to regain control.

"Calm down, calm down damn ye," he was yelling and then, just as he knelt down beside the still unconscious Monica, and just as he shouted at Lorna Rogers to fetch the school nurse, there emerged from the inside of Monica's desk the biggest and juiciest of the worms, the one that Vic had so proudly caught only half an hour before, making its slow, slithering bid for freedom across the dry, unfriendly landscape.

Although our punishment was to take place in the headmaster's study, such had been his disgust and trauma at the cruel nature of our offence, Mr McGrain had asked if he might be allowed to wield the cane himself. His wish had been granted by Mr Catchpole; he didn't seem the type to enjoy the more physical side of punishment, unlike most of the teachers at the school, so he had happily concurred and was to make do with a more adjudicating role in the matter. That, and the moral lecture that was delivered on pernicious and evil bullying, of not only somebody weaker than us, but a girl to boot.

"Where is the gallantry today," he was asking, "the chivalry of past generations that made this country what it is? In my day a man would sooner cut his own throat than harm a woman. It just wasn't done. You're a disgrace and you are extremely lucky not to be leaving this school. Do you hear me?"

"Yes, Sir," we chorused, the four of us standing in a row, facing the headmaster's desk with McGrain to one side, stick in hand, itching to be at us.

Catchpole got up from his seat and turned to look out of his window.

"Have you anything to say for yourselves," he growled, still with his back to us?

We were silent.

"Well?"

"We didn't know she would pass out," said Vic. "We wouldn't have done it if we had known that. Would we?" he said, bringing in the rest of us as support.

"No, Sir," we wouldn't, agreed Billy. "We thought the worms would give her a little shock, that's all."

Catchpole spun round on his heels and stared at us.

"Little shock! Little shock! You damn near killed the girl, you bunch of imbeciles," he ranted, his face red with anger. "Let this be a lesson to you. That poor girl has a genuine fear, a phobia even, of worms – it is a phobia isn't it, Mr McGrain? Yes a real phobia, and, and…are you laughing boy?" Suddenly he was looking at Billy, who had put his hand to his mouth and stifled what to everyone had sounded like a snigger but which with consummate skill he had managed to turn into some kind of a sobbing sound.

"No, Sir, no," protested Billy with fantastic conviction. "It's when you put it like that, like the way you did, then it makes me realise how wrong we were. I just wish I had obeyed my instincts and not got involved." He gave a few more sniffs for good measure and wiped his eyes with thumb and forefinger.

Vic, Pybus and I stared at each other open-mouthed. Of course it had been Billy's idea, although we hadn't taken much persuading, but to claim that he had been somehow coerced into it. He was a crafty sod sometimes and no mistake.

Catchpole and McGrain looked at Billy suspiciously.

"Is Monica alright, sir?" asked Vic, as if concerned.

"Mr McGrain?"

"Yes she is alright," snarled McGrain. "No thanks to you lot."

"Thank the Lord for that," said Vic in a pious voice I had never heard him use before.

There was another sob from Billy but he stifled it.

Catchpole looked long and hard at Billy and then at all of us just to make sure that we were all taking him seriously. By this time I was, and I think Pybus was too, because he had started to whimper alongside of me in that nervous way he had. We could both see McGrain and his bamboo cane and the longer this went on the more I felt he would be building up a head of steam. The anticipation on his face was obscene.

"You do know that I am duty bound to inform the girl's parents and that means informing your parents too? You do realise this, Gibson? As the new boy in the scenario I would be looking long and hard at the company I am keeping."

"Yes, Sir."

"Pybus, I'm shocked at your involvement," said Catchpole. "Shocked and disappointed."

"Yes, Sir," Pybus said in his trademark whimper.

"As for you two," he continued, glaring at Billy and Vic. "Well I'll be watching you both. You mark my words. I will be speaking to your fathers and advising them that any more of this nonsense and you will be looking for a new school because I will not have reprobates in mine. Am I understood?"

Billy and Vic muttered under their breath.

"AM I UNDERSTOOD?"

"Yes, Sir," they choroused. "We understand."

"Right," said Catchpole. "Hold your hands out. Three on each hand, please Mr McGrain, and don't hold back.

I was first and I held my hands out and waited for the cane to fall. I saw the snarl on the lips of McGrain and the effort in the muscles of his neck as he raised the stick and then brought it down on my soft young fingers. I saw his eyes bulge, his mouth glisten with spittle and the bald head bob, as with joy and relish he struck me, and the skin on my left hand felt as if it had been ripped from my bones, turned inside out and set alight, such was the pain of it.

Chapter 8

THE MAGICIAN

Straight after the cane we were obliged to take our throbbing fingers outside for two lessons of compulsory games. Our class was standing on the recreation ground shivering. It was only September, yet what felt like an ice-blue Arctic wind blew down the Ladybrook, under the seven arches and right on to the cold raw skins of the boys on the football pitch, our thin white limbs draped with inadequate football kit, the cotton damp with light drizzle, clinging to our bodies, making humiliating patches. Half of the boys, Billy, Vic and I amongst them, were charging around after the old leather ball, its great lace, proud in both senses of the word, richly adorning the centre like bright yellow sutures and raised slightly from the hard surface. Only the bravest of boys or the most stupid would dare to head the ball and if you weren't poleaxed by the sheer density of the rain-soaked leather then you were likely to end up with the exact reproduction of the lacing reprinted in a painful image upon your forehead. The other half of the class, Pybus and his ilk, hung around miserably, arms clasped around their own wheezy chests or kicking vacantly at puddles. These little knots of sorrow were largely ignored by our group of boys who played, red-faced and exuberant, blowing great clumps of air from their lungs, like steam trains, and by the large, bespectacled teacher with his baggy shorts, which allowed a tantalising glimpse of hairy knees. Mr Bream was his name and around his neck he wore a whistle on a vivid green ribbon, which he would blow only occasionally, because he liked a free-flowing game. He was proud of his leniency and his purist attitude, which allowed the boys' skills to flourish and allowed him to indulgently show off his own, because he wasn't averse to getting stuck in himself and showing these youngsters a thing or two. He had once had a trial with Port Vale and if he hadn't been such a talented teacher he may well have pursued an alternative career, but the call to academia had won and his glories were restricted to double games sessions on the recreation ground. It was this benevolent attitude which allowed him to largely ignore the pockets of non-combatants. The fewer boys involved the better, so as not to over-clog an already overcrowded pitch, so the odd 'come on, lad, get involved' or 'put yourself about a bit then you won't get so cold' was all the advice wasted by Mr. Bream on the less able boys.

You didn't want to get on the wrong side of him though. Like most of the teachers, he had a violent side to him if riled. Lionel Adshead, bored and cold, kicked the ball deliberately into a puddle of sludge in the goalmouth and then retrieved it by doing a swallow dive into the puddle. Adshead emerged, covered top to toe in mud, hoping and expecting to be sent back to the changing rooms for a hot shower and the chance for a smoke before the last bell, but Mr Bream wasn't having any of it.

He put his whistle to his lips and blew hard, and the game stopped suddenly, boys on the ball turning indignantly to see why they had been halted.

"Adshead, come here!" shouted Mr Bream at the top of his reedy voice and Adshead shambled over with a grin on his face. He was quite a tough kid, with mousy hair like wire wool and sticky-out teeth, but even he wasn't prepared for Bream's method of retribution.

"I've dealt with harder boys than you, Adshead," he said, "real hard nuts, not big girl's blouses like you, lad," and then with his thumb and forefinger he very delicately took the hairs on the side of Adshead's head, that tender space where in a year's time the hairline would meet the whisker line, and he pulled.

"Aaargh!" yelled Adshead and his head went up at an angle to take the strain. Then Bream pulled these small tender hairs harder, and harder, and then with all his strength, forcing Adshead to yell even more in acute pain and stand up on tiptoes to try and reduce the pressure. But Bream just pulled harder still.

"AAARRRGGGHH!" screeched Adshead. "Let go, Sir, please. Please Sir, SIR!" he was saying and the whole football field was laughing out loud at his predicament.

Then he could stand it no longer and begged for mercy.

"I give in, I give in. Let me go. I'm sorry," and Bream eventually let go.

"Next time you mess me about, Adshead," said Bream, "I'll have you doing country dancing with the girls," and as if that threat wasn't bad enough, he made him stand for the rest of the lesson in the middle of the pitch as the elements, sun and wind mainly, dried him to a crusty, brown scarecrow, immobile and barely conscious as everybody else played around him. Although everybody had laughed, we had seen this teacher in a new light and we were all wary of him after that.

Those boys who had a 'bit of talent', amongst them Lenny and Billy from our crowd and a few from the rest of the year like Joe Dempsey and Sammy Stevens, were given the full consultation. The whistle would blow and Bream would get his favourites in a big huddle and they would discuss what brilliant new skill they could try next. Then, waving his white, hairy, stripey-socked limb in the air like a drunk dancing at a wedding, he would reiterate the kicking technique that must be used if the ball is to stay on target while his protégés tried not to laugh. To cap it all he was a Liverpool supporter, and at any opportunity he would regale us with stories of what it was like to stand on the terraces of a real club and sing with twenty thousand others and then when a goal was scored to rush like a wave down the steps of the Kop out of control and in a red heaven. It never bothered me to hear all his crap but some of the other lads who were followers of Man United were close to jumping him on occasions when he wouldn't shut up, to hell with his new-found reputation.

It was rare to play football as part of the school day, they'd rather have us doing PE in the hall, which was a lot cleaner and less bother, but out of school at that time, as the cold winter days drew in, we played football, or at least practiced every single waking moment. If it got too dark for the recreation ground, then we'd play in the street under the streetlamps. In those days there were far fewer cars and kids played on the roads all the time, but it was getting harder and harder because the police were always coming around and putting a stop to it. They'd sneak around in their Morris Minor; two fat coppers who pretended they were just making us aware of road safety, but really they were just having a laugh with us. We would put younger kids on watch but they came around so often that soon it was just easier to go to the rec. We'd play for hours and we must have been at our fittest. We played penalties, or three and you're in, or if there were more than just a few of us we'd play a game end to end with our discarded clothing as goalposts. Occasionally a bunch of lads we didn't know- older, maybe, and tougher, would invite themselves in, and we'd endure a nervous ten minutes or so while they ran rings around us and we'd let them, until they got bored and they'd go off with their girlfriends, laughing and showing off. The high-pitched squeals of the girls carrying across the dusk-filled recreation ground, their painted fingers with cigarettes held high in the air, their mini-skirted arses wriggling as they walked.

When it rained, which in Manchester is every day, or that's how it feels sometimes, we played in the streets. It was hard to find somewhere to play where you wouldn't get bothered by the residents or by the coppers that they called out, but one time we found a more or less perfect place. It was in a crescent that backed onto the football field, at the bottom of a long hill. There was a row of garages to one side, in front of which stood a solitary car, an old Consul with a bullet hole sticker in the back window, which you got with three gallons of petrol. There were a couple of houses away to the left, but the beauty of the position was that it was in the road, so dry, yet with an escape route down to the river if the rozzers appeared. Priory Hill, which was the first part of the crescent, was long and steep and we had often ridden our bikes and our bogeys down it, so if a police car did appear at the top, there was usually plenty of time to get away. There were also a couple of decent street lights that shed great semi-circles of yellow light when darkness came, and that meant we could play as late as we liked in the floodlit road.

The first time the man appeared, we didn't take much notice. He asked us to keep the noise down, 'after all, it is 8 o'clock in the evening', but we ignored him and carried on playing. The next afternoon Lenny King kicked the ball into the front garden and ran in and fetched it out. The man came to his front gate and for the first time I looked at him closely. He didn't seem very big, but he had a black beard and short dark hair. He was well-dressed in a dark suit and tie and he walked with a slight limp. He didn't shout at us in a Manchester accent as we were used to, but spoke softly with a foreign accent.

He said, "Boys, if you want to fetch your ball from my garden, can I trouble you to at least ask me first? It is the respectful thing to do, after all."

We all looked at him with our mouths open. He had a strange way of speaking, sort of polite. I was all for leaving it at that, but I could see Billy and Lenny looking at him hard.

"What if we don't?" said Billy.

The man sighed.

"There is no need for that. Ask for your ball, don't just take it, that is all I'm saying."

"We'll see," said Billy, and he turned and marched back to the road. "Who's that get!" he said, as mouthy as ever, to no one in particular.

"New bloke just moved in," said Linton. "My dad says he's alright."

"Your dad's not had his football almost nicked, has he? I tell you, if he does it again, I'll chin the get. You watch me."

"He's Jewish," said Linton.

"So bloody what?" said Billy loudly.

"Nothing, I'm just telling you, that's all."

"What, like Jesus?" said Vic.

136

"I suppose so," said Linton.

"How did he get here then?" said Billy. "Jesus lived miles away."

"A lot came after the War," I said, "from Germany."

"Well they want to go back there then," Billy ranted on, "and leave us English to play football in peace."

"Are you sure he's Jewish?" Vic carried on. "I mean he looks nothing like Jesus did."

"I'm positive," said Linton. "My dad told me and my dad knows everyone around here. He says he's the only one for miles. They're mainly over Didsbury way. He says he's alright though. A bit strange, but alright."

It was only a matter of time before the ball went in again. The rest of us were happy just to play, but every time Billy got possession, he tried his best to get it in the garden just for the conflict, but he was such a piss poor shot that it took a while. Eventually, Lenny hoofed it in and we all waited to see what was going to happen. Before we could blink, Billy was over the low wall of the house and looking for the ball in the shrubs, so we all dutifully climbed the wall and followed him in.

I have to say, in the short time since he had moved in from God knows where, this bloke had made a beautiful garden. Most people round this way couldn't be bothered, but this man had put a lot of effort into it, you could see. The lawn was like a sponge and moved up and down when you walked on it, like those greens down at the golf course that we sometimes ran across to annoy the old codgers playing there. But there was more besides. Loads of bushes and small trees still tied to their wooden stakes, some already starting to bloom. There was a fragrance to the place that conquered the smells of tarmac and petrol outside, a sweeter perfume of leaves and pine needles and flowers. He had made a crazy paving path that weaved its way from one end of the garden to the other, and at the end of the path stood a funny little wooden building like a Greek temple, circular with only one door and no windows. It was dark inside, no artificial light, just one streak of sun that lit up a simple looking wooden chair, nothing fancy. It looked like the place where the man came to sit in the evening. It was even further away from the road and the rest of the estate, and I could imagine him sitting there in front of his little goldfish pond, pretending to be somewhere else. Anywhere that wasn't Manchester. Even the big trees, especially the huge horse chestnut which probably belonged to next door, were dense enough to keep out all but the heaviest rain, so you could forget about the miserable bloody weather as well. I started to understand why he was so protective about his garden. It was his haven, his peace away from the outside

It was obvious that the house was his pride and joy as well. While the rec was waterlogged from last week's rain, and we were in the street outside, I watched him paint the whole place from top to bottom, using white masonry paint over the pebble dash, and light blue around the roofs and guttering. It took him ages and he was so meticulous, so careful. Like a real artist. As if he was painting some masterpiece and not just his ordinary old suburban house. He spent hours perched up on that ladder and I was so fascinated by his dedication to the job that I'd find myself distracted from our football game and watching him instead, trying to work out what bits he was going to do next. He must have been quite strong, staying up that ladder the whole time, and he must have had a head for heights. Considering he had a bit of a funny shape, big arse and stomach and not very muscular-looking, he was pretty agile up and down and around the top of his ladder, skipping around and leaping on ledges like a bona fide window cleaner, not quite Burt Lancaster in *The Crimson Pirate*, but nifty enough. Part of my interest in him was because he always looked like he might fall, but he never did, even though he sometimes stretched so far from his perch to paint an awkward bit that even I felt like shouting at him to 'get back on your ladder, you daft get'. And all this whilst wearing the same old dark suit, only removing the jacket if it was really hot; up there on that ladder like a businessman who had been locked out and was getting in through his own window. We never saw his wife or kids so we just presumed he lived on his own, although to look at him he didn't look lonely. In actual fact he looked quite contented, but there was something else about him. It was hard to explain.

One evening as the midges from the river came inland and flew around our heads, and little kids sat around listening for the 'Greensleeves' chimes of the ice cream man, Billy Skinner, for the first time in ages, kicked the leather ball right into the old Jew's garden. We all stopped and Billy laughed, and you could tell that he was hesitating to go, but we knew, and he knew, that he would have to retrieve it, so he jumped the fence and disappeared into the area where the lawn was. We stood around waiting for him to emerge, but he didn't come back, not straight away anyway. The rest of us stood around shuffling our feet, except Vic, who had gone off to the river for a piss.

"Where is he?" said Pybus eventually. "He's been in that garden for ages."

"God knows," I said. "You know what he's like. He's probably having a snoop about."

"Maybe that old bloke's got him and he's locked him up in the shed," said Pybus.

"He's probably having difficulty finding the ball, that's all," I said. Besides, in weather like this, if the old bloke's not up his ladder then he's probably out."

"He was out, but not for much longer," said Vic joyously as he returned from the undergrowth. "He's in for it now."

"What do you mean was?" I asked.

"Turn around," said Vic.

So we all turned around and walking down the hill was the old Jewish man in his trademark black suit and wheeling a little shopping trolley behind him, like one of those things the little old ladies use. He walked down his little pathway and let himself in through his front door.

"Bloody hell!" I said.

"What are we going to do? Warn him, somebody." Pybus was sounding panicky.

"Billy!" I shouted as discreetly as I could. "Get back over the fence, he's just got back in." We all listened closely for any response from Billy but there was nothing.

Minutes passed and still no sign of him.

"He must have found him by now," said Pybus. "Billy can't have stayed hidden for this long, he hasn't got the patience for it."

"Oh no," said Vic, trying not to laugh. "Coppers. Boy is he in trouble. He won't know what's hit him."

We turned around again and, sure enough, cruising down Priory Hill at snail's pace, but fast enough for us, was one of those new Morris Minor police cars with the two huge, red-faced coppers inside, looking like they had got stuck and were slowly suffocating.

BILLY!" I yelled again in a soft voice. "GET OUT NOW. HE'S ONLY GONE AND CALLED THE COPPERS."

Unfortunately the coppers hadn't got stuck, and as soon as they saw us, probably in their eyes acting suspiciously, they leapt out of their seats as gracefully as ballerinas, and shouted at us.

"Oy, you lot, over here," they demanded in not very friendly fashion.

The decision was mine in the absence of Billy – they all seemed to be looking up at me to make it, even Vic, which was unusual. It was probably the unfamiliarity, not to say suddenness of my new role, that caused me to make the decision that I did. After all, we weren't really doing anything wrong, but like the soft lad that I was, I felt like we were.

"RUN FOR IT!" I yelled at the top of my voice, and the four lads remaining, myself included, ran off in a mad panic.

The coppers were too apathetic to give chase, but our quick exit gave them enough suspicion to investigate further, and it was only a matter of time before they unearthed Billy in the garden, ball in hand.

I could see from my vantage point how angry Billy was. I could see how red his face was even from a distance and that was a bad sign. Over the following days we would find out how much. Most of all, he was angry with the old Jewish man in the black suit who he blamed for the whole episode. He blamed him for his humiliation in the street, he blamed him for his so-called friends betraying him, and he blamed him for his mother's tears and his father's heavy hand.

The two coppers brought Billy home to his front door, talking about charges of trespass and vandalism, which would not be pursued on this occasion despite the seriousness of the offences. "Keep an eye out for your son, Mr and Mrs Skinner. We don't want him down the Borstal road, do we? Better nip this nonsense in the bud."

After they left, Billy's father took his own belt to his son's behind, while his mother stood in attendance and cried. Billy's father could thrash with the best of them and he left marks, but Billy, far from subdued, came out fighting. He wanted his revenge and he wanted us with him in the wreaking of it.

Billy reasserted his leadership on the building site with a meeting, and the mobilisation started. On a day that was cold and full of black angry clouds we met down where the old farmhouse had been. There was almost no trace of it, everything razed to the ground; it looked a bit like one of those First World War pictures you see with the odd raggedy tree left but mainly piles of trampled-down clay and puddles. Billy and I hadn't been down to the farm since the day we had fallen out over the rafting incident, but he didn't see fit to mention it. He had other things on his mind as he gathered us all together like a general and outlined his plans for revenge against the man from the immaculate house. I'm not so sure what Lenny and Vic and Pybus and the rest of them felt, but I wasn't so sure that it was as simple as that. However I kept quiet. Linton, since the first incident, had kept away. Anything involving coppers and he disappeared, on account of his own dad being one. 'More than his life was worth', he told us.

Billy, I knew, was itching to raise the question of us all running off and leaving him to the police and, if truth be told, we were mindful of our disloyalty, not to say cowardice in this matter. So although there was a growing feeling of unease, I stayed and listened and cheered with the others at the sheer audacity of Billy's plan.

I hadn't been the only one who had noticed how much time the Jewish man had spent on painting his house, how proud he was of it. It shone from its glow of new white paint like a beacon and it became the main target of Billy's revenge. He was careful to wait until he was sure that the painting was completed. In the meantime we assembled all bikes and bogeys because this attack was to be a mobile one, like a commando attack. Get in, bomb the place then get out again quickly before anybody could realise what was happening. Like 'The Dambusters.' All vehicles in use were to be repaired and in tiptop condition and we were to wear disguises, hoods, hats, balaclavas and scarves to cover our faces. If anybody crashed, or was wounded by retaliatory action, they would be left to fend for themselves ("like I was with the coppers," said Billy, glaring at us), but they were not expected to talk, even under the toughest of conditions.

"Right. Any questions?" said Billy to the assembled troops.

A little kid of only about seven, who we didn't know, wearing a purple balaclava, put his hand up.

"Who is he?" said Billy.

"Haven't a clue," I said.

"Yeah, kid, what is it?" asked Billy.

"I'm sorry to trouble you, Sir," said the little nipper. Billy grinned at that, he liked that kind of respect from the younguns.

"One of your soldiers had the wheels off me mam's pram when she left it outside the grocers," the kid continued. "He put it up on bricks with our baby Priscilla still in it. My mam's livid and she's told me to get the wheels back."

"Who's got them?" said Billy wearily to everyone in general.

No response.

"He has," said the kid pointing at Vic, seizing his moment before it disappeared forever.

"Give them back, Vic. Don't nick off prams that are being used. There's plenty of old wheels around," said Billy. He was enjoying his power.

Vic glared at the kid and then walked off to where his bogey was parked to return the stolen wheels.

"Right, let's get going. Pybus, how's the mud pool coming along?"

Pybus was using a big stick to stir the mud. This would be the main ammunition. "Yeah fine, Billy," he said "we're almost there." He flicked a bit of mud at some kid's back and it splattered onto his anorak.

"Yeah. Sound, " said Billy with real approval.

"Billy," said another of the younger ones. "Can we put bubble gum cards in our spokes so we sound like motorbikes?"

"What do you think?" said Billy scornfully. "Considering that we're trying to surprise the bloke and do some sort of commando raid. What do you think?"

"It's not a bad idea, Billy, from the point of view of scaring people," I said. "Just think, if we all did it, how much noise that would be. People won't know what's hit them when we ride past, that's for sure."

"It could sound really impressive, Billy," said Pybus, still stirring his mud. Scare them to death in that street."

"Yeah," said Lenny, "all those people that laughed at you when you got arrested. They won't know what's hit them."

Billy raised his arms up to settle his troops. He had yet another announcement.

"All those riding bikes in the attack must have cards on their spokes. We're going to make one hell of a racket. Nick the clothes pegs from your mums to fasten them with. Anyone short of cards come to Pybus, he's got loads."

"They're my collections," moaned Pybus.

"Stuff your collections," said Billy. "This is war."

So like the Sioux lined up against General Custer, or like the Zulus lined up on the ridge above Rorke's Drift , an assortment of bikes, scooters and bogeys ridden by one, or sometimes two, masked members of our gang, gathered in a long line across the top of Priory Hill. We wore scarves or balaclavas across our faces like bank robbers and most of us carried sticks about two feet in length, on top of which was a round piece of semi-gelatinous mud. These mud-balls were about the size of a small snowball, and had been meticulously prepared and loaded by Pybus and Vic back at the farm.

The lined formation became a vanguard, with Billy at the apex and his trusted lieutenants, me and Vic, on his right hand side. We left Pybus behind at the mud pool making more ammunition, and besides, he was useless on a bike. Our target was the house of the little Jewish man, and I could just see him at the bottom of the hill, in his garden tending his flowers. As we waited and soaked up that feeling of battle, the quietness of the air, the grey dry day perfect for our mission, there was a sudden cold gust of doubt in my stomach and my right leg, resting on the pedal of my bike, started to shake. Vic, who was my passenger because he never did find any wheels for his own bogey, was breathing hard against my neck. He carried a stick, and so did I. There was, however, no time for my doubt to grow. Our leader, Billy, raised his arm in the air and shouted, "Let's roll!" like John Wayne would have said at some point in most of his films, and like a huge wave, the twenty assorted vehicles, with thirty masked lads on board, cruised down the hill. All sorts of wheels squeaked, tyres roared on the tarmac and Pybus's bubble gum cards pegged to our spokes flapped manically, as we rode down the long slope into the bowl of the cul-de-sac at the bottom.

Then, as we reached the target, we fired, in a synchronised burst, globules of mud from our sticks at the pristine white walls and dark reflective windows of the Jewish man's house. We rode close to the little privet hedge up on the pavement then down again like real raiders, flicking the sticks as we passed, and the mud flew off and made splat sounds against the walls and more musical clunks against the window panes. As each bike or cart passed the house, more mud flew, until the whole wall was covered in little rivulets of brown stain, like hot treacle on icing. The house lost its pure white crust.

Then, as we turned to ride back up the hill to reload from one of the supply bogies, the next wave passed by. Another load of mud was fired at the house and suddenly, in amongst the splats and the thuds, there was the unmistakable clinking of broken glass. And then another.

Two broken windows. That batch of mud must have been contaminated with stones somehow, and when the mud balls had been hurled they had broken two of the front windows. This was not mud that could be washed off. I felt sick to my stomach. We had crossed a line and now the whole operation was in danger of backfiring. Out of the corner of my eye I saw the man, dressed in his black suit as always, run from his garden to his gate. I heard him berating the passing horde loudly and angrily, but with sobs of emotion in his voice, as he himself looked back to see what the mud had done to his precious paintwork. But it was the broken glass that seemed to enrage him. His voice sounded like the howl of a child, or a dog even, such was his confusion at the punishment he was receiving, the violation of his home.

As I rode back around the crescent, legs pumping me back up the hill with that clown Vic whooping with exhilaration at the back of me, that feeling of forboding returned. I returned to the farm and the meeting place where the celebration of the success of the operation had already begun, but in amongst the gloating and glorifying from my fellow raiders, my own joy was muted. No matter how much I justified our actions to myself, or even just trivialised it, I couldn't get the noise of the man's cries out of my head.

Those days at school were days of expectation, waiting for the calls to come. If he wasn't going to the police, then surely he must pay a visit to the headmaster and if that happened, well we were all for the cane. Or even worse, expulsion. Every assembly we waited for our names to be read out and to be summoned to Catchpole's study, and every day, as every other miscreant in the school, from first year to fifth, had their names called out, our names remained uncalled. For two weeks after the incident, there was no sign of the police and no sign of the Jewish man. Maybe it wasn't so bad after all, maybe I was taking it too seriously. The others had forgotten all about it, why shouldn't I? But I had heard his cries. I had heard his agony from deep down, his voice carrying a young child's words, "Please don't, please leave us alone."

Then his anger. English words, spat out with hate and fear in a foreign accent, "Criminals! Barbarians!"

Surely he would act. Sooner or later he would find out who had attacked his home and when he did, he would come looking for us.

Sure enough, the following day, as we all lined up for assembly, the little man in his dark suit walked into the school building, pulling his little shopping trolley behind him. Vic saw him first.

"He's here. He's here. I knew he'd come after us," he exclaimed, hopping about from one foot to another.

Strangely I felt calm. It was what I'd been expecting every day for the last two weeks and I was almost pleased that he had finally arrived.

"Where's Billy?" I said.

"In the toilet," said Lenny "Probably hiding."

"Or shitting himself," said Vic.

"Someone fetch him," I said, once again going into leadership mode.

"You bleeding fetch him," said Vic. "Who do you think you are, ordering people around, Winston Churchill, you cheeky get?"

"Alright," I said, "I will."

"Hang on," said Pybus, "why fetch him? He's no bloody good in a crisis, as we all know. He's better off in the toilet out of the way."

I groaned. "Look, I don't bloody care anyway. If he's here to see Catchpole, then so what. I'll be glad to get it over with."

Then Billy appeared from the toilet with not a care in the world, chewing gum, his big red cheeks working furiously.

"Look who's here," said Vic and, nodded his head in the direction of the headmaster's study, where the man in black was waiting patiently.

I could see Billy visibly pale under his red raw skin but he carried it pretty well, I'll give him that. He gave one glance over to where the man stood and said, "I couldn't give a monkey's about that get. He can squeal all he likes. He's still got to prove that it was us and since we were masked up I don't see how he can."

"He knows it was us," I said.

"Of course he does, soft lad," said Vic, "and forget proof. Since when do this lot need proof to cane you? They'll do it for fun."

"We'll be lucky if we get the cane," I said. "Catchpole could expel us for this. He said he wanted to after we put the worms in O'Hagan's desk. This might be the final straw for him. If he expels us, I might as well leave home now because I tell you I am dead."

"What's it got to do with the bloody school?" hissed Billy. "We did it on a Sunday."

"It doesn't matter when we did it," Vic hissed back at him. "You know what Catchpole is like. It's always school business."

"That's it," said Pybus "We're bloody done for."

"I'm going into assembly," said Vic, "we're safe in there until I get a chance to think. C'mon. Let's go. Maybe we can get out the back way."

Suddenly half the school started to move and teachers, blocked out by the crowd, were forced to stand on tip-toes and shout directions so as to prevent a stampede: "Wait your turn, fifth form first, Adshead you're a cretin, what are you?" and other messages of support, in deep scornful voices, overpowering the sheer volume of adolescent hum that had threatened to take over. Eventually some kind of order was resumed and under the cover of this teenage wave we slipped into the hall, and away from the headmaster's study. Feeling temporarily reprieved we sat down and waited for the teachers to file in, and as they did so, then the whole school stood in unison. We remained standing, waiting, as was the custom, for the headmaster to bring up the rear which he did... with the little Jewish man beside him.

Together, making an incongruous pair, they walked up the main aisle to the podium at the centre of the stage. I looked at my friends down the row either side of me and they wore the expressions of condemned men. I heard Vic, to my left, whisper almost incredulously, "They've only let the bastard follow us in. He's in here with us."

"That's it," said Pybus, "we are done for. I think I'm going to faint. Hold me up Billy."

"Shut the fook up, Pybus, yer big girl!" said Billy, bright red with rage and rising panic. "Or I'll batter you here and now. I don't bleedin' care where we are."

There was no escape. In front of the whole school we were going to be dragged out and humiliated, and I could feel my whole body going hot and cold under my clothes and a feeling of faintness, bright lights in my eyes. I looked to the big windows all down one side of the hall and the sunlight coming in seemed to smash them into a thousand pieces. I wanted to be out in the sunshine on my own walking across the playing field and home, not here in the hall.

The headmaster walked to the front of the stage and began to speak, his loud voice booming around the auditorium. The whole school was quiet, half watching the headmaster, half watching the Jewish man, standing right behind him, everyone listening, curious and expectant. The teachers in a row behind both men sat, arms folded and grim-faced. Already this didn't feel like normal assembly.

On the film screen at the back of the stage area there was a sudden movement, flickers of black and white, fragmented at first but then rejoining to form an image and make some sense. There was a clicking sound from behind us, which like the image transformed into a whirr as the projection machine cranked into life. Across our heads shone a long triangle of white light, cutting through the semi-gloom of the hall like an axe head. It was so gloomy outside that the teachers hadn't even bothered to pull down the blinds. In the projector light, previously unseen particles of dust and flies danced a frenzied jig and on the screen we at last started to make out some of the images, although the first one or two had us puzzled. It showed schoolchildren standing by a big wide road. Around them were houses that, although not destroyed, were badly damaged. Some of the front doors in the picture had big letters in white paint written on them, and these letters spelt the word *Juden*. The children carried their schoolbooks secured by little leather straps and although they smiled for the camera, it was easy to see that there was fear and horror in their eyes. The little Jewish man, by now standing at the lectern, spoke out and his soft foreign voice carried all round the assembly hall.

"Boys and girls," he said, "my name is David Ashton. David is my real name. Ashton isn't. It used to be Rosenberg but I changed it when

I came here. My friends told me it would be easier that way. I regret that now. Still."

He paused for a moment. We could see him peering at us from the lectern, one hand clasping a sheaf of notes, looking as if he was about to run away. But he wasn't.

"Some of you may know me already," and as he said this he looked deep into the crowd assembled below him.

He continued.

"I came to your beautiful country from Germany at the end of the War, when I was fifteen, the same age as many of you here, I suspect. You see I had to come, because there was nothing left for me in my own land. It had rejected me and my people. In November 1938, when I was much younger than you, about eight years old if I recall, there was a turning point for my people. It was called *Krystallnacht*, which means in English the night of the broken glass." He stopped again and looked down. I swear he was looking directly at the five of us sitting in a line about twenty rows back from the stage and we all shrank down in our seats.

"That night the Nazi Stormtroopers, fascist bully boys, call them what you will, destroyed our property and businesses and beat up thousands of innocent people across the length and breadth of Germany. This was done solely and simply because we were of the Jewish race and it was the final realisation for my people, for many of us too late a realisation, that Germany wanted rid of us, absolutely and unequivocably. No matter how much we wanted to believe otherwise, the writing was on the wall, in many places literally. *Juden* the signs said, and these signs, which were hung on doors and windows and placed around the necks of children and respected academics and business people and old ladies alike, singled us out for a very special treatment. You see, *Krystallnacht* meant broken glass from thousands and thousands of broken windows, but it also meant hatred and fear and the beginning of the killing."

He stopped again, a long pause in a sea of silence that was a Monday morning assembly going rapidly wrong. I felt faintly sick.

Then he nodded to the back again, and I saw that he was prompting the man in charge of the projector. There was another click and another black and white image. A wave of humankind crammed into trains with no room to move. A few looks of anguish, but mainly looks of grim resignation on their faces. A couple smiled, as if they were going on holiday. The image sucked me in briefly, and I felt the closeness, the suffocation. How could they breathe like that, crammed together like sheep in a pen? The little dark figure on the podium paused again and looked around. The whole hall was quiet and expectant. Even the bigger lads at the back who were always mucking about had gone quiet. Then he spoke again.

"By now, although I didn't know it at the time, all my family were dead. They had died at the hands of the Nazis in death camps all across Europe but somehow, by God's will, I managed to survive." He pointed to the screen behind him.

"That's where these people are going, to the death camps, although if you look at some of the faces they don't all know it. But trust me, boys and girls, most, if not all, in this picture were dead quite soon afterwards. I survived because I was a magician and it amused the officers in my camp to keep me alive, so I could entertain them on the long, cold winter evenings. He smiled to himself, a sad, sickly smile. "I was a very nervous performer. If my tricks failed, well I could be shot. Luckily for me my tricks never failed."

The projector made another click and the next frame came up on the screen. This one showed row upon row of wooden bunk beds, from which malnourished, defeated eyes peered. They were mainly women and children and many were wearing a coarse striped uniform a little like pyjamas; the few men there, were unshaven and hollow-eyed and frightened.

Click and another picture of more women, some determined looking but most just looking confused, and children, mainly solemn-faced but some, in their innocence, smiling. Click again, yet another stark image, totally shocking in its degradation, in its humiliation of fellow human beings, in its desecration of a moral taboo. Young male

German officers surveyed a line of people. Most were old, all were naked. In the foreground, an old woman, with the gentle face of a grandmother, stood, looking straight ahead, unbowed, proud. The young officers seemed to be laughing at her wrinkled skin and empty breasts and her stomach sagging over, yet the old woman, on some greater level than her captors would ever reach, stared straight ahead into her own private heaven.

Somebody at the back of the hall whispered "phwoar" but was immediately met with a "shut up" from one of his associates. A few of the girls around the hall began to sniffle and I could see a few handkerchiefs dabbing at eyes.

I felt the skin on my face tighten and my eyes and throat start to burn. I had never seen anything like this before. Sure, pictures of dead soldiers; *All Our Yesterdays* was always on showing the War. But I had never seen women, children and old people shown so cruelly treated, worse than animals even. I felt sick to my stomach. I looked at Skinner, who looked at me then looked away. Click, another picture, then another and another. At the end a pile of bodies, the colour of chicken, stacked up one on top of another like long grey bags of rubbish. Another picture, more of the same, but this time with British soldiers standing in shock, as if in a trance at what they were seeing. Then the film stopped and the hall went dark except for where a spotlight shone down onto the man at the podium. Then he walked out to the front of the stage with the light still on him and stood looking out across the hall. In the silence and the gloom his distinctive voice called out. "Do you have any questions?" he asked.

Nobody put their hand up. Not at first. Then somebody shouted out from the back of the hall.

"Were you in one of these camps?"

"Yes. Yes I was. It was called Bergen Belsen and it was like hell. I was no older than you are now, young man. I am afraid you saw the pictures."

"What happened to the Germans after the war?" Another question, this time from some kid in a row near us. I could feel the others alongside me keeping their heads down in case the Jewish man glanced along our row and saw us.

"They were taken away to prison or shot. Some were killed as soon as the liberation started, by the prisoners themselves. A lot got away." Then he laughed a sad ironic little giggle. "There may well be SS guards living on the streets of Manchester, maybe even on your street, young man. Have you thought about that?"

"How did you manage to survive?" This time from one of the middle rows.

"I told you, by magic. I was a magician." Then, as he saw the questioner looking unconvinced, the Jewish man elaborated.

"I'm sorry, I am being flippant. It wasn't just because I was a magician, although that was part of it. But I stayed healthy because I wasn't put to work like the others and I was lucky too. Not all the officers were psychopaths. There was one who helped me more than the others. Who protected me. Who kept me alive."

"What happened to him?" shouted another voice from the back.

"He died at the liberation I think. I never knew for sure. He was a good man in an evil place."

I found my hand going up.

"Put your bloody hand down," said Billy. "He'll recognise you." He spoke out of the side of his mouth, his own head ducked down behind the chair in front. I ignored him.

"Yes you." The man beckoned to me for my question. He showed no sign of recognising me.

"Excuse me," I said, "what was your best trick and do you still do it?"

He looked at me long and hard. "Well, my boy, I will show you my best trick. Do you believe in magic?"

"I'm not sure," I replied, "I've never seen any good magic. Only on TV."

So he clasped his hands together with a loud clap as if to warm them, and then unclasped them all in one movement. There, standing on the open palms of his hands, was a beautiful snow-white dove. He raised his hands slightly upwards, and the dove flew away up to the windows at the top of the hall. Then he did it again and again and each time a beautiful white dove appeared from the palms of his hands and then flew to the windows. There were gasps and cries from all around the hall.

"You see," he continued and I had the strange feeling that he was talking just to me, "those Germans loved this trick with the doves. The fact that the dove is a symbol of peace was lost on them, or maybe the notion of peace was never a consideration for them. After the officers had eaten and before their women arrived, as they were drinking brandy, they always called for me to come and do some magic. The one trick they always wanted me to do was with the doves. And the reason for this was because as the doves flew to the open window to escape outside – look, just as this one is doing now– well they would take out their pistols and shoot them. Their intention was to shoot the dove before it left the room."

"Did they?" I shouted to him. I was oblivious to the rest of the hall now, but the whole school was quiet, waiting for his answer. "Did they kill the doves?"

The old Jew smiled. "They thought they did. They saw the red blood and there was the flutter of dying wings but no, there was no way they could kill the birds because it was magic." Then he opened his arms and what felt like a hundred doves flew up across the hall and out through the open windows to freedom. All, that is, except one. Just one pure white bird seemed for a moment to lose its way. It flew down to the rows of pupils and, before I knew it, settled on my hand. I had forgotten to take my hand down from when I had first asked the question and my arm was still stuck up in the air and this stupid bird, by some fluke, had flown right on to it. Only for a moment though, because no sooner had it landed and looked at me with its beady eyes then it flew off again, out of the open windows to join its friends on the outside. When finally the last dove had flown to freedom through the open window, I looked back to the stage, and I saw immediately that the magician, much to the relief of my friends, had gone as well.

Chapter 9

THE MOORS

For the next few days I avoided Billy and Vic and I stood at the top of
the black cinder lane and watched the lorries going into and out of
the building site. As they went past, the drivers waved at me and a lot
of them gave the thumbs up or down and said "swinging" or "dodgy"
depending on how they felt. One of the drivers was an Indian, not
from America like the milkman, but a Sikh Indian from India. He
wore an orange turban on his head and he grinned down at me from
his cab, his white teeth a gash of a smile in his voluminous black beard
and his head nodding as if on a spring. His name was Sid (abbreviated
for the sake of understanding, he told me later) and he came to work
in a collar and tie and wore very serious-looking black-rimmed glasses
when he stopped to read a map, which he did by the big oak tree at
the site entrance. From the neck up he could have been a business
man and he was very proud of what he did. He was proud of the
strength in his arms and hands. "You'll not find no office Wallah with
hands like these, young boy," he would tell me later. He owned his
own lorry, he told me that day, and he was happy to be bringing
aggregate and sand "to help make the houses for decent people to live
in."

The first conversation Sid and I ever had was when he stopped his
lorry at the top of the lane to turn out into the main road. He was
empty so I presumed that he was off to get a fresh load of sand or
gravel. Then a meaty brown hand jolted out of the driver's side window,
making the thumbs up sign.

"Swinging?" he asked me in his funny accent, allowing the one word to resound around his mouth like an echo. I was so pleased to be acknowledged by this great man in his lorry that for a moment I didn't respond, but then my little fist popped up with my thumb turned down to the ground and I could hear my thin little voice against the noise of the engine.

"Dodgy," I replied and the Sikh gave me a big grin then stuck his great big lorry into gear and throbbed away up the new Cheadle road to fill up his wagon. I waited by the tree for the rest of the day to see if he would return but he didn't come back and I resolved to wait for him tomorrow. This went on for days. Straight after school I rushed home and waited by the tree at the entrance to the site. Then one day Sid stopped his lorry full of stones going in and leant out of his window.

"Hey young boy," he said in his rich, exotic voice. "How come you are always here? Have you no friends to play with?"

"Yes," I said indignantly, "I have friends."

He smiled down at me, his head shaking slightly from side to side. I got used to those shakes of the head later. He was acknowledging my answer not disputing it.

"I would just rather watch the lorries, that's all."

"Oh very good. Now tomorrow is Saturday I believe?"

"Yes," I replied.

"Not a day for school I believe?"

"No not a school day," I said, suddenly cautious as to why he was asking.

"Well," he said, "if you were to get permission from your mother and your father perhaps you could ride over the hills with me tomorrow to get some sand from the quarries. What do you think to that?"

I couldn't believe it, I was that happy I whooped. "YES!" I yelled up to him. "That would be great. Shall I wait for you here?"

"No," he said. "It'll be perfectly fine I am sure but it would be more discreet if we met further down the road."

155

"Eh?" I said. I found out later that he spoke like this sometimes.

"Meet me down there away from the site," he repeated. "But be sure to bring a note from your mother. I can't take you without a note. But don't tell anyone else. I'm not meant to take passengers, but I make exceptions for lonely boys."

For once my dad was home for his tea, although he always ate it away from us in front of the telly. I wanted to ask him questions but I could see that he wanted to watch the news. There was something about those missing kids again and pictures of a mad-looking woman with blond hair, but I wanted to ask him about the lorry and whether I could ride over the hills with Sid.

"What?" he said to me, one eye still on the television. My mother stood in the doorway, arms folded across her apron, a look of horror on her face at the unfolding news. Behind her from the kitchen wafted a smell of bacon and eggs, which we often ate at tea time.

"What are you on about? What's this about a lorry?" said my dad munching on a piece of toast.

"He says I can go with him to Huddersfield to pick up a load, but he needs a note from you."

"No!" snapped my mother, without taking her eyes off the telly.

"Hang on a second," said my dad to my mother, not to me.

"He's called Sid and he's a really nice bloke. Can I please, Dad?" For some reason I left out the bit about him being a Sikh from India with a lovely orange turban. I didn't think that my parents would object to somebody from another country but I didn't want to take a chance. With these kids going missing my mother was anti anything that moved. Even the Pope himself would have had trouble getting me out on a day trip the way she was going. But despite all this I could see that my dad was wavering.

"Please, Dad," I said, keeping the pressure on.

"There are kids going missing from all over Manchester and he wants to go off in a lorry with somebody called Sid," said my Mum. "That doesn't seem very sensible to me."

"You say he works on the site with all the other builders?" quizzed my dad while pointedly ignoring my mother. "And they all know him?"

"Yes. Yes," I assured him. "They all know him down there. Please, Dad, I swear he's a nice bloke and he won't do it without a note from you. Please."

"It sounds alright to me. When are you meeting him?"

"Tomorrow at 8.00 am. Down by the oak tree at the cinder lane."

"Excuse me. Do I have an opinion here?" asked my mother, getting annoyed.

"It'll be a good experience for him, get him out and about," said my dad, his decision already made. But my mother wasn't finished. She didn't give in that easily.

"He's always out and about," she countered. "In fact I never see him. Except for meals or when the pop lorry comes." Mum took a deep breath and shook her head from side to side, a sure sign that she was digging in. "He treats this house like a hotel and me like a skivvy," she continued. "Come to think of it you all do. You and our Sandra, and as for Stevie; I haven't seen him for two days."

"Well I ran wild as a kid and it didn't do me any harm," said my dad, ignoring the very obvious signs that mum was getting upset. Her voice was cracking and I could tell she was close to tears and I couldn't understand why my dad was still pushing it. This was becoming a war.

Then she lowered her voice in an effort to stay in control, but even I could see that there was no going back to rational argument.

"There were no cars when you were a kid to run you over."

"Yes there were," he said. "How old do you think I am?"

I sat quietly and miserably, quickly realising that they were careering to yet another row, and this time, it was all my fault. Bloody lorry driver, I wish I had never set eyes on him.

"It's alright I won't go," I said trying to defuse the tension.

"You bloody well will," said my dad.

"What about these then?" said Mum, pointing to the telly.

"What, The Hollies" said my dad facetiously. *Ready Steady Go* had followed the news and they were stood there, all suits and guitars, singing a song about looking through any window or some such thing. They should take a look through our window, that would give them something to sing about.

"You know what I mean, damn you!" she screamed at him. "I mean these monsters they've caught today. The two on the news, who killed all those kids and buried them on the moors. Those kids ran wild and look what happened to them."

"So what do you want to do? Lock all the kids up until they go out to work?" He was shouting now, the big vein in his forehead starting to throb like it always did when he was angry.

"For God's sake, woman. You won't keep them in for ten minutes. They'll be off and I wouldn't blame them. Wouldn't you, kid? You'd be off down the bloody road and I'd be right behind you because I can't stand the bloody mithering."

"I am a mother and I have to protect my kids," said mum persevering, convinced that she was right. "All of the mothers think the same."

My dad went quiet, his mouth set in an angry, resistant snarl, and that was as ominous as when he was shouting. But if my mum saw these as warning signs she chose to ignore them. She wasn't finished. I wanted her to stop, to let it go, but she was like a dog with a bone. Our George, hearing the noise had come down from his bedroom and he stood there, in his pyjamas, shivering tears, understanding like I did, that this row was even worse than all the others. "Stop, please stop," I begged them, but neither of them could. They were drowning in a flood of recrimination and were past saving.

"We've talked about it," she went on. "None of us want to be like that poor bloody woman weeping on the news because she's lost her kid. She was only ten for God's sake. The same age as our George, just a baby. Those people killed her in cold blood and now she will never grow up and get married and have babies of her own. All this roaming has to stop. They can both stop around here for a while." Then she started to cry and no more words would come.

My dad stood up and for a horrible moment I thought he would lash out such was the anger in his face. His skin had gone pale and there was a sheen of sweat on his top lip.

Then he spoke in a measured tone and I felt like crying myself because I knew he was preparing to leave the house again and these were his departing words.

"The kid goes out tomorrow and the next day and any bloody day he wants to wherever he wants, and if some murderer gets him then that is bloody tough. It's highly bloody unlikely, but tough if it happens. No son of mine, whether I am here to see it every day or not, will be frightened out of living his life by any other living man or woman. I will not allow you or your hysterical friends to turn my son into a bloody nancy boy, frightened of his own shadow. Do you understand me?"

My mother wept now fully and without restraint. She could no longer resist and merely sat, her head lowered, tears spilling into her lap, out of love with her husband, he out of love with her and me in the middle of them both, cowering and shaking in the wake of my father's rage and my mother's despair. My father walked through the kitchen to the back door and stood by the counter for a few seconds writing on a piece of paper. He turned round and beckoned me over. His eyes were glazed and watery, the same look that he had had at the river and the look he seemed to carry almost every time I saw him; a look of desperation and unhappiness.

"I wrote your note so make sure you're on that lorry," he said then he ruffled my hair. "Sorry kid," he said, "I might not see you for a while," then he walked out the back door and into the dark night.

Deep down I think I didn't believe that my dad would really leave us. At twelve years old I suppose I could just about understand a husband getting angry with his wife enough to leave her. But what man would leave his children? I know Stevie and Sandra weren't his, but George and I were. His own flesh and blood. So in the beginning at least I refused to believe my own father would desert me forever. He would be back in a few days, like he always was. It would be like a long shift at work in Manchester, then he would return dirty grumpy and tired. But he would return.

My feelings of unease at his going were bolstered by these rational thoughts, all my own work lying in bed at night, sleep refusing to come and relieve me of my worries; but I was also helped by the new adventure with Sid that I was about to embark upon.

Half the fun was the clandestine way we went about it. Sid had drummed it into me that he'd lose his job if I blabbed, so the whole trip had an air of danger about it. Down the road from the site, so as not to be seen, I climbed into the cab of the old lorry that was Sid's own pride and joy, with its own peculiar smell, a pungent mix of leather, petrol and Sid's tobacco pipe. He drove along with that pipe sticking out of his mouth at a right angle blowing great gusts of smoke like Popeye the sailor man. I sat alongside him high up and proud looking down on all the other drivers below me, or I looked out of the window as row after row of houses were replaced by green fields with cows in, which in turn were replaced by more rugged and spectacular scenery as we headed towards the hills. The very same hills that I had looked at for hours on end, from the top of the apple tree down at the old farm that was now a building site.

Sid and I didn't say much as we rolled along, and then even less as we started to climb up the hills, because he drove in deep concentration, juggling the gears skilfully to keep the revs up, the old lorry whining as it strained every rivet in its engine. Then when we went down the other side he used the gears again, whirring and clunking to save the brakes. Finally we were on a flat straight bit and the Pennines stretched out all around us, a rolling land of browns and greens, crowned by jagged granite outcrops on top of the peaks, silver in colour against the harsh light, like waves on an inland sea.

At this point, with most of the hard driving done, Sid pulled over into a lay-by, and we climbed out of the cab to look at the view. He had started to talk again and his happy self returned. The view from the top where we were was amazing, and he pointed out the little farms with their outbuildings and the long lines of dry stone walls that separated field from moor. We could see for miles and miles and miles.

"Look at that country, boy," he said, "look at it. It is so beautiful, so green, so fertile, like a Garden of Eden. God's own country." I looked as he commanded me to do and although I could never have put it into such enthusiastic words I did feel the freshness of it all, especially after the estate where we lived, with its cars and houses and all its people. Up here there was a lot of sheep but no people. And I could feel the weather properly, the sun and the wind. I could feel it in my eyes and my mouth and in my hair and on my skin. It felt good. Maybe it was just moorland, but to me and Sid, it was freedom.

Then in the distance, maybe two or three hills away to the west, I could suddenly see movement. Like lines of black ants but in some sort of formation, there were people walking across the landscape from left to right. They were moving so slowly as to appear almost stationary, but moving they were because Sid and I watched them off and on for twenty minutes or more. Some reached the brow of that hill and went over it while still more replaced them from the valley floor, almost as if they were rotating from under the hill itself. It was as if we were peering into a secret parallel world colonised by people we could never be close to.

"Who are they, Sid?" I asked, looking up at him to one side of me studying the distance with a puzzled look.

"Do you know," he said, "at first I thought they might be those beater fellows for scaring the birds into the sky for the rifle shooters. You know there's a lot of that sort of sport in these parts. I have seen them before when I have crossed the hills in my lorry."

Then he gave a great big sigh that came from the bottom of his stomach up through his throat and whistled out through his beard.

"I think they may be policeman," he said finally.

"Why?"

"It breaks my heart," he said, "but I think they may be looking for the lost children. Do you know who I mean?"

"Yes I do," I replied. "You mean the ones that got murdered?"

"Yes," he said, "by those evil monsters Hindley and Brady." Then he spat onto the ground and said, his voice a growl, "May they die and rot in hell."

We watched the policemen for a little while longer then climbed back into the lorry and continued on our way. For a long time though I couldn't get those lost kids out of my mind and I thought again of my mother and how she would feel if I was buried up here and they couldn't find me even with a hundred policemen looking. An unpleasant wave of guilt hit me for a moment until I managed to shrug it off with a question to Sid.

"What about your country, Sid?" I asked him. "Is it like this one at all?"

"Never," he replied. "My country is hot and brown and dusty and hard to farm. Hard to live in, even. When the rains come, the monsoon we call them, it rains too bloody much and everything just washes away. It is very annoying. No, this is my country now and I am very pleased to be here. Thank you very much!"

"But don't you get homesick? I mean if I left here and went to a place, no matter how much I liked it I would still get homesick. What about your family?"

For a moment Sid was silent and I took my eyes off the view for a moment to look up at this unknown man beside me. I studied his great long beard that rolled all the way down to his chest and that started at his neck and ears and high on his cheekbones and disappeared up into his turban in tendrils of fine black hair. I studied his dark slightly pockmarked skin which crinkled round his eyes, friendly eyes full of unshed tears, always watery from smoke and dust, sometimes smiley, sometimes sad. Sad at this moment as we drove and he thought of his family in India, and his spiritual home, and his sacred temple, and where he found it so hard to live. Then he cleared his throat with such a violent sound, almost a growl, long and low in his throat, a sound I later came to know as 'hawking' and in so doing he fetched up from the depths of his lungs an almighty gob that he rolled around in his mouth for a few moments before despatching it out of his driver's window and onto the landscape. He spat gob like a giant would, arcing it to fall like a missile and under my breath I swore "fooking hell" half disgusted, half impressed. To him it was a regular gesture; it meant nothing and each time he hawked he carried on as normal straight after.

"Thank God most of my family are here in Manchester," he continued. "That's why I have to work so hard," he said with a laugh, "because there are so many of the buggers I have to provide for."

He was glad of my company I think and was probably pleased that I didn't ask too many questions. When we got to the great quarry where we were to load the gravel I munched on the cheese sandwich that I had made myself that morning in the kitchen, when it was still dark outside and the whole house had been asleep. One of the quarrymen gave me a cup of sweet tea and it tasted better than lemonade. Sid parked the lorry under this great funnel that was attached to a big metal silo and I watched cascades of gravel hit the metal tipper with an almighty rattle, like hailstones on a tin roof, then gradually fill up. The rattling turned to a swooshing noise as the load increased, and then finished in a peak like a Mr Whippy ice cream. The whole process only took about five minutes and then we were ready to go back to Manchester. On the way back, through grey skies and patches of mist I kept an eye out for the policemen but they weren't to be seen and then we were going down hill again, Sid crunching his gears as we descended into Manchester from the Huddersfield side down through Oldham and into Gorton and east Manchester. There was still time for Sid to unload at the site, but he dropped me first by the oak tree so as not to be seen, and I ran home half full with my own adventure, but worried about my mum nonetheless.

There was no sign of my dad and I didn't dare ask her where he was; that's assuming she knew. She said nothing, just gave me my tea and went back to watching *Take Your Pick* with Michael Miles, fag in hand, stone-faced. Not a word about where I had been, or what I had been up to. I tried conversation but she cut me short with a "Michael, I don't want to know" so I gave up and munched on my toad in the hole, half listening to the hysteria of the TV audience: "Open the box!", "Take the money!" "No open the box!", all that shite.

The next week I went with Sid again, and this time we went out onto the moors on another road. I looked out for coppers but saw none. As we had done the time before at the top of the climb Sid stopped his groaning lorry and we got out, scattering the native sheep, and spent a full twenty minutes taking in the views all around us. I never thought at the time how strange it would have looked to other travellers seeing a young lad next to a big Sikh, in a bright purple turban this time, standing on top of a green bank letting the wind blow into us, our eyes watering with the cold pure air that blew across the ridges and the crags of the Pennine hills.

On this day the loading took longer and there seemed to be some dispute with the paperwork, because it was later than usual when we started for home. The light was already going and the hills looked shadowy and sinister and the long road in front of us lonely and empty. It made me think of the children again and what they must have wondered when they passed through the same landscape on their final journeys, that's if they were alive to see it.

"Sid," I said, "I can't be too late. My mum worries, especially now after those murders."

"You are safe with me, boy," said Sid.

I grinned up at him. "Yeah I know, but trouble is she worries when I'm not with you. On my way home. To-ing and Fro-ing. I tell her there's nothing she can do. I mean she can't lock me up, can she?"

"They have locked those two away now," said Sid. "Things are better."

"She just says there's more where they came from. She says, "just watch, they'll all start appearing like rats out of the drains.""

Sid laughed.

"It's not funny, Sid. It's gone too far. It's not so bad for me, but my younger brother can't do anything, and she's there. All those mothers are outside the school gates again waiting for the kids after school. They haven't done that since they were five. Before they didn't care, we never saw them. Now we can't get rid of them."

"Sons and mothers," said Sid. "They are a very fine combination, but sometimes like dynamite, like combustion." He kept his eyes straight ahead as he spoke but his head bobbed up and down in time to the bumpy moorland road. He was always using these big words, like combustion, always trying to show me how good his English was. I didn't care how well he spoke, in fact I liked it when he spoke his Punjabi. Tried to teach me it. Sometimes it came out like the rattle of machine guns. Tat tat tat tat. I knew quite a few words of his once, but I've forgotten most of them now.

The next day at school, as we queued to go into assembly, a policeman dressed in his blue uniform and carrying his helmet under one arm came in and knocked on the headmaster's door. For the second time in a week we were thrown into turmoil, a group panic with no outlet, with no place to run to because we were trapped at the doors of the hall by five hundred boys and girls all lined up to go forwards not backwards.

I was completely taken aback by this latest turn of events. I had honestly believed we had got away with it, and that we had in a strange way been forgiven by the Jewish man.

"I knew it," said Vic, looking around wildly for an escape route. He didn't like being trapped at the best of times. "I knew he had spotted us. All that old guff with the film show. He's probably been all round the schools using that old film as a ploy to find us. He'll have his revenge, you mark my words."

"We're done for," said Pybus.

"This is all your fault," said Billy, turning on me, red faced and flint-eyed with anger. Sticking your bleeding hand up and asking the bloke questions like you were in Sunday School. If he didn't know who we were when he came in before, he bloody well did after you had finished stroking his pigeons, you soft get."

The whole school had filed in to the hall and we were sidling down our own familiar row one after the other, just as we had done last week. Just as we did every day.

All around us were the murmurs of voices, wondering what the copper was there for, girls giggling, teachers shouting orders from their positions at the side and on the stage, chairs scraping on the wooden floor. I tell you, our school assemblies were like a cattle market.

"Those coppers warned my dad last time that they would take me away if I got into more trouble," Billy was hissing into my ear. "I got the bloody belt from him for that."

"You should have thought about that before you started slinging mud at his windows," I hissed back at him. "It was all your big idea, Billy. We just went along with it. We should be mad with you for dragging us in. We weren't the ones caught in his garden."

Then, as if somebody had turned the sound off the whole hall went quiet. The only sound was the clicking of shoes on the parquet floor as the headmaster, accompanied by his guest policeman, walked down the middle aisle and climbed onto the stage. In the hall yet again you could have heard a pin drop as the school waited expectantly for an explanation. In our row yet again our hearts were trying to leave our chests as we waited for certain exposure and humiliation.

"This is Sergeant Williams," began the headmaster, "and he is here to tell you about the sad discovery of some of the murdered children up on the moors which has been on our televisions and in our newspapers this past week. He is here to give you advice. Advice I would suggest it is worth listening to and taking on board because if you don't, well then I am afraid, without being too dramatic about this, it could become a life and death situation. For any of you."

The headmaster paused and looked over the top of his glasses at the six hundred or so pupils in the rows before him, and saw that he had the attention of every last one of them. He wasn't to know it but at least five or six of those before him had such a feeling of relief that they felt like standing up and singing at the tops of their voices. He wasn't there for us after all. He hadn't been sent to arrest us for breaking windows.

166

We sat there with joy in our hearts listening to what the sergeant had to say.

He looked quite tall and slim with a young fresh-faced look, short dark hair and a clean white shirt, but he had a deep voice that easily carried to the back of the room and his youth seemed at odds with the experience that showed in his words and in his demeanour.

He told us about the murders and the bodies that had been found on the moors and the others that they expected to find after more searching. He hinted at the brutality of the crimes, of the callous way in which the bodies had been disposed of, how young and how vulnerable the children were. He told us about the agonies for the fathers and mothers of children who had gone missing, who had to wait for news, always fearing the worst, waiting for their children to be found.

He did not mention the two people who had been arrested in connection with the murders, although we all knew their names, Myra Hindley and Ian Brady, and we all knew they had done it. It didn't matter that the trial was still months away, we knew they were guilty. So did the policeman, probably, although he wouldn't have been allowed to mention anything to do with the case, but he gave us the warning. Some others could have done with the same warning but it was too late for them; not too late for us though.

"Do not, under any circumstance," said Sergeant Williams, "go with any adult, male or female, that you do not know to be a completely trustworthy person. Personally I would advise that you keep it to relatives only but family friends have to be trusted.

However, do not alone or even together go with somebody you don't know, no matter how honest or friendly they appear to be. Certainly you must never get into a car with them. Am I clear? It is vital that you understand. Am I clear on this?"

"A bit fookin' late for those poor bastards," said a soft voice from one of the older boys and there was a murmur of agreement from the speaker's friends, boys and girls alike.

"Am I clear on this?" asked the sergeant again, this time in a louder and more forceful voice, not hearing the words but sensing a mood change nonetheless. There was a pause, a moment when there could have been a sudden gust of dissent or anger, but the moment went and the emotion subsided again to stillness, as quickly as it had risen. Then the whole hall mumbled a collective "Yes, Sir".

The policeman had one more piece of advice.

"If somebody you don't know does approach you in a suspicious manner, make your excuses immediately, as politely as you can, and walk away. Then tell a policeman or your mum and dad and they will make the decision as to what to do next. You have to use your own judgement to a certain extent of course. For instance, if a little old lady with a walking stick asks you to walk her across the road you hopefully will not run to the nearest police station to report her."

There was a ripple of weak laughter from the hall for that little joke, then back to the serious stuff.

"But there are bad people out there," continued the policeman, "and we can't catch them all, so just keep your eyes open and your wits about you. Ok. That's it. Good. Thank you all for your attention. Thank you Headmaster."

Sergeant Williams walked off the stage and out of the hall and back to his investigations, and we, the lucky ones, the forewarned ones, armed with fresh wisdom and fresh suspicions, went to our classrooms.

Chapter 10

THE GUARDIAN ANGEL

Sid had been right. It had been rows of policemen that we had seen on the hills and they had been searching for the lost children and, when I got home from school on the day that policeman came to talk to us, they were still searching for them. Only this time I was watching them on the TV and not standing up on the moors. My mother was watching the evening news and it was the leading story, more details having emerged over subsequent days about the fate of the little girl. They had found her remains buried on Saddleworth Moor; the little girl had lain ten months in a cold, wet, shallow grave while her distraught family had searched high and low, getting ever more desperate as time went on. My mum shed a lot of tears in that month of October and not just because my dad had gone. I can remember her sitting there on our maroon sofa watching the old black and white news pictures, tears rolling down her cheeks.

"What that poor woman must be going through," she kept saying. "My God, what it must be like to be in her shoes. That poor, poor woman."

Later we heard how they'd found the little girl in her makeshift grave. Those monsters had buried her, curled up naked in a foetal position, her favourite blue coat and the rest of her clothes thrown callously into the grave beside her.

That's when the anger started, and that anger grew to a crescendo of outrage as more and more information was released by the police. The wrath of the people seemed even more pronounced because it was a woman who had been arrested. Never mind Brady. Men would always be killers and the most evil of them would even kill children. But Hindley was a woman. That was what got my mum and all her friends so angry. How could a woman do this to a child? That was the question they asked each other time and time again.

There was never any debate as to whether she did it or not. The women of Manchester, and elsewhere for that matter, already knew, like the police and the press and maybe even the judge and his lawyers who would be sent to try them knew. That they were guilty was not in dispute. At this stage nobody knew how many children there were. Neither did they know of Lesley's ordeal at the hands of Brady and Hindley, how she had been tortured, how they had photographed her and taped her agony, her words begging them for mercy, and how they had eventually killed her. Nobody knew any of this yet, but there was enough now in the public domain to make my mother and her friends despair and to make me shiver in my bed at night.

I lay there and I couldn't sleep for thinking about it. I was imagining her lying outside, under rocks and earth, all cold and dirty with soil and stones in her mouth and ears and eyes and nobody knowing where she was. Her thin white body scrunched up and made to fit in her grave, like a rag doll forced into a small tin box. All alone, miles away from her family and those who loved her.

Then Stevie came in, turned the light on like he always did, as if he was the only one in the room, but this time he saw my face and straight away saw that something was bothering me.

"What's up, our kid?" he asked.

So I told him how mum and me were both feeling about the discovery of the body, and how possibly there were more up there all alone, without anybody to watch over them.

"Perhaps," said Stevie, "there was somebody to watch over them. Guardian angels, like."

"Nobody believes in angels, Stevie. It would be nice, especially for mothers of murdered children, but they probably find it hard to believe in anything after their kids have been taken."

"Why not?" said Stevie. "I've got a story that I could tell you that sort of proves it."

"Oh no," I groaned, "not one of your stories. I'm not in the mood."

"This is true," said our kid, suddenly all serious. "I wasn't going to tell you because this only happened to me a couple of weeks ago and I still can't believe it myself, but if I do tell you, you're not to tell anyone. Promise?"

My brother always began his stories with this sort of dramatic introduction, but there was something different in his tone this time and my attention was caught.

"Go on then," I said more casually than I felt. "Tell me what happened."

"You're to tell no one or I'll batter you. People will think I'm a nutter if this gets out. Do you understand?"

"Yes, yes," I assured him. "Now go on, tell me."

So he sat down on the edge of my bed and began his latest story.

It concerned a staff nurse on one of the children's wards at the hospital where Stevie worked, who was pretty and vivacious and adored by the kids. They all used to look forward to her coming on duty, so much that even the sickest of them would smile and get excited even though they were often literally on their deathbeds. All the staff loved her too, except for some of the other nurses who Stevie reckoned were just jealous of her popularity with the kids and the doctors alike. Stevie said most of the doctors were 'up themselves' and thought they were too good to speak to a humble porter like himself, but some of them were alright. And all of them liked this staff nurse. She was called Emma.

My brother liked her too and had toyed with the idea of asking her out, but had lost his nerve because she was a bit too well-brought-up for our Stevie, who preferred his women to be up for a pie and a pint. Apparently this Emma wasn't that type.

I remembered that I had had about a week of him asking me "What do you think I should do, our kid, should I ask her out?" and me saying "Yeah go on, she can only say no," as if I was any expert on the matter. But he never did, at least not to my knowledge, and then he started seeing Glenda from across the back and that was that; no more about Emma. Until now.

"Do you remember me talking about that nurse, Emma, who worked on the kiddies ward?" he began.

"How could I forget her," I said, "the amount you drivelled on about her? Don't tell me you asked her out."

"It's a bit late for all that," he said matter-of-factly. "She's dead." He saw the look of shock on my face but carried on talking and as he did, I knew he wasn't joking or winding me up. He was upset himself so I let him talk, only interrupting him when he went off track.

"Tuesday evening two weeks ago," he continued, "on her way in to work the night shift. That storm we had. Apparently her car skidded in the rain and she hit a wall. This was over Woodford way. She died at the scene. 5.00 pm that evening. Nobody else involved. Only twenty three years old she was, with a two year old daughter. Husband had pissed off to work in Australia and had never come back."

Stevie was sitting on the chair, his elbows on his knees, and staring at the floor. He paused for a moment then said, "I saw her."

"When?"

"Afterwards. After she died. Twice in fact. I saw her twice."

What do you mean? You saw the crash?"

"No," he said. "Not then. After it all happened."

"You mean you saw her dead in the hospital?"

"No, I saw her alive in the hospital but after she was supposed to be dead."

"Bloody hell. You mean you saw a ghost?"

He nodded unhappily. "I don't like to say it but that's what I saw."

"Are you sure? You could be mistaken."

"No," he said emphatically. "All the others said that but I know what I saw. I saw this girl."

I stared at him, unsure as to what to say, but there was still more that Stevie wanted to tell.

"That hospital, our kid, well you've got to see it to believe it. It's old for a start. Well over a hundred years, and it feels like it sometimes. The way it's built. Great big long corridors with hardly any light in them. Great long stone staircases shining in the dark with little bits of flint in that sometimes I have to climb up and down when I'm in a hurry and the lifts are not working. I hear echoes from rooms I have never been into and sometimes you can hear what people are saying three flights up. Sometimes you'll not know a sunny day when you're working there, some of it's so dark. They do their best with the wards though, which are generally at the top of the building, especially the children's wards, which are painted in bright colours and have quite a good atmosphere. Mostly though I'm down on the lower floors where the work is, casualty theatres and the outpatients and not forgetting the mortuary which is out at the back, a little rectangular building standing on its own like an oversized garden shed. Ordinary people walking by would never guess that inside that little brick building are fridges full of bodies. Bodies with little tags on their toes. Like items in a shop all neatly labelled. Bodies all shapes and sizes, all ages from nought to a hundred. Then I suppose that is what a hospital is like. Lots of things, good and terrible alike going on inside, while Joe Public walks around on the outside oblivious to it all."

Stevie was rambling a bit now and I was beginning to wonder if he was ever going to get to the point of the story. I didn't want to spoil his mood but I wanted to go to sleep.

"Stevie," I said "What happened with this nurse?"

"I'm getting to it," he snapped. "Show some patience, our kid!"

He continued his story. "Anyway, it's about 8.00 pm and I get a call to the childrens' ward to change an oxygen cylinder for one of the younguns that's struggling to breathe. I'm happy to do it because there's always nice nurses to chat to up there, and they usually make me a cup of tea." My brother paused again and took a deep breath to compose himself.

"Yeah go on," I said softly by way of encouragement, "then what?"

"Then I walk into the ward and it's dark. All the children are asleep and there are no staff that I can see except for one. I couldn't see who it was exactly but this nurse is standing next to the bed of little Edward, who is a lovely little kiddie, but is probably the sickest one in there. All the staff love the kid, because he's only seven years old and he has leukaemia and his chances are not good. Anyway, as I'm standing there, with my eyes trying to get used to the darkness, there's a sudden movement behind me which makes me jump, I'm so far away into myself. I turn around and it's Sister Wilkinson, big and blue in her uniform and her frilly little nurse's hat on her head which doesn't suit her. She's a dragon and makes the student nurses' lives a misery but she's always very polite to me.

'Ah thank you, Stephen,' she said, 'can you change that one over by Susan's bed, she will need it later.'

'Oh Sister,' I said, taken aback, 'I thought it was going to be for young Eddie.'

'No,' she replied, 'not Eddie. Eddie has oxygen but he needs our prayers more I'm afraid' and I could see how sad she was that the little lad was dying and it made me sad too, I can tell you. So the sister left me to it and I changed the cylinder by Susan's bed, but all the time I was glancing across to Eddie's bed at the end of the ward by the big window, wondering where his mum and dad had got to, although at least the nurse was still with him. That same nurse, just standing by him, with her hand resting on his head.

Then as I got up to leave, suddenly the moon came out from behind a cloud and there was a narrow strip of light that came in through the window and shone on the area around little Eddie's bed and I could clearly see that the nurse who was with him was Emma, and that reassured me because I knew that the kid loved this Emma and that she was the best one to be with him. I thought briefly about going across to them but I didn't, and I don't know whether I'm sorry about that or relieved. Anyway I went back downstairs and that's when I heard."

"Heard what?" I said.

"That's when I heard that Emma had been killed in a car crash on her way to work that evening."

"No," I said in a voice that masked the chill that I had suddenly felt. "You are kidding right?"

"She had died in her car that very evening," my brother persisted.

"You are telling me that you saw… you saw this Emma. No I can't believe that."

"Look," said Stevie, "I know what I saw. You don't have to believe me. I saw her clear as day. Well clear as moonlight which is clear enough for me. It doesn't matter what you think. I'm just telling you, that's all."

"Alright," I said, "I believe you. But let's get this right. You saw this nurse, this Emma, several hours after she had been killed in a car crash?"

"Yes," said my brother, "as clear as I can see you now."

"God that is spooky. How did that make you feel?"

"That's the point. I didn't know straight away. When old Johnstone the head porter told me after I went back down, he didn't break it to me exactly gently."

"What do you mean?"

"Well he said, 'Steve, I've got an interesting job for you. Do you want to help me with it?'

'Yeah sure, what is it?' I said.

'One of the nurses who works here apparently. She just came in DOA. Brown bread mate. Her car hit a wall in Woodford or Poynton, somewhere like that. God knows what speed she was travelling at. But she was in a right mess. They're just finishing off in casualty then you and I will take her up.'

'Who is it?' I said, not too worried at this time although not relishing the job. Not like Johnstone, the morbid cockney bastard; he loved the mortuary. Even loved the smell of it, he did.

'Emma, Emma,' he looked down at his bit of paper, 'Emma Ridley. She worked on the childrens' ward apparently, poor cow.' He looked at me. 'Did you know her?'

'Can't be her,' I said. 'I've just seen her up on that ward, looking after little Eddie.'

Johnstone looked closely at me. 'I know the name they gave me,' he said, and that was it. 'They don't make mistakes like that. You know that. It's probably you that's getting your nurses mixed up. Girl mad, that's your problem.'

'It was her,' I said. 'It was Emma I saw, not ten minutes ago.'

'Look, are you alright?' he said puzzled. Then taking the piss, because Johnstone thinks it's a man's thing to handle a dead body- the more gruesome the better. 'You look like you're coming down with something. I can call Jack if you're not up to it.'

"That was the second time I saw her after she had died; when Johnstone and I took her up to the old grey mortuary building out of the way at the back of the hospital. Once in and out of sight, standing there in the glaring white light, the two great enamel slabs with their drains before us, the smell of the chemicals burning holes in my nostrils, we could resist our curiosity no longer. I had still not convinced Johnstone that I had seen Emma on the ward, and I really had to persuade him to let me peek at her face to make sure it was the girl I had seen. It was more than his job was worth as senior porter to start messing around with the bodies, although if the sheets sometimes fell open because the nurses had been in too much of a hurry, well there was nothing he could do about that. As we laid her down on the steel rack to place her head first into the fridge, we opened the sheet that covered her head and I was able to see her. I hadn't wanted to but I had to know if it was Emma lying there. I knew that I would have lain awake in my bed for years wondering how she should have looked that night if I hadn't had that one peek."

Stevie paused and took a deep breath, not to keep me in suspense, although I was in suspense, I can tell you, but because even I could see that the whole experience had taken it out of him a bit. However, I was in no mood to wait.

"Go on then." I urged him on loudly. "Was it her or not?"

"It was her alright," he said. "No mistaking her even though she was bashed about from the crash."

All I could say was "Bloody hell". I could see that he was upset.

"It was horrible," he said in a quiet voice. "She must have gone through the windscreen because she was cut pretty badly, but worse than that, there was a big hole in her head at the side where she must have hit something. They'd stitched it up a bit, but not very well. Johnstone is beside me saying stuff like 'That hole probably killed her. She wouldn't survive that.' Then he said 'The cosmetic guys are going to have a hell of a job getting her right for the family viewing,' and when he said that, I just wanted to get out of there. I kept thinking of her little daughter all alone missing her mum, and just before Christmas too. It was enough to break your heart. So Johnstone opened the fridge door and rolled her inside and the metal tray she was on made a clanking sound as it hit the back. She didn't even have a bloody fridge to herself. She was on the bottom shelf but there were two other bodies above her. Just like the bloody butcher's shop. It hadn't bothered me before, but with Emma in there I couldn't stand it any longer. I had to get out. I just said to Johnstone, 'I've got to go.' And I went straight down to the pub. Do you remember two weeks ago when I didn't come home? That was then. I was too bloody drunk to leave the Railway Arms. They let me kip in an upstairs room. I suppose in a way I was in shock.

"Anyway," Stevie said finally, "I've thought about it a bit since then and I know what I saw and I know I'm not going mad, although some of my mates would think so. But you know what, in a funny sort of way it gives me a bit of comfort."

"What do you mean," I said, "comfort?"

"Well you're talking about that poor kid up on the moor and being all alone like. Well if little Eddie had his guardian angel on the ward as he was going off then why not her? Emma, on her way to God knows where, made a little diversion to go and stand at the bed of that little lad and tell him that she would wait for him on the other side, most probably. I don't care what anybody says, I saw her there. Well maybe, up on the moor that Lesley had somebody watching out for her. Maybe all those missing kids have. Perhaps we all do. Wouldn't that be good?"

"It would be nice to think that," I agreed, "even if we couldn't know for sure. It makes the cruelty of it easier to bear. It would make it easier for her mum if she could believe something like that. It would be nice to tell her the story one day, maybe ease her pain a little bit."

I lay awake for a long time after he told me that story, just going over it again and again in my own mind. I'm sure Stevie below me was doing the same thing. I was thinking about Emma's little girl. One day she goes off to work. Did she give her a last kiss? Will she always remember it? Did Emma, when she had finished with Eddie, nip ghost-like across Manchester to watch over her own little girl? I bet she did.

I went to sleep thinking, would it be a good idea when the daughter is a bit older, to find her and tell her that my brother saw her mum after she died and she looked alright, not frightened or damaged, just sweet, and beautiful like she had been in life? And I bet myself that if I did find her one day and told her what Stevie had seen, Emma's little girl would say to me, 'Yes I know all that because you see she came and said goodbye to me that night as well.'

A month later, I was lying in bed, this time with no Stevie around to tell me scary stories, when the phone rang downstairs and I heard my mothers voice answer, "Hulme Hall two nine oh three," in the posh telephone voice she used. Then I heard no more, though I strained my ears. It was probably for our Sandra. For a second in the back of my mind I hoped it was my dad but I dismissed it. If truth be told, since he had left, things had become a little quieter around the house. Stevie and Sandra were glad to see the back of him, they never said as much but you could tell. He was not their father and they didn't care about him and although they loved their mum they thought she was better off without him. And our George was either too thick or too young to realise that he had gone at all. It was only me and mum who missed him; it was obvious to me that she still loved him and wanted him back even if he was a grumpy old bastard when he was there. Every day after he first went I'd come bursting in from school or the river or the rec, wherever I had been, hoping that he had changed his mind and come home. But he was never there. Even after weeks of this I never got used to him not being there and the sharp pain of missing him never seemed to dull. Not for my mum either, although she had a different way of dealing with it. Sometime I would get home and find her crying quietly at the kitchen table while our George sat eating marmite soldiers and watching Zoo Time on the TV oblivious to all the drama going on around him. So I would walk her upstairs and lay her down and kiss her wispy brown hair like I was the mother and not the other way around and she would sleep for a while. Then a couple of hours later she would come bounding down the stairs as if nothing had happened and start on all her chores that she had abandoned that afternoon. This didn't happen every day but it was too often for my liking.

It was on one of these occasions, one afternoon when I came home and found her that she confessed to me that we were short of money. I looked at her tired face, swollen under her green eyes, her once clear skin starting to mottle with cold and age. I saw wrinkles around her mouth for the first time, so rarely did she smile these days, and of course I saw her hair. Always her hair. How she must worry about that.

She told me that since he had left, weeks ago now, he had sent money at first but that had dwindled then stopped altogether. She had telephoned him and he had promised to send more but then it had stopped again. She thought that he may have been out of work or ill but since he didn't answer her calls or her letters anymore it was hard to know. She told me that she was coming to the end of her tether and that she was thinking of sending Stevie around but she was worried they may fight. I offered to go round and see him but she thought that was not a good idea since he lived too far away. We may go together, she told me, if things didn't get better. At the moment Stevie's and Sandra's wages, were keeping us afloat, but it was a real struggle. I said, "Doesn't he love us anymore?" and she cried again, which was not what I wanted, and said, "Of course he does, he's just finding it difficult to show it at the moment."

I told her not to worry and that I would get another job, find another milkman maybe (someone a little less dangerous, I thought to myself), and she laughed through her tears and ruffled my hair, and said that when I was around I was a tower of strength and that I would make somebody a lovely husband one day.

I knew she was worried because it seemed to me that her hair was falling out at a faster rate than ever, and had been for some time. I don't know whether my dad leaving had accelerated it, but she had had this nervous habit of pulling on it for quite a while now and it seemed to me that if she wasn't careful she was going to run out of the stuff altogether. It must have devastated her at the time because her hair had been her pride and joy and she had always said it was her saving grace, her golden halo. In the end when she felt she needed to wear a wig to cover up the sparseness, it was never discussed, never declared openly and none of us would have thought to mention it because we would not have deliberately hurt her for the world.

In those days they didn't have the medications that are around now, but she bought all sorts of wigs: black ones, gold ones, brown ones and even a red one. She must have spent a fortune on them. Her favourite one had been a blonde wig with the hair piled quite high, not quite a beehive but close to it. That's the one she started to wear all the time, the one she became quite comfortable with, even to the point where everyone just assumed it was her real hair. Then when they caught the moors murderers and they showed that picture of Hindley, the infamous one with the blonde hair, in every newspaper and on every television in the land, my mother thought the likeness to her, in her blond wig, too close to bear. Nobody ever said anything but she stopped wearing it overnight, and her mood changed back again too, which was a shame.

When she had started to wear her wigs she kissed me less, or at least seemed to. I don't think it was my imagination. At first I thought she would be worried that when she bent down her hair would slide off and that it would frighten the life out of both of us. As a kid she had always come up to my room as I dropped off to sleep and I would wait for her lips to touch my cheek. I would pretend that she was too late and that I had already dropped off. I would feel the wetness and the softness of her lips on my skin and I would hear her murmur that she loved me, but when the wigs came that stopped. I would wait ages for her to come up but those times got less and less and eventually went altogether. Even on those days when she had been asleep in the afternoon and she was not so tired in the evening, even then she didn't come up. Not to me, or our George. She thought us both too old, which was probably true so we learnt to kiss her before we went up, so that we wouldn't have to lie there and wait anymore.

On this particular evening she did come to my room. She came right over to the bed and sat down and I smiled up at her in the gloom. "Are you alright, Mum?" I asked.

"That was your dad on the phone," she said.

"What did he want?" I asked, feigning disinterest, but when my mother did not immediately reply, I leapt up in my bed in a sudden surge of hope. "Is he coming home?" I blurted out.

"Sssschh," she said, "you'll wake the whole house up."

"Oh Mum, please tell me he's coming home. Please."

"No love," she said hurriedly. "He's not coming home yet. Maybe one day, but not yet. Look. He has asked me to tell you and George that he has to go away over Christmas to work."

"Over Christmas?" I said, as I sank, along with all my expectations, back into the bedclothes. "Over Christmas? Jesus Christ," I said bitterly.

"Don't blaspheme," reproached my mother half-heartedly.

"Well we can't mean that much to him if he can't turn up at Christmas." I looked up at my poor mother, her face set hard in the half light of the bedroom.

"He's found work in Scotland over Christmas and New Year. God knows how. He says it won't be forever, but the money is really good and he'll send us some home."

"He hasn't sent you any for weeks," I pointed out. "Why should we believe him now?"

"I know he hasn't given you much of a reason, but he is your dad and he does love you."

"He has a funny way of showing it."

My mother sighed. "I know but he did tell me to tell you that he would keep your birthday free in January. He promised to take you out. He said he would try and get tickets for the football."

"I'll believe it when I see it," I muttered, but part of me rose up again, in that childish way that wants to believe the best in our fathers and mothers, despite evidence to the contrary.

"We'll see," she said and smiled and touched my forehead with her left hand, a hand that I noticed was clean and clear and silent, unburdened by its usual jingling adornments of wedding rings, bracelets and gold watch. I was too tired to ask her where they were, although I wondered, then I heard her say, "Now get to sleep," and she bent her face down and kissed me for the first time since I could remember.

Chapter 11

LEAVING STEVIE

Everything changed in my life on January 4th, 1966, the day of my thirteenth birthday. The day my father had promised, a lifetime ago, would be special because he would come and spend it with me. Mum had done her best at Christmas but the house was empty without my dad moaning and groaning and getting in the way and I wished for it to be over, so I would be allowed out again and not made to sit around and play stupid games with our George because it was the family thing to do. Our Stevie and Sandra were out most of the time anyway, with their mates in town. Mum had tried her hardest; I could see that with the amount of food she had cooked, and the presents we had received, but for me it just wasn't the same without my dad, although I never would have told her that, not in a million years. January 4th felt like it was a long time coming, but eventually it arrived. The fact that it turned out to be the saddest day of my life is in no small part due to my brother Stevie, yet there was a lot I didn't know about at the time that I have had to piece together from what other people have said. I was there at the beginning and then right at the end of the day but not in the middle and the middle part of the day was when most things happened. Even Linton's dad was able to tell me stuff that he had heard from other coppers.

That day I got up and dressed next to the heater because the house was freezing. Outside the sky had that grey, overcast, snow-filled look, like it wanted to burst at any minute, but it hadn't done so yet and the ground was still dry. Oh but it was cold. As I dressed I could see my own breath in the air. I went downstairs to get some breakfast.

I could hear the sound of coughing, almost retching, from the bathroom, which must have been our Sandra because Stevie had gone out early to do a couple of hours of overtime.

In the kitchen mum was smoking a cigarette and reading the *Daily Mail*. She was wearing her black wig, the one that made her look like a vampire. The radio was blaring out 'Love Me Do' by the Beatles and the whole place smelt of burnt toast and cigarettes. When she saw me she put the fag down in the ashtray next to her piece of toast. I hated that; the way she could almost eat and smoke at the same time.

"Come here, my darling," she said, her red hands clasping either side of my head and her lips planting a succession of kisses on my face.

"Thirteen years old," she declared in mock disbelief. "Thirteen years old. What happened to my little boy? Where's he gone?"

"I'm still here, Mum," I said, not quite sure of this new-found affection. "I haven't gone away."

"You're getting so big and handsome. Those girls are going to be flocking round. You mark my words, you'll have to watch out."

I tried to change the subject. "Where's our George?" I said, although I couldn't have cared less where he was.

"He's out playing football," she replied and I heard the strain in her voice. "They called him in because they're short of players. I think he's too young but he was desperate, and that Mr Sherwood who runs it says he'll be alright. He says he's better than most of them there anyway, even though he's two years younger. He says he has potential."

"He won't see dad," I muttered.

"He may be back in time," she said and I saw her take a deep breath like people do when they're nervous or worse, about to cry. Maybe she was worried about seeing him again. After all it had been quite a while. "Anyway," she continued, recovering her composure, "it's your day really. It's more important that you see him."

After my bacon sandwich I went outside to wait for my dad, although he wasn't due for an hour yet. There was a smell of a bonfire in the cold wintry air and further down the street some younger girls played in a big circle, clapping and stamping their little feet, some with their arms aloft. I could hear their thin voices singing happily, words clearly carrying up to me perched on the garden wall.

The wind, the wind, the wind blows high,
The rain comes scattering down the sky.
She is handsome, she is pretty,
She is the girl of London city.
She goes a courting a-one, two, three,
And Paul Harding will you marry me?

Who the hell is Paul Harding, I thought to myself, then Vic appeared over the brow of the hill and I groaned inside.

"I can't leave the house, Vic," I said.

"What's up?" he said, persistent as ever. "He can come and find you, can't he?"

But I was not for budging.

"I don't want to take a chance. It's alright for you, your dad wants to come home every night."

"Yeah," said Vic, "worse luck. I wish he were a travelling salesman and not a warehouseman. Who knows, I might get some peace."

"Well mine doesn't come home. I haven't seen him for weeks and I don't want to miss him because I'm off with you somewhere."

Vic wandered off to find Billy and an hour later I was still sitting there on the wall.

I went back inside and found my mum washing dishes.

"What time did dad say?" I asked.

"Oh about now," she said, "he'll be along any minute."

I wasted another quarter of an hour inside the house and then went and sat back on the front wall. Even though it was cold just sitting there, I could see right up the road and that helped. Even if, for the moment, that road was long and black and empty, it was still better than the four walls inside.

Mrs Milner came by. "Hello, love, are you waiting for the bus?" She was having a joke. Buses went from half a mile away. I smiled weakly at her. It was now 11:30.

185

He should have been here by now. Maybe he had a flat tyre. He could phone. We were on the telephone now.

I stood up and did some running on the spot and moved my arms. I gave myself some bearhugs. I put my balaclava on, even though I felt a bit of a twat.

Something made me turn around and look back at the house and I could see my mum standing there looking at me. She smiled and waved a little wave. She had changed her wig to the brown short-haired one which I much preferred.

I held my hand to my ear to try and imitate a telephone and I must have done it pretty well because she knew what I was asking. She shook her head and I carried on pacing and stomping, blowing cold air. My nose began to run. A car came up the road and crawled past looking for another house. A blue car, not green, not the car I wanted. The man driving gave me a look as if wondering whether to ask for directions but then dismissed the idea. Probably thought I'd send him the wrong way. Probably would have done too, the mood I was in. There was a clanking of a milk float in the distance. Not the Red Indian. Hopefully he's back in America. I could also hear the Duncans' vicious mangy dog barking in the distance. That sharp little yap. I wished they would shoot the damn thing.

It was gone 12 o'clock, and still my dad didn't come.

I went back into the house trying to act cheerful and unconcerned but inside I was burning. "Has Dad called yet, Mum?"

I watched her gulp her words. "No, love, he hasn't. I'm sure he'll be here soon." She was tight-lipped and angry and trying not to show it but it was easy to tell. My mother never could hide her emotions very well, although she tried her hardest to do so. She was being optimistic for me, while probably deep down realising that the father of her child was not going to show up yet again.

I went back outside yet again and tried to stare up the road as far as I could see. And then I tried to stare up where I couldn't see, to imagine the road on which my father was making his promised journey. Up Claremont Avenue, I went in my imagination, along

Queens Road through Cheadle High street out to Kingsway and then through Didsbury, all the way to the little house in Manchester where he now lived and never took me to.

After this day happened I tried to go over in my own mind the sequence of events using other people's accounts to fill in the gaps. I found out by talking to some of Stevie's mates and some of my dad's mates that while I had been sitting on the wall waiting for him he had been sitting on a barstool in the Rose and Crown Tavern out on the Stockport Road. He had gone in early after a night shift, well-intentioned and determined to stick to his promise to me. He could get in that early because he knew the landlady, an old peroxide-blond widow from Blackburn who he was romantically involved with off and on; this I found out from his less discreet acquaintances. Our Stevie, who had been called up at work by mum and asked to go and look for him, followed a trail of his regular haunts before getting lucky fifth time. However, as the story goes, when Stevie walked into the rose and Crown at midday looking for my dad he had already been in there nearly five hours and he was too drunk to stand up never mind take me to Old Trafford. What is more, he had been in possession of two tickets for Man U against Liverpool but had sold them to a bloke at the bar who had gone himself and taken his old dad with him. The men I spoke to later said that at the time Stevie was so angry that they thought he might beat my father to a pulp, drunk and incapable as he was, but he merely took his car keys and most of the cash from his wallet, to pay for his son's birthday treat, he told the amused audience of morning drinkers, and then walked out, leaving him slumped at the bar.

Then Stevie, illegally driving my father's second hand Jaguar, his pride and joy and a direct reason why my mother was always short of money, as I realised later in my life, came to look for me.

It was gone 1.00 pm and I was still sitting on the wall, although I had just about given up by this time. Periodically Billy and Vic had come by to tempt me away but I had refused and eventually they had wandered off to look for adventures elsewhere.

Suddenly I saw the red Jag coming down our road and my heart leapt because although I was angry I would forgive him if we got to the match; ninety minutes to kick off, there was still time. I was stone-faced as the car pulled up, just to show that I was really pissed off with him, but when the window wound down on the driver's side, it was Stevie's big blond head that popped out, not my dad's.

"Alright, our kid?" he said.

"Where's my dad?" I replied. "He's never letting you drive his car, you jammy get?"

"Your dad can't make it, Mike," said Stevie. "He sends his apologies, but something came up, something really important."

"You're joking?" I couldn't quite believe what I was hearing.

"You know what his job is like."

"Yes, I do," I said, snarling back at Stevie, the bearer of bad news. I was trying hard to keep my voice from cracking. "It's more important than me. That's what his bastard job is to him."

"C'mon, kid," said Stevie gently, but I wouldn't let him finish.

"He bloody promised me. I've waited ages for this day. It's not bloody fair," and by now I was close to tears. That was the last thing Stevie wanted and he was madly trying to get me back onside.

"Look, look, it's alright," he soothed. "I'll take you. He's leant me his car. We'll go down there ourselves."

"Have you got the tickets?" I asked, on the verge of snivelling.

"No it's alright we'll get some down there."

"You bloody won't. It's a sell out is this," I answered, in a scornful voice which normally would have got me a clip from him.

"Look," said Stevie, "you cheeky get, there's always touts. I've got a bit of cash on me." As he said this he patted his jacket pocket. "I don't mind forking out for my kid brother on his birthday."

At this point, mum walked out of the house.

"Where is he?" she said in her hard, stern voice. "Over four hours the lad has been sitting on the wall. I'll bloody swing for him, I swear to God."

"It's alright, Mum," I said in a hurry, because I could see she was upset, "our Stevie's taking us. Dad's busy."

"I'll explain to you later, Ma," says Stevie. He takes her to one side and I could only hear bits and pieces of what was said but it didn't take a genius to realise that both of them were very angry with my father.

"I'll bloody kill him when I see him," I heard her say, then, "Alright love, you take him but watch yourself in that bloody car. Don't drive too fast."

"I won't, I won't," our Stevie says. "Bloody hell, Mum, trust me for once, will you. C'mon, our kid," he said, indicating, me, "jump in before all this mithering loses me the will to live."

So with our Stevie, constantly trying to cheer me up and partially succeeding, we went up our road, arms waving from the windows as we went on our way. If my dad couldn't be bothered then to hell with him, I thought, at least I've got my brother. I looked out of my passenger window as we left the estate, and in the wing mirror I could see the distorted image of my mother in her flowery old apron, brown wig on, waving at our disappearing backs. Even with an indirect view and from a distance of thirty or forty yards, I could clearly see in her face that her anger had gone and only sadness remained.

I had to admit that even without the basic legal requirements to drive my brother could handle my dad's car pretty well. God knows where he learnt how: all I know is that I felt safe with him, despite some of the speeds he was getting up to.

The first stop we made was outside a parade of shops in Rusholme.

"Stevie," I said, "What are you doing?"

"I'll tell you in a second. I just have to get something, wait, it will be worth it, I promise." Then he disappeared into a pawnbroker's shop, its old door opening and closing with a scraping sound, and the old bell making a shrill ring, to alert the owner. It was my imagination again, but I suddenly had this feeling that Stevie had gone in to rob the shop, and I was there to keep an eye out for the rozzers. I actually started to get nervous and I could feel the palms of my hands sweating up.

"What's up with you?" he said as he got back to the car. "You look like you're going to piss your pants. I wasn't that long, was I?"

"No you're fine," I said more calmly than I felt. "What were you doing?"

He was obviously pleased with himself, and bursting to tell me something, so I humoured him. "What did you buy?"

He was grinning at me as he took a big brown envelope from his pocket.

"Look," he said as if he was about to reveal the secret of life and he opened the envelope and delicately, for him at least, pulled out a man's wrist watch. This was no ordinary watch though. In fact, at first glance it didn't look like a watch at all but just a stainless steel rectangular bracelet, about an inch long and half an inch wide, still with the winding mechanism visible. It was, in effect, a watch without a face.

It was attached at either end by an ivory-coloured leather strap, the only part of the whole design that was familiar to me. Stevie chuckled at my puzzled expression.

"There's writing on it," I said. "What does it say?"

"It says," read Stevie, squinting at the small inscription on the metal fascia, "To Amy with love, Daddy, 1926."

Then Stevie put his nail under the winder and pulled. The steel back flipped out of its casing, rotated and then clicked back in with a crisp snap, revealing the beautiful watch, with its ornate Roman numerals set in gold on the shiny white face that I saw on my mother's wrist every day.

"That belongs to our mum," I said.

"Ten out of ten," said Stevie.

"I didn't know it had that writing on the back."

"Neither did I," said Stevie, "until just now when the pawnbroker showed me. A lot of men in the First World War carried those reverse watches to protect them from all the knocks and the mud, and all the bombs too I expect. Shrapnel and the like. Obviously mum's father, our grandad, gave her his, with an inscription on, just before he died. I always wondered how mum could be so protective of an old watch. Now I know. I think it's the only thing she has that belonged to him."

"What was it doing in the pawnbrokers?"

"She pawned it, soft lad, why do you think?"

"Yeah but why did she pawn it? That's her dad's watch. She would never risk losing it."

"She would, if she needed the money enough."

"Christmas?"

"Christmas," he confirmed. "She wanted Christmas to be as normal as possible, especially for you and George with your dad gone. I'm sworn to secrecy, so don't you dare tell her I told you. She would kill me if she thought you knew, and then I would have to kill you, I promise. She needed some money for presents and she's had nothing from the men in her life. Your father is worse than mine. As tight as a duck's arse he is."

Stevie then reached back into the brown envelope and brought out a little double silver photograph frame. I hadn't seen it before.

Stevie, as if reading my thoughts, said, "She keeps it in a drawer of her desk out of sight." Inside each frame was a photograph; one small black and white print was of a young, handsome but serious, looking man wearing an army uniform. It was a formal studio shot, one of millions taken of young men in high streets the length and breadth of Britain, just before they went off to France, often never to return. My grandfather stood erect and uncomfortable, wanting to be out of the hot studio and in the fresh air outside, an impassive gaze on his unblemished features, a face loved by my mother but not known by us, a face from long ago. The picture on the other side of the frame we did know and we did love, but it needed a little imagination to recall it. It was a photograph of our mum, although you wouldn't necessarily have known it because the photo showed a beautiful, carefree girl with long golden hair and blue eyes and a smile that would melt your heart. It's always a shock for a child to see that a parent not only had a life before they were born but that their old, careworn, snappy mother had been beautiful and vivacious and young.

"How come Mum didn't take the photos out," I asked. " She could have lost them if you hadn't raised the money."

Stevie grinned at me. "I asked the old man the same question. He said she risked ripping them if she took them out. Best left alone. That's what he told her. He also said that he had decided not to sell them on, because he could see how hard it was for her to leave them. Not sure I believe that. Those pawnbrokers are not the sentimental types."

For a while there was silence between us as we studied our mother's most treasured possessions.

"She was beautiful, Stevie," I said finally.

"Yes she was," he answered. "At least she was before she got saddled with us lot."

Then we were interrupted by a bunch of lads walking down the pavement towards us singing and shouting and carrying on. I could see in the wing mirror that they were Man United supporters, although not the sort that you would want to be next to in the crowd or on the train with. As they walked past the car Stevie saw them and leant over me to shout out of the passenger window. My heart missed a beat because I thought that he was challenging them, but it turned out that he knew them.

"Alright, Dale," he said to a big, mean-looking, bald-headed bloke who duly bent down to look in the car and breathed all over me in the process. He stank of beer and he looked glassy-eyed. I looked around him to his two mates and they seemed unsteady on their feet. One of them, a short, dark, Mediterranean-looking man they called Rico, turned around and took a piss up against the wall even though it was broad daylight and people were passing by, although they gave him a wide berth. He sounded like a horse, the water hitting the wall with a splash and then running down the pavement in a yellow river while pedestrians trying to get by stepped carefully over it. Some little kids laughed but the older ones knew better than to say anything.

"What are youse doing in that motor?" slurred Dale to Stevie in a thick Manchester accent.

"What d'you think?" said Stevie with his good natured grin. "Smart eh?"

"A've yer nicked it?" said the third one, a tall, lanky kid with bulbous eyes and tattoos, sticking his head in my window alongside Dale's. Their heads were jammed together now, like some fairground freak show, joined by the ears.

"No," said Stevie enigmatically. I noticed he was talking differently, brasher, acting tough. "I just borrowed it for a while. From his dad actually," and he indicated me, sitting quietly underneath these big men with their language and beery breath and whiskers. The bug-eyed one smelt of vinegar as well, and I felt faintly sick.

They noticed me properly for the first time and noticed my Man United scarf too.

"Who's this," said Dale mockingly, "all dressed in red? Your little mascot?"

"It's our kid," said my brother. "I'm taking him down Man U. It's his birthday."

"That's good," said Dale, "you can give us a lift down there."

"Have you got tickets? It's a sell out is this one," said our kid.

"We're not going in," said Dale.

"What do you mean you're not going in?" persisted Stevie.

"We're going to ambush the Scousers," shouted Rico into the window with a maniacal laugh. "On their way in from the station."

"Dale," said Stevie, "I've got our kid with me and I'm not going near any trouble. You'll have to get yourselves down there."

"We need you there and your car," said Dale menacingly. "Stroke of luck you having that. Fast getaway, like."

"Bring the kid too if you like," said Rico. "He'll have to fight with the rest of them though."

"He's only thirteen," said Stevie. "I wouldn't take him up there. They're worse than Leeds some of them Liverpool fans. No way."

"Well kick the kid out then," said Dale, "and let's get on our way. It's only an hour to kick off."

"Dale," pleaded Stevie. "C'mon mate. Let it go eh. I'll give you a lift to the station, but I can't stay for the fighting. I've promised our kid."

193

"I'm beginning to think that you're not up for the battle," said Dale.

"Are you calling me a coward?" said Stevie in his own dangerous voice that made it clear he would take so much but no more, and I made a mental note never to call him a coward even as a joke.

"Not me, kid," said Dale, backtracking. "I've battled with you. But you know what it's like."

"Yeah," said Rico, now nonchalantly picking at his fingernails with a small lethal-looking knife, he had carried in his back pocket, "Word gets around. You know what they're like, those others. Bunch of old women the way they gossip. You miss a big event like the Scousers and suddenly there's others in the pub saying why wasn't so and so there getting battered and slashed like I was. Before you know it you've got yourself a reputation."

"And a bad reputation," said the bug-eyed one, finally joining the discussion, "can be a dangerous thing."

Stevie, alongside me, gave a big sigh then went quiet. I think he was weighing up his options, but I was scared and angry because I had never seen him take this from anybody. Normally he was frightened of nothing, but these three had made him very nervous.

"Mike, get out of the car," he finally said to me. "You'll have to catch the bus back down the Oxford Road. I'll give you some money. Get yourself some sweets as well."

"Stevie," I pleaded. "Don't go with them. Let's just drive off. They'll never catch us in their state. Please."

Stevie got out of the car and came round to my side and opened the door.

"C'mon, get out, our kid," he said.

"Get the little runt out or I will," said Dale suddenly from the other side of the car.

"I have to take them," Stevie said. "If this lot start blabbing, I'll have half the Stretford End after me. Please, Mike, get out of the car or I'm going to have to drag you out."

I looked at my brother then and I could see the near desperation on his face.

"OK," I said in a soft voice and I saw his desperation change to relief.

I got out of the car and my brother pressed a ten bob note into my hand and gave me a weak apologetic smile.

"I'll make it up to you, I promise. I'll see you later tonight."

"Don't give me another promise, our kid," I said to him "I've had enough to last me a lifetime," and I saw that I'd hit home. I felt better in that moment because I had wanted to hurt him and the tightening of his lips told me that I had. Then he turned and got back into the driver's seat, and my last view of him was driving away from me with the other three already in their chosen seats and staring straight ahead looking forward to battle. I had a feeling of dread for my brother but as I crossed the road to wait at the bus stop, this feeling became too submerged in self-pity to last that long.

The first time I woke up that night I didn't open my eyes, I just lay there and felt the soft sweep of puckered lips on my damp forehead. I moaned in my dream, thought Mum but then the maleness of the touch made me think Dad. He had come after all, over twelve hours late, but he had come and that was enough. I would forgive him the rest.

The next time I woke up, I was freezing and I lay there, the covers up to my chin, looking at the ceiling and thinking about the previous day, hating Stevie a little, hating my dad a lot. I lowered my head to look under my bunk and saw that Stevie wasn't there and probably hadn't been, because his bedclothes lay undisturbed.

With an effort that took several counts to ten, I climbed down to go to the toilet. On the landing I stopped at the window, drew back the curtains and peered out into dawn light. The whole of the estate for as far as the eye could see was covered in a blanket of white snow. It was as if Sid had driven across the sky in a gigantic lorry and tipped a load out that covered everything, every house, every tree and all the roads and all the cars too, the few that were around then. It looked like a picture a child would draw with a grey sky all one tone, and a dense white landscape. Only when my eyes opened properly and I looked more closely did I start to see the finer details poking through. Like the windows and the gateposts, and the extremities of the buildings, the gutters and chimney pots which were fighting back against the deluge. Nature's constructions were resisting too and the light gusty breeze was starting to whip around the trees, and gusts of white powder were falling in clouds from the branches.

The only flaw on this virgin snow scene were the tyre tracks. Only one set, they came from over the white hill that was Queens Road and along the flatter track that was our road. But they weren't the tyre tracks of a careful, sober driver. These tracks wavered and snaked their way down the street, narrowly missing snow-laden trees and cars, until they finished under a red Jaguar parked halfway down our gently sloping drive at an unlikely angle.

A surge of hope and pleasure rose in my heart. My dad had worked my birthday but now he had weaved his way home in treacherous conditions to make it up to me and I was delirious with excitement to see him. I didn't think of forgiveness; what was there to forgive? He had come home at last. So, still half asleep, I rushed into the bedroom that he had shared with my mother, searching for him, seeking him out. But she lay there alone, as she had done for the past few months.

"Dad!" I was shouting, "Dad, where are you?"

My mother woke with a start but was almost immediately lucid, and surprisingly not angry with me for waking her.

"He's not here, love. I'm sorry."

"But he came in when I was asleep, I heard him."

"You must have been dreaming, Michael. It's a dream, that's all."

"His car is still outside though," I said.

"Remember yesterday," she said patiently, "Stevie had his car. I haven't forgotten because he dropped you in the middle of Manchester, which he'll get a clout for when I catch up with him, let me tell you."

"Oh," and my disappointment in that small exclamation made my mother reach up and take my small hand in hers.

It was all coming back to me. I remembered the pawn shop, Mum's watch and photograph, then his horrible Man United mates hijacking the car and having to wait ages for a bus back to Cheadle. Then walking home from Cheadle in the rain, and getting a telling off from my mother because I was soaked to the skin, even though it was Stevie's fault. Then, as I lay in my bed waiting for sleep and for Stevie to come home, my mother coming in to me and saying sorry about my dad. Yes it was all coming back and the strange empty feeling in my stomach that had been with me most of yesterday was coming back as well.

Mum was dropping off again, so I went back out and downstairs to look for my brother. He would probably be asleep on the sofa downstairs with the TV making a whining sound. But he wasn't there. I was puzzled now. Where could he be?

I opened the front door to look at the car, and a gust of icy air hit me four square in the chest, making me cough. It was bloody freezing. Then I saw Stevie still inside the car, his head just showing above the line of the windscreen. I could see his eyes closed and his head slumped onto his chest, and his body leaning at an angle against the driver's door. The windscreen was more icy than snowy and his image was hazy and distorted, like looking through polythene, but I saw a paleness in his skin that made me go straight to the car, even without getting a coat or putting anything on my feet. My first thoughts were that the stupid bastard had frozen to death in his own driveway.

I banged on the driver's window hard. "Stevie," I shouted. "Stevie, wake up. Then I noticed lumps and bumps around his face, traces of dried blood, sure signs that Stevie had been fighting and had received some heavy blows.

With a huge effort I pulled open the driver's door and Stevie fell into the snow outside, almost gracefully like a dancer, and lay on his back with his arms alongside him. There was more blood on his body from earlier superficial wounds, a black stain on his chest turned to red in the new morning light and then to pink as the sudden movement brought fresh blood flowing out of him in a rush, to mix with the snow on the ground. I sank to my knees beside him and tried to cradle his big handsome blonde head in my puny arms and for a

197

moment I thought his eyes were going to open like on those old films when the cowboy has died but if you look carefully you can see his eyes flicker. But not our Stevie. His eyes were never going to open again.

All I could say was his name over and over. "Stevie, Stevie" and "What have you done" but I must have been screaming and crying too because people started to appear from all over, my mother included, but they couldn't make me let go of him. Not for a while at least. But he had died right there in the snow, my big dopey brother, with nobody holding him in the actual moment, all alone, while I had been asleep upstairs.

I found out later that he had gone with Dale and Rico and the bug-eyed one to the game, got into a fight and been hit around the head. After a night celebrating in various pubs with his fellow warriors he had driven all the way home, head starting to ache from the blood clot rapidly forming around his brain, all the way back down through south Manchester. The sad thing is the doctors said that if he had got to a hospital, there was a strong chance that he could have been saved, but that only made it harder to bear, knowing that if Stevie had just turned right to a hospital, instead of left to our house, then everything would have been alright. They could have drilled a hole in his head, let his blood spurt out, and he would have been saved. But they hadn't and he wasn't.

With a great effort they managed to prise my hand away from his left hand, so they could get him into the ambulance at least. In the hospital, Stevie's right hand, also held in a tight fist, required another surge of strength from a doctor to unclench, and inside it they found my mother's watch, the one that had seen my grandfather more or less safely through the Great War, and also the tiny photo frame containing my mother's shining face alongside the more severe image of her own father. These two pieces that my brother had rescued from the pawn shop, to give back to my mother as a surprise, were eventually returned to her by the police, the ornate metal of both stained with the innocent blood of her firstborn child, and kept by her, her most precious of treasures, never again to leave her conscious possession.

After Stevie died, my mother was never the same again.

My brother was buried in one of those old Manchester cemeteries; that was when the coroner had finished with him and the police had stopped asking questions. They gave him a little plot, a muddy hole in amongst the endless rows of white marble angels and ornate crosses, paid for by the bereaved families of the city's glorious and wealthy past.

I composed a letter in my head on the day of the funeral and I mumbled to myself the words as our small, fragmented family stood around Stevie's grave, my father next to our George but keeping his distance from my mother and keeping his distance in death from the boy in the box, who was not his son and who he had never loved or even known really. My mother, still in a state of total shock, high as a kite on prescribed sedatives, stood moaning softly, me on one side of her, mumbling my own eulogy. Our Sandra was on her other side, dark hair piled high, her face a fierce grey mask beneath, at last feeling pain of her own. Other assorted relatives and friends stood in rows, according to, it seemed to me, the level of friendship that they had had with Stevie. In the front, Glenda, the girl he had been courting most recently, and some other girls who he had courted before, who maybe still loved him, because they were openly weeping, clutching tiny white hankies in frail white fingers, as if they still did.

Behind them, there were his mates, lads of all shapes and sizes, uncomfortable in their black suits and ties, some tough-looking, some softer from the hospital where he worked and where he had been taken to on that last day. Most just stood silently, their heads bowed, as the vicar spoke about ashes and dust and all that 'returned to the arms of Jesus' stuff that Stevie would have hated.

I spoke my letter to Stevie from my place at his graveside, trying to reconcile his live self who I knew and loved, with the body that he had become, the cold, grey, bloodless replica that lay in the light brown box by the hole in the ground. I told him that I was trying to feel his hugs and his blows, and touch his rough skin and have it touch me with his big hands, and see his big, handsome, blonde-haired face gazing down at me with his stupid grin as I was trying to sleep. I wanted his words back, making me laugh and cringe in equal measure, and I wanted to hear him sing Buddy Holly's 'True love Ways', which he had always loved because Buddy had talked in his normal voice on the front of the record, and I wanted him to be telling me again about the nurse who was a guardian angel and how he would always keep an eye out for me. I wanted to hear him snore and groan and cry out in his sleep like he always did and wake me up so that I got mad. How much I wanted him back. I told him all this, as I stood by the hole waiting for them to place him inside.

Yet I knew somehow, that the body that had imprinted all these images in my mind, was an empty body, that his blood had been washed off by the nurses and with it my fingerprints and the kisses that I had given him as he lay in the snow that day, and the tears that I had cried over him. I knew that his hair would have been brushed and his wounds made invisible by mortuary make-up, so my mother could see him and kiss him for the last time with the minimum amount of torment to follow. I knew that he would have been dressed in his best suit, the one that he would have worn to his own wedding, and then with no resistance or a cheeky smile or a comment that they surely would have got had he lived, some strong people, because he was a heavy lad was our Stevie, would have placed him in a wooden box like he was a piece of freight to be despatched, which in a way he was. But he wasn't going anywhere unless you believed in heaven, and I didn't and I don't think our Stevie did, although he did believe in angels. Well guardian angels at least.

But I knew that inside that wet, black earth, the box would rot, then the worms and the maggots would eat him and his bloody suit, and then his skin would go and those muscles that he had been so proud of would rot away over weeks or months, maybe even quicker, so that quite soon there would be nothing left except dust, as that vicar was trying to tell us, and it would be almost like he had never been. Deep down I knew that this would all happen, but that was too much to take in so I stopped thinking about him for the time being.

It pissed down with rain and I was pleased about that. I would have hated to have seen him leave a blue-sky world, with the sun blazing down, like being made to go to bed with the curtains drawn on a summer's evening, when there was still so much left to do in the day. Being put into the rich, black Manchester earth and having your light turned out forever didn't seem so bad on a day with one big grey cloak of rain hanging over it. On a day when nobody could do anything, except feel sad, and lost, and dead too in their own way.

Chapter 12

THE SEARCH

After Stevie died, I was quite ill for a while and I didn't have to go to school. At one point I went into hospital, and I can remember crowds of doctors standing around talking in hushed tones to my mother. On one occasion, I woke in the middle of the night and they had put sides on my bed like I was some kid in a cot, and when I started yelling, out of the blue my dad appeared. I don't think it was a dream, but I lay down again when I saw him, and when I woke again in the morning, he wasn't there. I was too tired to ask anyone whether he had been there in the middle of the night. I was too tired to ask anyone anything for that matter, and for what seemed like weeks I didn't say a word. Just kept my trap shut. Even when my mum begged me to speak to her, I didn't. I just couldn't be bothered at that time. I felt bad later because I knew it must have hurt her. She was pulling her own hair out because of her nerves, but I couldn't help myself, and I justified it by thinking that sometimes kids do stuff that is not personal, that hurts mums and dads, they just can't stop themselves.

In my case it was those weeks in hospital when I was awake when I didn't talk; when I knew my mother desperately wanted me to speak to her but I truly couldn't, no matter how hard I tried. The doctors and the nurses were trying but they couldn't make me talk. So they stuck loads of needles in me and sucked out my blood, like those leeches do in the Ladybrook, and then they manhandled me, and banged me and scraped me, but still no sound came from my mouth. They even brought our George and our Sandra in to make me speak, and that nearly worked because I was that close to telling them to 'fuck off,' but I stopped myself in time and just lay there, mute and unsmiling. They looked down at me like I was some kind of mental case, which in a way I was in danger of being, but I was happier in my silent world, away from all the crap.

I didn't eat either, because I just lost the urge for that. I must have been losing weight because they kept getting the scales out and making me stand on them in just my pyjama bottoms, in the middle of the ward for every bastard to see. It was humiliating but I didn't complain. Then they tried fattening me up with all that hospital food, all that mince and soggy potatoes and cabbage and suet pudding, but I wouldn't eat that either, although there were times when I wanted to.

They were all waiting for a big defining moment when one day I would suddenly start to talk and eat again and they could all throw their hands up in joy. But it never came. I think all the doctors and nurses got pissed off with their lack of progress. They had done all their tests, found nothing much wrong with me physically and eventually asked my mum to take me home so that they could have their bed back. She didn't complain. It had been almost a month and she was as sick of them as they were of us. So one morning she came and told me to get up and get dressed, we were going home. I did so with no fuss and no resistance, because I had had enough too, and in truth I was feeling a lot better about life. I had this real urge to talk, but I was mindful that it had been so long since Mum had heard my voice, that I didn't want to give her too much of a shock by talking out of the blue, especially given her own fragile state.

When we came out of the hospital entrance straight onto the Oxford Road, instead of turning left to catch the bus south out past Platt Fields, we turned right and headed towards the city centre. My mum was striding out in determined fashion and in my weakened state I was huffing and puffing and struggling to keep up with her. Eventually, when we were forced to wait at a junction while cars whizzed by at breakneck speed, I was able to whisper to her, above the noise of their engines, my first words since they had buried Stevie, four weeks before.

"Mum. Mum, where the hell are we going?" I asked, my voice croaky and with a sharp pain from my throat to my chest from walking so fast.

She turned and looked at me, her face red from her own exertions, in colourful contrast to the light blue headscarf that protected her ravaged hair from the Manchester drizzle. But she made no comment on my sudden return to speech, not even an observation on the sound of fresh words coming from me, which for weeks she had longed to hear.

As we stood on that junction, she bent and she kissed me on the cheek.

"I think it's about time we paid a visit to your father," she said. "I think he needs to be reminded that he still has responsibilities, and I don't just mean financial."

That day is a bit of a blur now as I look back on it, but there are still little things I remember with a vivid clarity, even thirty years down the line. I remember being surprised at how fast my own mother could walk, and, while I struggled behind her how slow I had become since getting sick. Last summer, with Billy and the others, I had been able to keep moving almost all day, be it on foot or on bike, especially if we had got out to somewhere like Alderley Edge to look for caves, or to the Ringway Airport to look at planes.

After a few blocks we turned east away from the city centre, into the back streets of Manchester, row after row of them, most made of those lumpy old cobble stones, which shone brightly in the light rain and were slippery when we left the pavement to walk across them. I kept wondering why we didn't catch a bus but I think my mum was in too much of a hurry to wait for one. Past red-bricked back to back terraces we walked, past house after house, their stone steps glistening from hard scrubbing, young mothers in twos and threes standing in doorways, or at the tops of the alleyways wearing old worn overcoats, their hair pinned back from their tired faces, holding babies, not minding the rain, or at least used to it. Their older children, still not at school, wearing shorts and Wellington boots, played in the small puddles at their feet. On the corners there were little grocery stores or newsagents, their grimy facades covered in familiar logos, Players Navy Cut cigarettes and Brooke Bond tea, but they didn't seem to be doing too much business. At regular intervals, as we moved through Gorton, then Audenshaw, and eventually into Ashton, there were big open spaces, some completely flat and clear, some overgrown with vegetation or covered in old debris, brick and timber and even, on one, an old abandoned black car, on which sat a couple of older lads with pointy shoes and shiny black quiffs, smoking cigarettes, bored and oblivious to all around them. These spaces, I learnt later, were the bomb sites from the War, or sometimes just slum clearance, where the houses had just got too rundown to live in, and I realised that these were the areas that the Spills had come from, and it all felt like a million miles away from our part of Manchester. Those areas that my mother and I walked through looking for where my father lived, were slowly but surely dying, falling away, to be swallowed back into the ground from where they had sprung a hundred years before, in more prosperous and vibrant times. I could smell the decay of it all, the must and the grime in the thousands of bricks in the buildings that never dried out.

As we walked past the ornate, wrought-iron lampposts with their old lights on top, and some with bits of rope attached which the kids would use as swings like we used the tree at the Ladybrook, I started to notice something else. Posted on almost every one were little photographs of the missing girl Lesley Ann Downey, her solemn face looking out from under her neat brown hair, her chubby cheeks, her innocent, unquestioning eyes. I remembered that same photo as being the one they used in all the news items and the newspapers. On the day she had been photographed, she had worn her favourite blue coat and it had been her mother's favourite picture of her. Her fate now known, her pictures in this street had been left intact, almost like a memorial; but time and those winter mists of smoke and rain that pervaded these streets every day, had now curled their edges like woodshavings and turned their colour from monochrome to sepia. Most were peeling away from their cardboard backs, leaving just faint flickers of her image, as if she came from another century, and not from the 1960s.

We arrived at number thirty two Sebastopol Street and stood outside, my mother holding the little scrap of paper that was the letter my father had sent her. She squinted down and checked the address on the page then looked up again at the number painted on the old black door. The rain had stopped for the moment but I could see her eyes watering in the fresh breeze that had come in its place, and with a glance at me she rapped her woollen gloves hard against the wood. No answer. She knocked again and I stood at her side, silently praying that he would be there and we could go in for a bit and get dry. Then we heard some sound from within, and I saw my mother take a step backwards and straighten her back, bracing herself, preparing to meet him, and I saw the hard line of her jaw and her eyes half closed, keeping her emotions in check, and in that moment I loved her more than any time that I could remember.

But the door opened and it was not my father but an old woman, her grey hair in curlers and wearing an old housecoat, its once vivid pattern faded with age and use. The initial disappointment that we both felt was tempered by the realisation that this woman must be his landlady.

"Yes?" she enquired, in a broad Lancashire accent, brusque, almost rude. "What can I do for you?"

"We're looking for James Gibson," said my mother, not put off. "He's my husband," she added for good measure.

The old woman looked my mother up and down, a slight sign of distaste in the downturn of her mouth. She had already made her judgement.

"He's not here," she said again in a rude manner.

"When will he return?" asked my mother, trying to keep her dignity and her temper in the face of such unhelpfulness.

"He won't be returning," said the landlady. "He paid me in full and left at the end of last week." She glanced down at the letter and sneered. "He obviously hasn't got round to informing you yet."

"Did he say where he was going," whispered my mother, close to tears. "Did he leave an address? Anything?"

"Only a crate of empty beer bottles, if that's any good to you? He left in a hurry, mind."

"Why?"

"Because I kicked him out, that's why. I can't have my lodgers bringing lady friends home. I can't have any of that nonsense under my roof. This is a reputable household."

"A woman, what woman?" cried my mother and my own stomach churned when I heard these words.

The old landlady placed her big red hands firmly on her hips and stared at us defensively.

"His fancy woman," she said, "I don't know. I don't care. I can't have it and I told them so. Take my advice, Missus. Forget him. He'll be nothing but trouble for you. And for him," she added, nodding at me. Then she shut the door and left us standing there in the street and we stood, the two of us, silently for seconds before, with no other course of action to take, we turned and walked to the nearest bus stop.

It took us three buses to get home and mum did not speak the whole journey back, except to ask for our fares from the conductor. She just stared straight ahead, constantly smoking, while I looked out of the window at the shops and the houses and all the people going home from work. At one point she turned the face of her watch inside out and pressed the cool metal back, the bit with the writing on, onto her forehead as if it was some kind of cold compress relieving a headache. Then she lowered it to her mouth so she could brush her lips against it and held it there for a while, getting some comfort from it. Then she lit yet another cigarette.

When we got off the bus at the other end, just by chance, Christine MacNeill from my class at school came walking down the street towards us. She had grown taller since I had seen her last, and she looked more grown-up, a little make-up around her green eyes, her fair hair styled. Even her freckles were fading. I thanked God she was on her own because I just wasn't in the mood to face all her mates as well, Monica and Lorna and the rest of them, especially since I hadn't been at school for a while and they were bound to ask questions about where I had been. Or, more likely, if they knew what had happened to my brother, offer up all that sickly sympathy, which would have been even worse. I couldn't have stuck that. I thought about ignoring MacNeill, but there was no way she was going to let me do that, and as it happened she talked to me in a straight sort of way, which I prefer. Better than all that pussyfooting around that most people go in for, trying not to hurt your feelings, but in so doing really pissing you off. MacNeill was different.

"Hello, Michael, hello Mrs Gibson," she said to us both, although to my knowledge she had never met my mother before. My mother just smiled a thin, tired smile and moved on a few paces, giving me time to at least say hello back.

"Are you alright now?" she asked. "I heard about your brother and I was so sorry."

"Thank you. I'm feeling a lot better than I was," I told her. "I'm back at school next week."

"Good. I've missed you. We've all missed you," she added hurriedly. "Those barmy friends of yours, Billy and Vic are hard work without you to keep them in control."

I smiled at the thought of them, but could think of no reply because my mind wandered back to Stevie. I shook my head a little to clear it.

"I wanted to write you a letter because you were away such a long time," she said. "But I lost my nerve. I'm so sorry."

"You should have. It would have helped."

"Next time I will. Oh I don't mean that. There, there won't be a next time I'm sure…"

"It's alright," I interrupted, "I know what you mean. A letter would be good anytime. I love getting them, but I hardly ever do. My dad is away at the moment, but he never writes."

"I like to write," she said. "You can say things in a letter that you can't say face to face. When you don't want other people to know, or when you are worried you may say the wrong thing."

"Yes, I know what you mean," I agreed, remembering the letter I had written in my head to my brother when he died, which I still kept in my head even now.

There was a pause, and we looked at each other awkwardly, both of us unsure whether to continue the conversation.

"There's Gypsies down at the Ladybrook," she suddenly said out of the blue.

"Where?"

"They're on the wasteland by the shallow crossing," she said. "There's trailers and a big tent and lots of kids. Oh and there's a couple of horses too."

"They won't stay long," I said, "Gypsies never do."

"No," she agreed. "Some people are already upset they're there at all. They're talking about getting the police."

"That would be a shame," I said and MacNeill nodded. There was a pause and we both stood for a moment, unable to find the words to continue.

"Look, I have to go," I said finally. "I'll see you at school."

"Can you tell your mum how sorry we all are... about your brother I mean. I didn't get a chance just now."

"I will and thank you again," I said, one eye on my mother, who was now showing signs of impatience.

I started to walk away, but MacNeill called me back and I turned round again.

"Michael," she said. "Could you show me the river sometime? Properly I mean, all its secret places. Lorna and the others aren't interested in going down there and I don't want to go on my own."

She saw my hesitation and read it correctly.

"Your friends wouldn't have to know," she added. "We wouldn't tell anyone."

"Alright," I said eventually. "I'll call for you sometime."

"Promise?" she said.

"Promise," I replied.

Chapter 13

THE GYPSY BOY

The first time we encountered the Gypsy boy, he was on his own doorstep so to speak. As MacNeill had told me, they had parked their caravan and trailer, and tethered a couple of horses too, down on the piece of waste ground that led down to the river from Grange Park. This upset the residents for two reasons. Firstly, because the waste ground was useful to them. It was used for all different kinds of reasons, from just having some space to play (a lot of the places didn't have gardens), to fixing cars and playing football. The other reason was that not many people either liked or trusted Gypsies. They were trouble, they were thieves and they were unsocialised; and back in 1966, the few home owners, but mainly rent-paying tenants of my south Manchester neighbourhood, didn't want them there. It didn't matter that they were only one family, a mum, dad and five scraggly kids, including this lad about our age whose name we found out later was Jody. The locals didn't confront them, but a minority whispered amongst themselves and so the rumours spread.

"With these people before you know it there is a whole tribe of them and it isn't safe to leave your house," they said to one another. So the locals called the police.

"Not our problem," they were told, "if they're not offending. They're only trespassing if they're on private land. They're on council land. Try them."

So the locals tried the council. "They're not doing any harm, are they?" they were asked.

"Not yet," the locals replied, "but it's early days."

"There's only one family from what I hear," said the faceless voice from the council. "Not too much for the residents to worry about."

"That's for now. More might come. Then it won't be alright. What about sanitation? He's got horses too."

"Look, we are aware of the situation and we're dealing with it. It's obvious they can't stay there forever, but these things take time. We have to think about the children. He's got children, I believe."

"They've always got children. Hundreds of the little buggers. Alright, we'll sit tight for now. But any hint of trouble and he's off. And if you won't do it, and the police won't, then somebody else will have to. If you know what I mean."

So for the time being the Gypsy family stayed and they became an item of curiosity for the locals, who would go and stand and just look at them, a bit like they were watching animals in the zoo. To be honest I was surprised how they could put up with it for so long, being stared at, although at least for the moment nobody was abusing them at all. Not yet anyway.

Billy, Vic, Pybus and I went and had a look at them. It was a warm spring day and we were on our way back from the river, so we thought we'd go by the waste ground and have a look. There were a few others from the estate kicking about when we got there, but the Gypsies were just getting on with their business, as if they were alone. The younger kids, a boy and a girl of about seven and eight, were running about playing. The mother was sitting down in a chair outside the door of her caravan, and she had a bundle of brightly-coloured cloth which she was sewing with a great big needle, up and down and through, not delicately, but really vigorously, like a fisherman with his nets, that I saw once at Whitby. The young lad, Jody, just looked at us, as if to say, 'What are you doing here watching my family?' He was about our age, not as tall but strong, you could tell somehow. He was feeding the two horses, his arms draped over their bobbing brown necks as if they were his best friends, and looking back at us as if we were the strangers. He was really dark-skinned, not like an Indian or an African, but much darker than us, and he had blue eyes and a smile that was hidden under a tough look, like he could be happy but only on his terms. Right now he was looking at four lads, who were looking right back at him and looking right into the way he and his family lived, invading his life, so it was not surprising he didn't smile. He was not scared either. I was impressed with that. I might have been, in his position, but this kid just looked at us as if he had a right to be there, and we were the ones who needed permission.

"Look at him, the cheeky get," said Billy to all of us. "Acting hard. Bloody gyppo." We all stared at him, but he just stared right back, not caring.

Then the father came out from behind one of the vehicles and walked towards the trailer. He wasn't much bigger than his son and he had the same proud look. He also didn't care that he was an item of curiosity. He was proud to live in a caravan. I could see how dark and well-muscled his arms were and also how bandy-legged he was, like a cowboy. On his forearms, almost hidden in the hair and the brown skin, were the faint blue lines of old tattoos. His face was strong and thin with blue eyes like his boy, and, like his boy, he looked at you directly, not aggressively, but not with any apology either. The same smile that might be there was also hidden.

He walked to a trailer that was parked directly behind the caravan, and which was covered with a huge canvas sheet that made it as big as a marquee. Then very carefully he found a gap in the sheet, pulled it apart and disappeared inside. We waited, but he didn't come out for ages, and we were all dying to know what he was doing inside this huge tent. Our imaginations were going, I can tell you. Billy Skinner thought he had wild animals.

"Tigers or lions," he said.

"Do you think we might have heard them by now?" enquired Vic sarcastically.

"Not if he's drugged them," said Billy.

"What about feeding them?" asked Vic, still sceptical. "They need loads of meat and there's none about."

"Maybe the butcher's going to deliver him some," I said.

"Maybe that's what the horses are for," said Pybus, and we all laughed.

"I'm serious," he said.

"Get lost, Pybus," said Billy. "What's he going do, chuck them in live or cut them up right here at the bottom of Grange Avenue? That'll go down well with the neighbours." We were all killing ourselves laughing.

"Maybe he's got snakes in there. They don't make a noise and they don't need that much food," said Billy.

"Some snakes do," said Vic. "Pythons for a start. They can eat a whole sheep with one swallow. My mum told me. Then they sleep for a week, she said."

As we speculated, the Gypsy man came back out from his tented vehicle and closed the flaps up tightly, his strong arms pulling the two sides together. Before he tied it back up, he looked across at us. He said nothing, just looked in that open way he had, not hard or nasty, just a glance that said you've looked for long enough, now go away.

We decided to go and explore up to the northernmost part of our territory where we had rarely ventured before and where word of mouth had told us there were some interesting old buildings, derelict and deserted and rumoured to be haunted. Pybus told us he had done enough for one day but Billy, Vic and I walked the mile or so up from the river towards the golf course and eventually found the buildings surrounded by a high wire fence. We had to walk the length of the fence until we found a gap in the wire to crawl through then we scrabbled through, cursing and moaning at the awkwardness of it. On the other side was a small copse of trees and then beyond that flat land with grass growing out of control almost to our chests. In fact, it was old wasteland from where buildings had been knocked down and cleared and where, with the passage of time, shrubs and grass had regained lost ground.

Unexpectedly, we found amidst the nettles and the dock leaves, with their pungent aromas of rotten vegetables, a tiled floor that had probably once been somebody's kitchen and which just sat there well hidden in the undergrowth like some modern day Roman mural. We would have been more pleased by our own discovery, if it wasn't for something even more astonishing dominating the near foreground. Rising up from this wasteland was the largest house we had ever seen. It was a huge black Victorian house with turrets and gothic windows, all angles and pointy arches, and it stood three storeys high.

We had heard about the house from other lads who had tried to explore it, and although its reputation preceded it, we were still taken aback by how spooky it looked and by the sheer size and scale of it. It looked like a house from your worst nightmares, not unlike that one in Hitchcock's *Psycho* film where the girl got stabbed in the shower, the one on all the cinema posters.

It was a huge deserted mansion, the occupants long gone, but I found out later, when I became more interested in the history of the area, that this place had once been a family home to rich industrialists, away from the urban sprawl of a Lancashire mill town where they had their business. A hundred years on, when this part of once rural Cheshire had also been swallowed up, this time by the growth of the more affluent suburbs, these people had moved on in search of a new solitude. They had sold their unloved mansion to property developers who, while waiting for the right time to rebuild, had let it fall into rack and ruin, a playground for very young children to play out their fantasies of murderers and demons, and for children not much older to play out their own games, no less adventurous and no less spine-tingling.

The building should have been made safe and there had been an attempt to fence the outside and post signs warning of the danger, but the signs had been torn down and holes made in the fence so there were no real physical barriers to entering the property, only mental ones. Who knew how many mad grown-ups there were out there just waiting for the right time or opportunity to murder innocent and unsuspecting children? That was enough to keep most of the kids in the area out of the big black house that stood on its own, cold and malevolent, an enticing playground for only the very reckless and daring. This was the first time we had seen the big house we had heard about so much and we could see why so many kids were scared to come here. But it wasn't going to stop us, not today at least.

"Bloody hell," said Billy finally, in true wonderment. "Look at the size of that place."

"Let's go in," I said.

So we charged in at a gallop, leaping over rusted bicycle wheels and all sorts of other debris. As we did, we had the discretion to at least slow down and then pause before we passed through the old front door, our boots crunching on broken glass. Some glass still remained in the doorframe itself, and great shards of stained glass in deep reds and greens, hung precariously from window frames like coloured icicles, left by the locals' stone throwing. Later we ourselves would not be able to resist some target practice.

The door creaked and groaned as in all the best horror films and we stepped into what would once have been a magnificent hallway. Despite the brightness outside, it was dark in the hall, the stained glass, even where broken, not shedding enough light to brighten the gloom. There was a sinister feel to the place, a house abandoned and unloved, and it fair gave me the creeps I can tell you.

All of a sudden there was a huge shout from Vic which made us all yell in unison.

"What's that, what's happening?" I said in a panic. "Vic, where are you?"

"Aarrgh!" he yelled again.

"Where are you, you stupid lump?" said Billy in a voice that disguised his nerves well.

"Bloody cobwebs!" said Vic. "There's bloody hundreds of them. All over me. Ugh! I can't move for them."

Suddenly I was caught by them as well. They stuck to my face and neck like musty candy floss.

"Aarrgh!" I said. "They've got me now. They're everywhere."

"They're only cobwebs," said Billy "They won't hurt you."

"True enough," I said

"Mind you," Billy continued "the spider that built them, now she might want a word, if you know what I mean."

"That's it," said Vic. "I'm getting out of here, besides," he added as he turned to leave, "I'm starting to get the belly ache. I need some fresh air."

"What about you, Mike?" said Billy. "You're not scared of a couple of manky spiders, are you?"

"I'm with you," I said.

"Well c'mon then," he said, "let's explore this heap of rubble," and together, although more carefully than before, we went further into the house.

Our eyes were slowly getting used to the light now and we could see various doors leading off in different directions. At the end of the hall through a great arch we walked into a much larger space and there stood what remained of a once magnificent staircase. It appeared largely intact so, with Billy leading, the two of us started to climb, picking our way carefully, avoiding the spider's webs where we could and on the lookout for any missing steps. Both of us had some experience of exploring old houses and knew it was wise to watch your step. At one point as we climbed the stairs, Billy stopped me with a very melodramatic hand to my chest, as if he was a commando in the jungle just about to walk into an enemy ambush. He pointed down and there was a gaping hole in the stair, almost as if some unfortunate explorer before us had met his end falling through. Then he put his fingers to his lips, which I thought was a bit unnecessary – he was just trying to scare me and he was doing a good job, I can tell you. I mean, who else did he think would be creeping around? Was he expecting to bump into somebody on the stairs? Then he waved us on as if the noise had passed.

On one of the landings there was a window that looked out onto the overgrown garden, and far below us we could see Vic bent double and with his hands cupped, creeping through the long grass deep in concentration.

"Look at that twat," said Billy. "What's he think he's doing?"

"He's looking for insects," I replied smiling in the gloom despite myself. "He's always doing it. He's probably after crickets because those things can really jump."

"Funny how he likes crickets but doesn't like spiders," said Billy.

"He's a funny bloke is Vic and no mistake," and I meant what I said.

"Let's lob something at him," said Billy. "Wake him up a bit."

He picked up a bit of wood and hurled it through the window. The missile went spinning soundlessly through the air and landed a couple of feet from him, but he didn't even look up from his bug hunt. It was strange watching him from inside the dark house, paddling about in the long grass in the bright sunshine, almost as if he wasn't in the same life as we were but in another dimension.

Billy threw another missile, this time a metal hinge from one of the doors, which fell closer to Vic and he must have heard the whoosh as it landed in the long grass. He probably thought it was a small animal (possibly even a rat which we were all wary of) and he stopped, looked hard at the ground from where the noise had come and then leapt up onto a tree trunk that protruded above the line of the grass.

Upstairs we were creased up with laughter and at the same time madly trying to find something else to throw down at him.

Billy had a great big piece of wood.

"You can't throw that, it'll kill him," I protested.

"I'm not going to hit him with it," said Billy with admirable confidence, "just scare him a little, that's all. He'll know it's us."

Billy took a run and hurled the piece of wood out of the window, and we watched as it rather disappointingly flapped down like a wounded bird rather than speared down 'javelin style' as was intended. Vic, at last hearing a commotion above his head, looked up in time to see the piece of wood fall out of the sky and land harmlessly ten yards away from him. He looked again at where it landed, then up at us as if he thought we were trying to set him a riddle, then mouthed, 'What are you doing?' or words to that effect, before jumping off his trunk and resuming his search for insects.

He had taken off his shirt and I could see his thin white torso bordered by his yellow and black snake belt holding his baggy khaki shorts up. Usually he would have gone missing by now but today he was staying put in the overgrown garden.

Back inside the house we had left the window to continue on our way and silence had overtaken us again. Suddenly, Billy made the same motion that had stopped us in the first place. He held his hand up and said with all seriousness, in a whisper, "Listen!"

Then I heard a noise, I presume a repeat of the one that had startled him. From some distance away came the sound of a groan, faint but discernible nonetheless, a long drawn-out groan that seemed to come from a young girl. I don't know how I could tell, I just could and I felt my heart, already beating rapidly, really start to pound. A cold drop of sweat ran out of my armpit and down the side of my hot chest and I had an urgent, but not unpleasant desire to use the toilet. Then there came, not just a groan, but a long gurgling scream that started low but then rose higher and higher until it hit a point so sharp that it pierced my skin and made me shudder with fear. I looked at Billy and his face was pale and contorted in astonishment.

"What the fooking hell was that?" he whispered.

"Somebody must be torturing her," I whispered back at him. "God knows what he's doing to her. What are we going to do?" Then, even more chilling than the scream, there came the sound of laughter, a deep man's voice laughing like the devil himself.

"That's it," said Billy "I'm off. I'm not hanging around here to be murdered," and he was up and away down the stairs two at a time.

"Wait for me," I hissed and I tore down after him, down into the grand old hallway, out through the old double doorway, with its shattered windows, and out into the beautiful warm sunshine, the long coarse grass stinging our legs as we ran for the perimeter and safety. We called to Vic as we went and he fell into a trot beside us, and we didn't stop until we were back on the other side of the fence, the old house a black ominous shadow a hundred yards behind us.

"What's up with you two?" said Vic "In a bit of a hurry, aren't you?"

"Didn't you hear that scream?" I asked him. "From inside the house?"

"No," he said, "I was busy."

"You could hear it in bloody Stockport," said Billy, his breath coming back, "it was that loud."

"Somebody being tortured or murdered," I said.

"No?" said Vic.

"That's what it sounded like."

"How close were you two then? To this murder?"

"Close enough and a damn sight closer than you," said Billy obviously annoyed at Vic's sarcastic form of questioning.

"Do you think we should tell someone?" I asked.

"Maybe the rozzers," said Vic.

"No way!" said Billy. "I've had it with them. Let them find it for themselves. I'm not doing their job for them."

"Maybe it was kids just like us," I suggested hopefully. "They could have seen us coming and decided to spook us."

"They did a good job of it too," said Vic.

"At least we got past the spiders, which is more than you did," said Billy, getting irritated.

"Maybe it's Hindley and Brady," said Vic, "you know, the ones who've been taking all these kids. Murdered them too they reckon. You could have been listening to a murder."

"They're locked up and you know it," said Billy. "I'm going to batter you in a minute, Vic. I swear."

"Alright," said Vic hurriedly, "if it's not them, what if it's copycats. That's what the police call them. Copycat murderers. My mum said they'll be like rats out of drains following in these two's footsteps. That's why she never stops bloody mithering me. All her questions. She thinks I'll be next, that's why."

"My mum says the last two were round here all the time," I joined in. "Looking for victims. I heard her telling my dad. You never know."

"If it's not copycats, then you probably heard ghosts," said Vic. "I thought there was something odd about that place. I bet it's full of dead bodies. I mean look at it," and he turned to look back at the house, getting ever more sinister as the light faded. "Look at it," he repeated. "If that's not a haunted house, I don't know what is."

"Alright, alright," said Billy, worn down now by our speculation.

"We'll go back, maybe tomorrow, but for now I'm going home for me tea. I'll get killed if I'm late again."

At that point the fading light was illuminated momentarily by a sheet of white light that seemed to cross the whole sky and everything around us for just a second shone with a dazzling clarity. Then gloom again and we all gasped. Seconds later a rumble of not so distant thunder, like the roll of a growl in a big dog's chest, brought us to our senses.

"C'mon," said Billy, "we don't want to be stuck in this horrible place in a thunderstorm. Let's run."

That was the second time we saw the Gypsy kid; on our way back from the haunted house as the storm came in. I don't know what he was doing so far from home. We were hurrying now, heads down tucked into our chests, along Queens Road, fleeing the rain that would surely come, the clouds chasing us, black and angry-looking, and the thunder getting louder by the minute. The day and the evening had been warm but now the temperature had dropped and all was quiet, no birds or traffic, no planes in the sky, no trains in the distance. There were no people on the street except us, and then suddenly, as if from nowhere, this bedraggled kid came running along. He was running fast, straight towards us, and he was frightened. We knew immediately he was not one of us, not from our estate, but at first we thought he may be a Spill and we braced ourselves for trouble, but then we realised that it was the Gypsy kid, the one from the caravan. The boy, without hesitation, ran right up to us and said, "Can you tell me how to get back to the Ladybrook?"

Even though this kid was lost and frightened, he tried not to show it. It was obvious he didn't recognise us from earlier in the day when we'd stood watching his family. He didn't plead with us to help him, just asked very casually for directions, trying to control his nerves. In a strange way this attitude annoyed us and it showed in our response.

"What part of the Ladybrook?" said Vic. "It's about ten miles long. Longer even."

"I dunno," muttered the kid, still acting cocky. "Near some houses."

"That's a big help that is," said Billy. "Near some houses."

The kid persisted.

"There's a street near there called Grange Avenue and there's a school not far."

Then for the first time he showed a bit of panic. "Can you help me?" he asked, his voice starting to falter. "I don't know how to get back. My mum will kill me if I'm caught out in this."

We all stood looking at him, enjoying the sudden change in his demeanor.

"What's your name kid?" enquired Billy.

"Jody," said the boy, starting to shiver despite his own best efforts.

"Jody!" exclaimed Vic. "What kind of name is that?"

"Not so proud now, eh, Jody?" said Billy. "You want to try saying please when you ask for help."

I don't know why, to this day, we acted like we did. I can't explain it. Maybe it's a boy thing. Even when the kid showed us he was scared we didn't help him, still didn't give him the directions he wanted even though since we had recognized him, we knew exactly where he wanted to go. I think we wanted to hear him admit that he lived in a caravan. Because his bravery and his aloofness unsettled us; because he was tougher than all of us. All these things and he was just a Gypsy of the same age, but how different his life was, how much closer to the wild he seemed to be.

Then we all went into mock consultation. The thunder grew closer but we no longer cared, for we were in a frenzy of humiliation and degradation and the moment was sweet.

"Now let's see," said Billy, "Grange Avenue. That rings a bell. Does it with you Vic?"

"Can't say it does," said Vic, in a mock snooty voice. "What about you, old man?"

"What's that about a school?" said Billy. "Anybody know a school?"

"Don't go to school," said Vic. "Gypsies don't, why should I?"

"What about you, kid?" said Billy, turning to the Gypsy boy. "Do you go to school?"

A great drop of rain, that would have filled a teaspoon, drops from the sky; then another and another and one drops onto the boy's face. He stands and looks at the group of boys who are taunting him and there is a silence between us and this raindrop is running down the Gypsy's face like a big tear and he rubs it away with his sleeve. Then there is a crack of thunder so loud it's like a bomb has gone off, which makes us all jump but which seems to poleaxe the kid, such is his terror of it. He bows his head into his shoulders like a tortoise and crouches right down, and then when the rumble after the blast finally stops he looks up and his eyes are wild.

All of a sudden I start to feel sorry for the lad and I want this to stop, but Billy has not finished with him.

"So you take a left then a right then left again and again down a long road up a short one round the block and that will get you back to your caravan. Is that clear?" he gabbled, relishing the kid's confusion. Then Billy and Vic went quiet and just looked at the kid waiting to see what he did, but at this point I piped up. I had seen enough.

"Billy," I said, "I think we should take him back."

They both look at me like I've gone mad.

"Fook off!" exclaimed Billy, contemptuously. "Let him find his own way. Gypsies are meant to find their own way home anyway. It's what they do."

He turned and looked at the kid, desperately trying not to shiver and shake in front of us. "Go on," he said, "get off home, but I'd get a shift on if I were you."

The Gypsy boy looked at Billy, who was twice the size of him, and said in a voice that would chill your blood. "I'll kill you for this, you bastard, you just wait." And then he set off again at breakneck speed down Queens Road, more towards the storm than away from it and in the opposite direction to the Ladybrook.

I could see that Billy, despite his normal bravado, was shaken by the kid's threat, sort of stunned by the power of it. Just a small kid but he meant it and Billy was unnerved. I was more worried that the kid was going to get struck by lightning and I made a decision in that split second that changed my friendship with Billy forever and altered my life way beyond its normal horizons for a few weeks thereafter. Against Billy's direct wishes, I changed direction and started running after the Gypsy kid. I could hear the shouts of the other two behind me as I ran from them, head down into the eye of the storm, in pursuit of the frightened Jody. In my head my thoughts were in turmoil because I wasn't sure I had made the correct decision. It was like night-time, it was so dark and the thunder and lightning were getting closer and I wanted to get home myself, and already I was half thinking how angry Billy was going to be with me, but I knew that I couldn't let the kid go off in the wrong direction when he was scared stiff already and there was no one else around to help him out of it. So I chased him and I really had to pump my legs because he was moving like a scalded cat. Eventually he heard me shouting behind him and he stopped and turned around and I could see that he was ready to fight me, and that there were tears rolling down his cheeks from his bright red eyes and that he was angrier and more frightened than any one I had ever seen. I really had to convince him that I was helping him.

"I'll take you back," I yelled to him, "calm down, just follow me." I said all this to him as sincerely as I could but it took a while before he trusted me enough to follow, not surprisingly, after our previous work.

"C'mon," I beckoned to him "I'm not messing you about I promise. I'll take you back."

I had to talk to him like I would a dog. Try to get his trust back slowly but surely.

Then eventually I'd convinced him that I was telling the truth and he started to trot back with me in the right direction away from the shops and the lights and the traffic and the roar of the storm that had arrived, the whole scene behind us like an old painting of a foreign city, the oils shimmering with rain and light.

So we raced back, half in half out of the storm, getting soaked to the skin, raindrops plastering our hair flat to our heads and our clothes to our bodies, but staying warm because our arms and legs were pumping. Back down Queens Road we ran, across Grange Road then down Claremont Avenue and I could see that his fear was melting away as he saw familiar landmarks come into view. Eventually twenty minutes later, we got back to the caravan and there was no-one around.

"Where's your family, out looking for you?" I asked and the kid laughed.

"No," he said "they wouldn't be looking for me. No way. We're expected to take care of ourselves, not like you folks."

"I have to go," I said, not mentioning the fact that I had just taken care of him by getting him home, but waiting for a 'thank you' at least. It seemed that I was waiting in vain, for he said nothing. Then as I turned to run back home, he called out to me.

"Oi you," his confident attitude had returned.

"What?" I shouted back, expecting that missing thank you.

"Tell your mate that I haven't forgotten him," and he made a cut throat motion with his finger across his neck. Then he turned and walked up the steps into his trailer without a backward glance.

The next day Billy and Vic were still angry with me for helping the Gypsy, but to be honest I didn't care.

"You went against your mates. That's betrayal that is," said Vic, in a sneering voice.

"It never is," I countered, prepared to stand my ground. "All I did was help that kid. You could see he was scared shitless. He was having a heart attack. We were all dead tight to him, and he'd done nothing. I thought he had had enough that's all."

"He's only a Gypsy," Billy ranted on, "why are you getting all sentimental all of a sudden? If I remember you were all against him to start with. What happened? Did you go all soft on us? Go on, piss off. Go and play with the gyppo, you sad get."

I looked at Linton and Pybus, who hadn't even been there, and were as usual not saying much, just going along with what Billy said.

"Right then," I said, "I bloody will. Oh and by the way, he's after you, that Jody lad. He told me he hasn't forgotten. I'd watch him if I were you."

Billy snorted with derision. "Tell him I'll have him anytime he wants, the runt. I'll bury the bastard once and for all. I ain't scared of no gyppo. He's got some mouth."

"I'm just telling you, that's all," I said and I walked off in the opposite direction.

Jody's mother, or it might have been his grandmother, you can never be sure with 'travelling' people, (sometimes they look older than they really are on account of the hard lives they live), told fortunes. She read tea leaves, she read palms, she even produced these brightly-coloured cards that she called tarot cards and read them. Apparently she could see the future in a whole variety of things. If you had brought your dirty underpants along, she probably would have read them as well.

After the Gypsy family had been there a little while all the women from around about started to get their fortunes told. It was also said that she had magic potions that she rubbed on their stomachs and other parts but I can't be sure of all that. The women off the estates quite liked the gypsies there for that reason, but of course they had to keep their visits a secret from the men, who were still hostile to them. The old woman had a constant stream of customers paying their shilling to have their fortune told and she would tell them about great wealth coming or tall dark strangers, all that baloney, which was what they wanted to hear. All this was a small but valuable respite from the reality of hard lives with drunken husbands that quite a few of them had to put up with. Or at best stuck in a small flat, with snivelling babies for company and with the rain pissing down as it always seemed to do in Manchester. Enough to make anyone want their fortune told with a promise of something better. I don't suppose the Gypsy woman ever told any of them, as she read those tea leaves or traced the lines of those work-reddened palms, that they were going to stay in the same house for their whole life or that their husband would get older and sicker and more useless or that in just a few years they would get cancer of the breast and find out too late and die leaving young children behind, which is what did happen to a couple of them I remember. No, the Gypsy woman told them nice things for the most part and even if it was misleading or giving false hope it was still alright and worth that shilling.

The day after my fall out with Billy and the others I wandered down to the camp to see if Jody had recovered from his ordeal in the storm. After a short time he appeared from one of the trailers and when he saw me nodded in my direction. But he didn't call me over, just bent down and whispered a few words to his mum, who was sitting on the steps peeling vegetables, then disappeared into the side of the big tent that his father was working in. After a minute or so just as I had decided to leave, Jody's mum raised her hand and beckoned me to come across to where she was sitting, and after initially hesitating I crossed the grass to her trailer, mindful that I had been invited over an unseen line into their camp. Then she asked me if I wanted my fortune told. I hesitated again because I didn't have a shilling to give her and also because I wasn't sure I wanted to know my future, but she persuaded me and said the shilling didn't matter on account of how I had helped out Jody, so I agreed to do it. She took my hand in her own hand which was brown and knobbly like a hard wood and almost clawlike in its shape, permanently open like an eagle's talon. She ran her old yellow nails down the soft lines on the inside of my palm and started muttering to herself. The skin on my hand felt scratchy and I wanted to laugh but I dared not. She was probably not bad looking once and she carried that same half smile that her family carried that made you want to find out more about them. She had blond hair with black streaks at the top where her parting was and she had dark intense eyes that didn't just look at you, they looked into you, right through into your head, down your spine and into your heart, at least that was what it felt like, which I suppose was pretty good if you told fortunes. Suddenly you didn't feel so critical and ready to laugh. She knew about Stevie and about my dad, not in an obvious way but she told me that was why I was sad a lot of the time and lonely. She told me that my mum would get better. It would take some time but she would live to be an old lady. I didn't really know that my mum was ill but Jody's mum seemed to know what she was talking about so I didn't contradict her. Besides, she said I was a good boy for looking out for her and that would make me a good man. She said her Jody had the same traits; he would make a good man too. I wasn't keen to hear any more than that really so I was glad when the old lady said, "Just remember, boy. Be true to yourself," and with that she finally let go of my hand.

So that was how I came to spend a few weeks in springtime in the company of Jody the Gypsy boy. After our initial rocky start, slowly we began to trust each other and we became willing to share our secrets. I showed him the rope swing and the arches, and he educated me in the way of the Romany. Or at least as much as he could say to a non Romany, which I suppose wasn't that much, but enough for me to appreciate that their ways were very different. He taught me in some fashion how to ride and we tore bareback up and down on the piece of waste ground on two of the old man's ponies. He never seemed to mind. One warm day in March we organised pony rides and charged the little kids a penny a ride and we made nearly five bob, which Jody spent on a packet of fags and I spent on bubblegum with the American Civil War cards in, that I was collecting. But it was in the countryside that his knowledge astounded me. As Jody showed me how to blend into the landscape, I came to realise just how much the other boys and I had crashed into it and disturbed everything in our path. When I was with Jody we moved along the paths and hedgerows quietly and with care, his little black and white terrier up ahead looking for game, and every so often he would put his hand up to stop me and his finger over his lips to shush me and he would point out a little piece of nature. He showed me little chicks in a starling's nest, he showed me weasels moving through hedgerows hunting rabbits, and he showed me a sparrow hawk hovering in the air, glossy wings holding the thermals, its tiny body with mean little face waiting to swoop on an unsuspecting field mouse. We'd rig up little fishing rods and tempt from the shallows coarse fish like gudgeon and tench, but always, because we couldn't eat it, remove the little homemade hook that he'd made and replace the fish back in its domain to pause briefly before spinning away in its silvery dash for freedom. Jody told me what fruits and berries it was safe to eat and which ones were so poisonous they could give you slow, agonising death, and we speculated on who we'd do it to. For Jody it was always Billy and I found myself protecting my old friend, I think because I had no doubt that Jody had the ability to wreak some horrible revenge even if ultimately he did not have the will or the vindictiveness to do it. I was quite surprised that he still felt that way after I had learned how worldly-wise and understanding he was in other things, but then I didn't know then how deep the feelings run of a Romany who has felt wronged. But I would learn and so would Billy.

After a while I got pretty confident on horseback. Jody could ride bareback like a Sioux Indian; just a rope for reins, leaning right over left and right to scoop up stuff from low down. I had an idea to fetch Nelson's sword from where I had been hiding it in the shed and we would take it in turns to slash the thistles and the shrubs with it as we rode. We had to be really careful though because the sword was still sharp and I didn't want to ruin it out of respect for Nelson's memory. One day though Jody turned up with a couple of huge marrows that he'd nicked, either from the front of the greengrocers or more likely an allotment somewhere. I didn't ask, and we cut faces into these marrows and hung them with string off a tree branch and spent a happy time with the sword, riding bareback and slashing the marrows with the sword in true cavalry style. Jody loved that sword and begged me to lend it to him and although I felt really uneasy about it I did just the same. He was so generous with everything he had, even his horses, or his father's horses as it was, but still; I felt I had to pay him back somehow. Anyway, he was better at hiding stuff than me and I was always worried that someone would find my sword and nick it so it was alright if he kept it for a while.

Jody's dad accepted me in the camp, welcomed me even, although he never said much more than a couple of words to me. He always had time for Jody and it was good to see the relationship they had. They never passed one another without a grapple or a playfight and even on a couple of occasions a full on boxing session, bare knuckle sparring with the old man passing on some of his tricks to the both of us. I could tell that his dad had probably been in a fair few scrapes, small as he was, and judging from the skills he showed us, had probably won more than he lost. He had the confidence of a man who can handle himself and he had, through his teaching, passed down that same confidence to his son. No need to strut about and play the big hard man, for Jody was quiet like his dad, but he had a self-assurance that gave him almost a peaceful demeanour, at least when he was in his own environment, running free. I found myself liking him more and more as the days went by.

Jody never took any notice of territory and wandered where he pleased. He wasn't wary of the Spills like I was and if he wanted to cross the river he did. One day we crossed with the terrier at Jody's heels to go and look for rabbits and as we scoured the fields looking for signs, me nervous and Jody unconcerned, sure enough the Spills appeared.

There were three of them coming out of the distance and walking towards us with that tell-tale swagger that tough kids have. My heart started to pump.

"Shit, Jody," I said, "Spills."

"What are Spills?" asked Jody, completely unworried by their approach.

"They come from those houses up there," I said, glancing across to the white sprawl of their new estate. "They're tough lads from the Manchester slums. You don't mess with them. I think we should run while we can, we're in their territory."

"They look alright to me," said Jody confidently. "Let's see what they say. You never know, they might be friendly."

I looked at them and they didn't look that friendly to me. I didn't recognise them so I think they might have been from a different tribe to the ones we had warred with before. They had that wiry, slightly undernourished look, mean narrow eyes and bad skin but big strong hands with scars on the fingers from fighting. They stood in front of us, thin legs in blue jeans, wide apart, arms hanging down like apes, unsmiling, watching. They were about our age, maybe a bit older.

"What the fook are youse two doing over here?" said their leader in a nasal Manchester twang.

Jody said nothing, just looked at them.

"Just walking," I said, trying to keep the nerves from my voice. "We're going back now."

"Fooking right you are," said the second Spill who carried a big purple bruise on his cheek from a previous skirmish. "Piss off back over that river."

"Yeah alright. C'mon, Jody," I urged.

"Jody. Jody," laughed the second Spill. "What kind of name is that?"

"It's a fooking girl's name, that's what it is," said the leader, and he mimicked a high voice.

"Jody, Jody," they all laughed.

I looked at Jody and his face was going pale.

"Ignore them, Jody," I whispered.

Jody wasn't going to ignore them though, I could tell.

"C'mon," I said. I was ready to run straight down and through the river, not even bother to go back to the crossing place.

Then from away to the right, diagonally about fifty yards up, came the sound of Jody's dog tearing through the long grass, yelping happily as it bounced over the clumps of nettle and thistle. Then, as if on cue, there was a deep snarl and the dog tore off in a zig-zag pattern, yelping and yapping, nose to the ground, legs pumping and then very quickly after, there came the sound of a short sharp attack. The dog trotted back to us with something in his mouth, sat down in front of Jody and looked up at him expectantly. Its tongue hung out and clasped firmly in its jaws was a young rabbit. I looked at the Spills and they were watching with rapt attention. I looked at Jody and he was watching his dog with his little half-smile. I looked at the rabbit in the jaws of the dog, still living and breathing, deep in shock, eyes showing a human-like fear. A young buck, his soft grey fur wet with canine saliva, head lolling, beautiful ears, gentle-natured, good to eat if you like your meat rich, an animal that loves his family, dying alone, feeling pain. Jody, much against his dog's wishes, took the rabbit from his jaws, held it up and looked in its eyes, like a midwife studying a newborn. It seemed like an age that Jody stared at this rabbit and then with one hand on the neck and the other around its head he gave a little twist of his fingers as if turning a door knob. There was a click, its eyes closed, and the body went limp and it died an instant, painless death. Then Jody pulled out a small but very sharp-bladed knife from his trouser pocket and made a long incision along the belly of the rabbit. From the bloody entrails that fell into his left hand he cut out the long black liver and with a flourish tipped back his head and lowered the shiny piece into his mouth with a delicacy of touch that belied the baseness of the act. The carcass he threw to the dog, who fell upon it and ate speedily, not to be denied its spoils for a second time.

Jody looked at me, then at the Spills who were staring at him with their mouths open.

"Good iron," said Jody. "Good for your blood, or so my grandad says." Then with a smile he wiped his lips with his sleeve.

"Fooking hell," said the third Spill, the first time he had spoken, "that's bloody mad is that. Are youse some kind of nutter, kid? I never seen the like. You're not with these posh twats," he said indicating me, "are yer? I can't see one of them eating raw rabbit."

"What's it do for yer?" enquired the leader with the twang, "eating its innards? Gives yer iron?"

"What it means," said Jody, "is that iron makes you strong and it makes you brave."

"Youse wanna give some to your mate," said the Spill with the bruise. "He's shaking like a bleedin' jelly."

"Who's shaking?" I said before I could stop myself. "I'm just cold, that's all. C'mon, Jody," I said, "let's go, I need to get back."

"Yeah, go on, Jody, take him home," said the lead Spill, "before he pisses himself. What you doing hanging around with a dick like that anyway?"

"He's alright," said Jody.

"Are we going to fight these or what?" said the third Spill impatiently.

"Nah," said the leader. "It'd be too easy. Wouldn't it, Judy?"

He had made fun of Jody's name and I braced myself for a reaction but Jody just looked at the three lads. He didn't move, just looked at them. For a horrible moment I thought he was going to go for them but he thought better of it. I don't know how good a fighter he was, but nobody I knew was good enough for one Spill let alone three of them. You can't count the Indian because he was crazy and he had a big knife but Jody was relatively normal as far as I could tell.

Sure enough he proved me right because he did nothing; just turned and walked aback down the hill with his dog and me very close behind. We didn't look back but we could feel the eyes of the Spills upon us and we could hear their insults carry us all the way back to the brook and across it.

The next day I went down to the Gypsy camp to call for Jody, and the family had gone. Suddenly, without warning and leaving virtually no trace of having been there, they had disappeared. I stood and looked at the embers of yesterday's fire still smoldering in the morning mist and wondered what had caused my friends to leave without even saying goodbye. It was two days after they had gone that I remembered that Jody still had my sword, hidden in some secret place in one of the trailers, and which I presumed had been taken with them in their sudden departure. When I realised, I was unsure whether I was angry or relieved that Jody had taken it with him, given the strange feeling that being in possession of that sword sometimes gave me.

A week after Jody left, Sandra and I were alone in the house. Mum was down the road at her friend Edna's drinking tea, and our George was playing football at the rec. It was one of those warm days with grey skies that you get in April, where everything goes quiet and you get a spooky feeling if you're in the wrong place. Normally being alone with Sandra anywhere is spooky but this day I was lying on my bed with the belly ache and I couldn't have cared less. I was trying to sleep but Sandra was making too much noise in her room; she had the radio on full blast, not with music but with some bloke blathering on about something, I couldn't make out what. I shouted at her to turn it down but she couldn't hear me over her own noise so I rolled over and tried to block it out with a pillow over my head and that worked for a while.

Then she must have left her bedroom and in so doing left her door slightly ajar because all of a sudden I could hear the radio as clear as a bell. What had previously been a muffled male voice droning on and on had suddenly become the posh voice of a radio news reporter. It was definitely the same voice, the same tone and resonance, the same slightly manic delivery, as if he was trying too hard to stimulate his unknown and unseen audience out there in the real world. He must have been talking for ages, but now instead of a flow of incoherent narrative there emerged a clear, concise and dramatic delivery of the day's news.

He was talking about the trial of Myra Hindley and Ian Brady, which was taking place at the Central Criminal Court at Chester assizes. As young as I was, even I knew that the whole country, even the whole world, had listened aghast as the details of the murders committed by the two accused had unfolded, and as I wandered out of my own bedroom across the forbidden threshold of my sister's bedroom to investigate the source of the noise. I too listened, horrified, to the summary of the trial.

"It was said in court that once they got Lesley Ann Downey from the fair and into the car they put a blindfold on her eyes. This was to serve a dual purpose. Firstly, to keep her calm, like a blanket over a cage calms a trapped bird, but more importantly so she would not see where she was being taken, although that implies that they hadn't intended to kill her, just abuse her. Whatever the reason it is hard to imagine just how frightened the little ten year old girl would have been in the hands of these monsters. Then they began their torture. To take obscene photographs of this shy, most modest of little girls, they forcibly removed her clothes. The clothes that she had put on that very day in the safety of her own bedroom. A ten year old's clothes. Despite her begging, her pleading, their cruel intentions became apparent. When the little girl realised that no matter what she said or did these grown-ups were not going to take her home, her fear would have taken her beyond reason, almost to insanity.

All that Lesley Ann was subjected to, from the moment that she first arrived at the house, was recorded by Ian Brady on his tape recorder.

In the hushed courtroom at Chester assizes, this past week, the tape was played as evidence to those assembled there, judge and jury, lawyers and court officials, the police and journalists. The presiding judge, Mr Justice Fenton Atkinson, ordered that all women be obliged to leave the court while the tape was played. The tape was played for a duration of sixteen minutes and twenty one seconds. What they listened to that day broke their hearts.

One woman, of course, had already heard the tape. Ann Downey, the mother of Lesley Ann, had, for purpose of identification, already listened to her own daughter's final moments on earth.

The little ten year old girl, naked and tied up, pleading and begging for them to stop what it was they were doing, pleading with all her might to be allowed to go home to her mother who would be worried about her. Her cries were heard again, echoing around the court; wanting to get home to her mum.

'Please,' she had begged them. 'Let me go home. I'll get killed if I'm late home.'

All of her pleading was in vain. The court could hear the harsh, uncaring voices of her tormentors shouting at her. Then, in turn, cajoling and threatening,

the woman's voice, Hindley's voice, prevalent amongst the pair. And contrary to
the instinct, the very core being of a woman, she showed no compassion. She
showed no mercy.

Those who attended said that to listen to those tapes was to cross from
heaven into hell, from civilisation into barbarism.

These tapes and photographs have not been released and hopefully never
will be but the journalists and the policemen who had heard and seen the
evidence have been able in small ways to convey the horror of those details to
the adult population, although they have been sworn to secrecy by the courts,
and to reveal anything would be seen as contempt of court. Most of us outside
the criminal justice system have been spared the details of the horrors that were
inflicted on the poor children by these monsters. Yet we do know that it was evil
and deranged beyond our understanding and that those who have borne witness
to these events through the evidence disclosed in the courtroom have to carry
that burden of knowing for us, and that knowledge will change their lives
forever."

That's where the report ended and there was still no sight or sound of
Sandra on the stairs so I ventured right into her bedroom to look for
her radio in order to turn it off. I didn't care that she would know it
was me, my head was starting to hurt as much as my stomach and I
was feeling a bit sick as well. I wanted peace and quiet.

Her room was a mess. Girls were meant to be clean and tidy, unlike
boys, but Sandra lived like a pig. No wonder she kept a lock on her
door. If anybody from the Health Service were to get in there they
would condemn the bloody place. There was a faint whiff of cheap
perfume but that was almost enveloped in a harsher stink of cigarette
smoke and something sour like unwashed laundry. Although the
window was open the curtains were drawn almost across, allowing
only fragments of natural light to break the gloom. In that half light I
could see that over the months that had passed since we had all been
excluded from her space she had made some attempt at decoration
and she had pasted pictures of pop stars all over the wall, all long black
hair and sulky looks. Her clothes were all over the floor, and her bed

was unmade. An ashtray on her bedside table was overflowing with cigarette ends, one day she was going to burn the whole house down and all of us along with it. She had one shelf, one place for displaying all her treasured possessions; but not for her ornaments and trinklets. Her shelf was covered with all sorts of weird figurines, dragons and goblins, unicorns and wizards and board games with strange cards and letters and pictures.

Then, as I looked at my sister's belongings in a haze of fascination and disgust, I suddenly heard her come back into the house. As I moved quickly back across the crowded floor of her room, stepping over underwear and candles and newspaper cuttings and suchlike, I heard her talking to her weasel boyfriend, Derek, who must have called by on his way home from work. As I got to the door of her room I heard a thump, thump, thump as Sandra's long skinny legs started to lope up our stairs two at a time. I made it back into my room by the skin of my teeth.

I lay back down on my bed, and buried my pounding head deep into my pillow. I waited, hardly daring to breathe, for Sandra to come bursting into my room, screaming at me for daring to enter hers, and then the slaps would rain down on me from above. I waited for the recrimination but nothing came.

I must have fallen asleep, but only briefly because a noise came into my head that was at first, part of my subconscious. But the noise changed in tone and volume and it surged out of me, broke free from my dream and startled me fully awake again.

The sound was familiar but it scared me nonetheless. As I sat up on my bed, already I was trying to remember where I had heard it before. As quietly as I could, I opened my bedroom door and tiptoed across the landing towards Sandra's room. My previous fear of being discovered by her must have been unfounded because her door was ajar, not wide open, but open enough to convey the impression that she felt that she and her boyfriend were alone in the house and would be undiscovered. At least that was what I thought at the time.

I could hear that noise again, a male laugh, not loud but a multilayered depth of sound, lust and happiness and cruelty lying in separate levels within. I heard the laugh and walked towards the gap in her door and peered through.

It took a while for my eyes to adjust, to make sense amongst the mess of her room that I had only minutes before picked my way through. Two people now lay there together, entwined and coiled like white vines, naked upon the unmade bed, and one of these people was my sister.

I saw the back of his head first, the curl of sweaty hair on his neckline, then his back, the spots on it so red and frequent, it was as if they had been painted on. Then I saw his backside, and below that, the long, thin white legs. Then I saw his whole scrawny body start to pump up and down and only then when he put his own head down on the pillow so as to work harder did I see the face of my sister alongside that head. The pale complexion and the narrow eyes black with mascara that ran with sweat and tears of joy. It felt like she was looking directly up at me but she couldn't have seen me. I had been too quiet and too well-hidden and besides, she had her mind too much on other things. I saw through the gap of the door their writhing limbs and I saw her face change from a benign satisfied smile, through to an idiotic grimace, and then finally as they both moved together, into that of an open-mouthed, eye-bulging gargoyle. I watched, transfixed, as she held this face for what seemed an age, a suspension of time, her muscles set in a grotesque rigour mortis until finally she let out a long, deep, high-pitched moan, a moan that broke free to become a scream. Laughing as he did so, the boyfriend placed his hand across her painted mouth to stifle the noise, but it was too soon for her and she resisted him. Then as I turned away to run downstairs and away from the house, I heard my sister's scream subsiding, moving down in volume through a series of childlike gurgles to a groaning and then into silence. It sounded to me, in my innocence, not like pleasure or love but like the most torturous of deaths.

Chapter 14

THE FISH

The river was where I ran to on that warm April day in 1966. I thought the others would be there, so I was braced for confrontation, but part of me wanted to be with them again, I wasn't too sure why.

Right enough they were down at the river, up from the swing because the Spills were now said to be using it themselves, and a little bit down from the seven arches, probably because they all figured that Nelson would be just the type to come back and haunt the place. I had left the house at breakneck speed, but at the river I slowed to a trot, my pumps pounding on the cakey track that ran alongside it, looking across to my friends for some kind of welcome.

Pybus and Linton were lying in the long grass on the riverbank and Billy was in the river right up to his thighs, trying to fish for gudgeon with his bare hands. When he saw me, he stood up and put his hands on his hips to ease his aching back and stared right at me, not smiling but not overly hostile either.

"Look who's here," he said. "Found out who your true mates are, now the Gypsies have gone?"

I shrugged, and Billy turned to the other two. I wondered where Vic was at this point. He was bound to have his say but, for the moment, he had disappeared as he usually did. 'Gone scouting,' he called it, 'like on *Wagon Train*.'

"I'll join up again, if you let me," I said, trying not to sound too desperate.

"What do you say, boys?" shouted Billy, across to the bank. "Should we let him back in?"

"Fine by me," said Linton and he grinned in my direction.

"Me too," said Pybus. "Although I don't know what Vic will say. You know what he's like."

"Let me worry about Vic," said Billy. "I'm leader of this gang and I say we let the bastard back in."

"Thanks, Billy," I said, grateful despite myself. "It's lonely out there with nobody talking to me. I'm glad to be back."

But Billy hadn't finished. "On one condition," he said.

"What's that?" I muttered, my heart sinking. He was going to make me do something stupid to get back in, I could feel it.

"That you never go off with a Gypsy again, no matter how much you feel sorry for him. Do you understand me? Never again side with someone that's not one of us."

I was relieved. Since I never expected to see Jody again, ever, that was not a difficult promise to make. I felt slightly disloyal to him because we had been good mates, but he would understand better than anyone that sometimes you have to do deals to get by in life. He would have done the same thing probably. Besides, he still had my sword, which made us even. At least in my book it did.

"Alright, Billy," I said. "You have a deal."

"I mean it, kid," Billy persisted, suddenly steely. "Betray me again and I'll batter you."

"I promise, Billy," I assured him.

This whole negotiation had gone on with Billy standing in the river and me on the bank, then he went back to looking for fish and I sat down in the long grass next to Linton and Pybus.

It was hot and I felt the heat of the earth on my hands as I made myself comfortable. Pybus's hair was wet with sweat and I could hear his breathing labouring with the hay fever he got when the pollen was high. I could smell the dried grass from nearby fields and I could see dots of pollen in the air, like molecules, so it was not surprising that he was wheezing, but it hadn't slowed him up at all. He was as talkative as ever.

Like everybody else in Manchester, they had been talking about the Brady and Hindley trial and as usual Linton knew more than his fair share.

"So, Linton," says Pybus, continuing where they had obviously left off. "Tell us about this trial. Was your dad really there?"

"He was," replied Linton. "They had lots of coppers there. He said not to protect the public from the murderers, but the other way around."

"What did he mean by that?" I asked.

"My dad said that he had never seen such an ugly crowd. Worse than any football crowd. Worse even than Man U v Liverpool. He said the crowd at the courts every day would have killed Hindley and Brady had they got their hands on them; and a lot of the coppers would have let them, given the choice. Especially after knowing what was on the tape."

"What tape?" asked Pybus.

Linton looked around him and then lowered his voice, although there was no one within a hundred yards of us, except Billy, who was still annoying the fish.

"This is top secret," said Linton in a serious voice. "I overheard my dad telling my mum last night when they thought I was asleep, and he said that he would lose his job if this ever got out, so you've got to swear not to tell anybody."

"Not even Billy?" I asked.

"Especially not Billy," said Linton. "Better just the three of us."

"Alright," said Pybus. "We promise not to tell, don't we, Mike?"

"Promise," I said.

"Well, there was a tape apparently that Brady had recorded of them torturing the little girl."

"I heard something about that. What were they doing to her?" I asked, my voice sounding thin and reedy to my own ears, only partly wanting to know the answer to my own question.

"Well I don't exactly know what they were doing, but I could hear my dad saying that the whole court had to listen to this girl begging and pleading to be allowed to go home to her mum and begging them not to do things to her."

"What things?" asked Pybus.

"I'm not sure. Rude things I think. Things a grown-up should never do to a little girl, that's for sure. Apparently the woman's voice could be heard talking quietly, trying to calm the girl, but when that didn't work she shouted at her and you could hear it all clearly on this tape." Linton paused to shift his position on the bank, and I pulled at a green stem of grass to place in my mouth. I sucked for a moment then spat a green stream through the gap between my teeth, waiting for him to continue.

"By this time," he went on, "I was almost at the bottom of the stairs trying to listen to what my dad was saying so I only heard snatches. He said the judge sent all the women out so they wouldn't have to listen to it, but even so a lot of the men who had stayed behind in court cried when they heard the little girl's voice begging for mercy, policemen as well. Real tough coppers he said, wept at the cruelty, but Hindley and Brady sat stone-faced throughout."

"Bastards!" said Pybus with more feeling and aggression than I had ever heard from him. "It makes you want to go out and kill them yourself."

I just felt sick to my stomach thinking of how scared these kids would have been.

"Just a few months earlier and they would have been hanged," said Linton. "That would have made a lot of people happy. Now they'll just get life."

"Then they will still have hope," I said.

"Hope for what?" said Linton.

"Hope that they could escape, or get let out when they get old."

"No," said Linton dismissively. "They will watch them night and day and nobody will ever let them out. Not after what they've done."

"Bring back hanging, that's what I say," said Pybus, "or the electric chair like in America." His heavy features were still set in an angry scowl. He hurled a pebble into one of the pools near to where Billy was fishing.

"Oi pack that in," shouted Billy. "I'm trying to fish here. You lot should get down here and see the size of these gudgeon."

Billy was half bent in the river concentrating hard, eyes staring like a goalkeeper facing a penalty, but with his big hands open just under the surface of the water.

Linton called over to Billy in that know-all voice of his that irritated him almost to the point of violence.

"You won't catch them without a rod and line, I'm telling you now," he said. Straight away I saw Billy's neck turn red. He took the bait quicker than the fish.

Billy shouted back at Linton, oblivious to the fact that his voice might disturb the very fish he was trying to catch.

"My dad doesn't need a rod and line when he goes after trout. He tickles them underneath and then just flips them out. I've seen him with my own eyes, smart arse!"

Linton persisted. "There are no trout here. These are gudgeon. Different sort of fish."

"So bloody what?" Billy replied, starting to get angry. He was so easy to wind up there was almost no challenge to it.

"Maybe they're not ticklish," said Pybus.

"And you can shut up as well," said Billy. Then almost straight away he said "Hang on. Hang on." Then a long drawn out "Hang on" and with that he flipped out of the water a silvery fish about six inches in length and held it in his hand. The banter stopped and Billy looked across at us with a mixture of surprise and triumph. From the bank we stared back, equally surprised.

"Oh no," I heard Linton mutter to himself.

"Bloody hell," said Pybus. "He's only gone and caught one."

Then in slow motion, within the vessel that is Billy's big hands, the gudgeon started to jump and shake. Its sudden movement broke everyone's trance and there was a barrage of advice from the bank.

"Flip it."

"Chuck it."

"Get rid of it."

"Get it over here."

And finally he did just that, flipping the fish with one deft flick of his wrists in our direction. It travelled in a silvery arc as if radar guided and fell on the softest part of the bank, a flattened-down piece of long grass, where it lay in the sun gasping for breath, probably wondering what the hell had happened to it.

Billy followed rapidly behind it, splashing ashore like some mad Viking ready to claim his prize, glaring protectively as if one of us might elope with it. The four of us, Vic was still off scouting, stood in a circle looking down on the fish as it flipped and jumped, its intricate little mouth opening and closing as it struggled for life.

Finally Pybus said, "What are you going to do with it?"

"Nothing," said Billy matter-of-factly.

"What do you mean, nothing?" I asked.

"Nothing," he repeated. "Just look at it."

"You should put it back, it can't breathe," said Linton.

"I caught the bloody thing. I'll decide what I'm going to do with it," countered Billy.

"It's cruel," I said. "If we don't put it back now, it's going to die."

"Yeah, he's right," Pybus backed up. "It's cruel to leave it like that."

Billy had a stick in his hand and he gently turned the fish over in the grass to inspect its other side. The three of us watched him uneasily, wondering what he was going to do.

"It's not as if you can eat them," continued Linton. "It's well known that gudgeon taste horrible."

Billy ignored us and continued to inspect the fish with his stick. I was looking at this poor little fish, his little black eye looking back up at us. Then I looked at his mouth and his head and the hundreds of silvery scales on his body, all perfectly formed in exactly the same patterns, and the different colours within the scales, not just silver but hidden blues and reds. And growing seamlessly from the spine and the belly and the tail of the fish, various feathery fins to help propel and guide it through the reedy shallows of the brook. Where did fish come from, I thought? Why were they made so beautifully, just to end up on a slab in a fish shop or on the bank of a river? Too much beauty and engineering, just for a stupid fish.

"Chuck it back in, Billy," I said. The fish had stopped jumping but its mouth was opening and closing rapidly and it was obviously struggling.

"You lot can piss off," Billy replied with a sneer. "Fish don't feel anything anyway."

"Chuck it back in or I will," I said. It was the first time I had directly challenged Billy and I was surprised at myself.

"You bloody won't," said Billy, "watch this." He took his stick, and brought it down onto the fish, hitting it somewhere in the middle and immediately drawing blood onto its silvery scales.

We all gasped in shock, but then he brought the stick down again, then again. The fish jumped at the power of the blow and wriggled and struggled.

"That's cruel," I shouted at him.

"What's the point of that?" said Linton, real astonishment in his voice. "What's the poor thing ever done to you?"

Billy ignored us and brought the stick down twice more on the fish, and finally it stopped moving. The green grass around it was pink and sticky from where it had bled and the body was dented and broken and some of its scales were missing. I know it was only a fish, but in some way it felt as if Billy had murdered it.

Now he had finished beating it, he stood wild-eyed and sweating, his anger gone but still defiant. He was panting, taking huge gulps of breath.

I had never seen Linton so angry. "You shouldn't kill what you're not going to eat. You're a nutter, you are, Billy, I swear to God."

Billy's anger returned with a vengeance. "I'll make you bloody eat it if you don't shut up."

"Go on then," said Linton. "Make me. You're all bloody mouth, Skinner, and everyone knows it."

"Linton. Please shut up," said Pybus. "You're making things worse."

"No. I won't shut up."

Billy bent down and picked up the bloodied fish from the ground and walked towards Linton. He held the limp fish by its tail and pushed it into Linton's face, who recoiled in disgust.

"What was that about eating, copper's boy. You want to eat my fish?" Billy's voice had gone softer and as a result more menacing.

"Leave him, Billy," I said, but he ignored me, his mind set on the humiliation of Linton.

"Please, Billy," said Pybus, but he ignored Pybus too.

"No," he said in his new voice. "The grammar school boy wants to eat my fish," and in one swift movement, still holding the fish, he put one leg behind Linton and flipped him over onto his back. He then sat astride him. Although Linton was tall, Billy was much heavier and held him down easily.

"You're mad, Billy," said Linton, who was now close to tears.

Billy, with one hand pressing down on Linton's chest, dangled the dead fish over his face.

"Get off me," said Linton, trying to get up, but he was held tight by Billy's bulk. "Get off me!"

"C'mon Billy, get off him," I said tentatively, mindful of my recent reacceptance by him. Pybus was hopping around on one foot whimpering with nerves. He knew Billy better than all of us and what he was capable of.

"No. He wants to eat my fish and I'm going to let him," and he dangled the bloody carcass down towards Linton's mouth.

Linton screwed his eyes up and tried to turn away but the fish was getting closer.

"Don't you dare, don't you bloody dare!" screamed Linton and his eyes filled with tears.

"Eat it," said Billy, placing the head of the fish on Lintons's lips. "Eat the fish."

"Billy," I shouted. "That's enough," but he wouldn't stop. He was torturing Linton now, brushing the fish over his face and leaving a thin pink streak of fish blood on his cheek. Linton was spitting and retching in disgust.

"Pybus," I said, "we have to get him off. He's like a madman," and Pybus agreed, although I could see that the last thing he wanted to do was to start wrestling with Billy. But we were desperate now, and I could see no alternative. We were just about to pull Billy off and hang the consequences when there was the sound of crashing through the undergrowth and Vic ran out into our clearing, red faced and breathless.

He stopped dead in his tracks and looked at Billy sitting on top of Linton.

Then he looked at me. "What's he doing here?" he asked.

"He came crawling, so I let him back in," said Billy from his position astride Linton.

I wanted to object to that particular summary of what had really happened, but thought it best not to antagonise Billy further.

Vic looked at me with contempt, but made no further comment. He was more interested in Linton lying prone but distressed, underneath Billy.

"What's going on?" he asked.

"Oh nothing," said Billy, acting all casual now. "Just feeding Lint some old fish I caught," and with that he jumped to his feet leaving Linton lying on his back in the grass. As if to finish the episode once and for all, Billy flung what was left of the fish back into the river.

Vic, meanwhile, only slightly registered what had been going on, his clever little eyes darting around from Linton to Billy to me, and back again. But he didn't care, he had far more interesting news of his own to reveal.

"Hey you lot," he said, barely able to contain himself, "guess who I've found further down the river?"

"Not those bloody Spills again?" groaned Pybus.

"No, better than that," said Vic. "C'mon, follow me."

"This better be good," growled Billy, still in his strange mood, "or someone is going to get battered."

We followed Vic down the path alongside the river. All of us, that is, except Linton who had climbed to his feet and was walking the other way. If anyone else saw Linton they didn't say anything and I let him go without a word, because I knew he wouldn't have come anyway. I heard a sob from him as he went and knew that he had had enough for one day.

We walked along the bank for what seemed like ages, to the point where we were thinking it was another one of Vic's wild-goose chases, when suddenly, from the front of the line he stopped, held up his hand and shushed us. We all bumped gently into one another, like the Keystone Cops.

"For God's sake, Vic, where are you taking us?" growled Billy.

"Shush," Vic whispered, finger over his lips. "We're here. Come and take a look at this."

Vic beckoned us to join him. He was peering through a little hole in the trees that revealed a small clearing right next to the river, and about twenty yards away, sitting in a line on the bank, bare legs dangling in the water, were four girls from our class at school.

"Bloody hell!" exclaimed Billy. "It's MacNeill and that Lorna Rogers, and that moany old bird who got us caned for putting worms in her desk. What's her name, Monica O'Hagan."

"That's her," said Vic, "our Monica with a mouth like an organ." He looked at us expecting appreciation for his wit and getting none.

"Where? Here, let me have a look," said Pybus, bursting through the undergrowth with me right behind him.

"Quiet," hissed Vic, "they'll hear us."

"There's another one as well," said Billy, his hand cupping his eyes to shield the reflection from the water. "It's that Jenny Turner, who went out with Joe Fenners for a while. Until she realised what a nutter he is."

"Look at them there," said Pybus, "showing their knickers and everything they've got. It shouldn't be allowed."

From where we crouched in the undergrowth we could hear their chatter and their laughter. Occasionally one would sing a few lines from one of their favourite songs.

"When people ask of me
What would you like to be
Now that you're not a kid anymore
You're not a kid any more"

"Listen to them," said Billy. "They're like the cat's choir," and we all laughed as quietly as we could.

These girls were so different on their own. We only saw them occasionally around the estates and whenever they saw us their attitude changed completely anyway. They would turn into different people, often hard-faced and unsmiling, as bad as the older lads that they sometimes hung around with, trying to look tough. It really annoyed us but they seemed older than us somehow. But here by the river they looked just like normal happy girls, splashing and playing, singing and laughing, off their guard.

I liked MacNeill too; I wasn't sure about her mates but MacNeill was alright. Ever since I had seen her in the street that day and I saw her for her true self. I knew she wasn't like everyone else. She was nicer than she sometimes made herself out to be, just like most people were, not really true to herself. But then, like the rest of us, she wasn't fully grown yet. They say people get nicer when they get older, but even I know that's not necessarily true. I remembered that I had promised to take her to the river. She was not to know that three times I had gone to her door to call for her and three times I had lost my nerve at the last minute. She had obviously got tired of waiting.

The four of us watched them for a while, their distant voices carrying to us upstream still singing their favourite song.

"I want to be Bobby's girl
I want to be Bobby's girl
That's the most important thing to me…"

"Let's spook them. It might make them stop singing," whispered Billy.

"Yeah," agreed Vic, "let's lob some stones. They'll think it's the Spills. Not hit them like, but the water next to them."

"Good idea," said Billy and he started to look for some stones to throw while the girls kept singing.

"And if I was Bobby's girl
If I was Bobby's girl
What a faithful, thankful girl I would be."

Taking careful aim, Vic lobbed the first stone and it landed with an audible plop in the water about ten yards from the girls. They looked up in alarm, all four together like a clutch of frightened squirrels. In the clearing we'd all got our fists in our mouths trying not to laugh.

"Your go, Billy," said Vic and Billy stood up and hurled half a rock to the right of where the girls were. It hit the river with a flat splash like some kid belly flopping into a swimming pool. At this point the girls jumped up in a flurry of sand and grass, their hair and clothing askew.

The scrawny girl called Monica shouted out to the empty air.

"Who's that? Who's throwing stones?"

"Who's that? Who's throwing stones?" Vic mimicked her high-pitched voice and lobbed another rock.

"It's not funny, it's dangerous. One of those nearly hit us," shouted mouthy Lorna, her deeper voice carrying easily across the clearing, although you could tell that they still weren't sure where we were.

Then I heard MacNeill's voice. "It might be those Spills. Maybe we should go."

"C'mon," said Billy, "let's rush them and scare the crap out of them. C'mon."

So in true ambush style the four of us rushed from the trees towards the girls, screaming and yelling. Then the girls all started screaming and clasping each other, like girls do when they're excited or frightened, and jumping up and down, at which point we'd almost reached them because they were never that far away. So we pulled up short because we couldn't exactly bash straight into them, and we stood there just in front of them, tongues out, panting like dogs, smirks on our faces, while the girls stood calmly now, dignity regained, still clinging to each other, but with a look of slight contempt on their faces. There was a long silence and then MacNeill said, "Oh it's you lot, we should have known."

"Aren't you the little heroes, scaring us like that?" said Lorna. "Now what are you going to do, ravage us?" I tell you, she had a bit of a tongue on her, that one.

Still panting, we just grinned at them like idiots. Billy, who was in the front, turned to us for guidance. I don't think he understood what ravage meant.

"We thought you were the Spills," piped up Jenny Turner, who was second nicest after MacNeill, not far behind her but miles ahead of that Lorna. "Proper scared us you did."

"What!" said Billy, in disgust. "Spills don't come down here."

"If they did, you wouldn't be here, would you Billy?" said Lorna with her snakey tongue.

"What does that mean, Rogers?" challenged Billy. I could see his face going red, getting angry.

"It means you're scared of them and don't try to deny it. Your gang got a good hiding from them, that's what we heard, didn't we girls?" They nodded their agreement.

"Yeah," said Vic. "That's because there were fifty of them. There were only three of us. Besides that was months ago. They don't bother us now."

Pretty Jenny and scrawny Monica started giggling. MacNeill was trying not to.

"What are you two laughing at?" said Vic.

"Nothing," said Lorna and then all four of them broke out into fits of laughter and the four of us, for want of anything to say, just stood and glared at them.

Then Lorna spoke directly to me and I felt my arms go cold.

"You don't say much, do you, Michael?" she said. "Are you shy?"

"No," I grunted. I could see MacNeill, with a little smile, not joining in.

"I think he is," said Jenny.

"No I'm not."

Billy changed the subject, thankfully.

"What are you dopey girls doing round here anyway?" he asked obnoxiously.

"Actually we're allowed to go wherever we like without your say-so, Billy Skinner," said Lorna.

"Alright, I was only asking. Actually I couldn't care less where you all go."

"C'mon," said Pybus, who had been uncomfortable throughout. "Let's go back to the rec and play footie."

Vic and I laughed. Pybus never ever asked to play footie if he could help it. He had to be made to do it, and even then he was always made to go in goal.

"If you really want to know," said MacNeill suddenly, "we were talking about which boys we fancy."

We had started to lose interest up to this point, but MacNeill's words hooked us right back in.

"Who would that be then?" said Vic, trying not to sound too interested.

"That's for us to know and you to find out," said Jenny.

"C'mon," said Pybus.

"Hang on a minute," said Billy. "Alright, tell us which boys you fancy."

"Well we don't know if we really fancy them. It all depends." This was said by Lorna in a teasing drawl that she had learnt off some film star. It was working too because we couldn't wait to hear what she had to say.

"Depends on what?" said Vic, with a mixture of curiosity and scorn.

"It depends," said Lorna in that drawl again, "it depends on how good a kisser he is," and she looked us full in the eyes while her three friends giggled into their hands.

251

"You see," she continued, "we can like the way a lad looks, we can even like the way a lad is, but we can't know for sure what he's really like, until we've kissed him."

"Bloody hell!" moaned Pybus, then more loudly, "kissing's unhealthy, my mum said."

"Shut up, Pybus," said Billy, who then said, in a not very assured fashion, "so are you… do you… do any of you, fancy any of us?"

"We might do," said Lorna, "but that would be telling."

"We would have to kiss you first," said Jenny with a big grin on her face and they dissolved into their stupid giggling again.

"C'mon, let's go," said Pybus again, persisting.

"Who's it between then?" said Billy, ignoring him.

"What?" said MacNeill and Jenny together.

"Who's it between? Which one of us do you think it could be?"

"You'll have to find out, won't you," said Lorna.

"So let me get this right," said Vic, slowly and deliberately, "when you have kissed us, you will know which one you fancy?"

"Well in actual fact," said MacNeill enigmatically, "we've all got a fair idea already. It just needs confirming."

"Where would we do this kissing?" I said. I thought I'd better say something before those girls started on to me again.

"Hang on," said Billy "I haven't said we'll do it yet."

"Ooh Billy's playing hard to get," said Jenny and that set them off giggling again.

Eventually Lorna said, "Oh it's got to be on the lips, it's got to be proper kissing."

"No that's not what I meant." I was trying to keep my voice steady and matter-of- fact. "Do you mean here and now down by the river," I persisted, only I've got my tea in half an hour."

My question made them all laugh, for some reason.

"No," said Lorna, who seemed to be doing all the organising. "Not here, not now. Besides, they can see us from the flats. No, we know a place, a really good place. Our den."

"Where's that then?" said Vic.

"We're not going to tell you unless you agree to it," said Lorna. "Otherwise you may just go and wreck the place."

"Hang on," said Billy "we have to discuss this first," and he motioned for us to gather around into a huddle. "What do you think lads?" said Billy. It was like a team talk.

"I don't mind giving it a go," said Vic.

"Me neither," said I.

"Pybus," said Billy, "what about you?"

"No I ain't doing it, you lot go on," said Pybus, without any hesitation.

We all half turned and looked at the girls, who were about ten yards away looking disinterested. Monica was picking flowers and Jenny was standing on one leg with the other one outstretched doing ballet. She looked like a skinny wading bird. None of them appeared bothered as to whether we would accept their kind offer or not.

We all turned back into our group.

"Alright," said Billy decisively. "Alright. I think we should do it, but I'm telling you now, I'm not going to kiss that scrawny one."

We went back to the girls and Billy spoke as if he was accepting some dangerous mission on our behalf, which I suppose in a way he was.

"Alright," he said, "we'll do it. We just have to arrange a time and a place."

"Oh sorry," said Lorna, "we should have said, but is it alright if Pybus doesn't come? The den is not big enough for all of us. Sorry, Pybus."

I looked across to our friend but he seemed unbothered by the rejection. Maybe he was used to it.

"Suits me," he grunted. "I wasn't coming anyway. You can all catch some horrible disease for all I care."

"That's fine," said Billy, "If Pybus can't come then you can leave Monica behind."

At this point Monica let out a wail that would chill your blood and then burst into floods of tears.

"God you're a cruel bastard, Skinner!" said Lorna outraged. "You've really hurt her feelings. What did you say that for?"

MacNeill and Jenny had their arms around Monica, trying in vain to console her.

"Well you said Pybus couldn't come," said Billy. "It's like for like int'it?"

"It's not the same and you know it," said MacNeill, her arm still held protectively around Monica. "We'll call the whole thing off if you're just going to be mean. Won't we, girls?"

They all nodded their agreement.

"C'mon, Billy, let her come," said Vic.

"Yeah forget Pybus," I said. "He doesn't want to come anyway. He said so himself."

"Alright. Alright. She can come." Billy pretended to relent, but in fact he was the keenest out of all of us to go kissing, and there was no way he would let a small point of order jeopardise that.

"Where is this place?" asked Vic.

"Do you know the road up to the golf course off Queens Avenue?"

"Yeah."

"Do you know the empty house on the corner?"

"The haunted house?"

"It's not haunted."

"It bloody is," insisted Billy. "We heard things, didn't we, Mike?"

"We heard some screaming and laughing. It was horrible," I agreed

"When?" persisted Lorna, who remained unconvinced.

"A month back."

"That's ages ago," she countered. "We weren't even there then."

"Are you sure?" said Vic.

"It wasn't us. We only went there a week ago for the first time. It was probably other kids."

"It wasn't kids," said Billy. Was it, Mike?"

"No," I agreed. "It didn't sound like kids."

"Well that's where our den is now, and we haven't heard anything since then," said Lorna.

"Ok," said Vic. "Well we'll meet you up there then."

"11:00 am tomorrow," said Lorna. She turned to her friends. "Is that alright, girls?" and they all nodded, all three of them, even Monica, who had finally stopped snivelling.

The girls turned and walked slowly away back towards the flats on Grange Avenue, each one in turn unable to resist a slight backward glance at the group of bamboozled lads standing watching them. We watched them all the way, and we saw their different shapes and heights and movements as they went, their summer dresses in pink and yellows clearly visible even after they had passed through the low trees and out onto the steps to the flats. Even as they went out of sight the sounds of their chatter and laughter carried through on the still evening air.

Chapter 15

THE KISS

So the next day we were back in the haunted house, although downstairs and across the other side from the room that we had heard noises from. The girls had made a den, a real home from home, and we sat there now, the three of us, perched uncomfortably in broken armchairs around an old tea chest table that they had cobbled together. The girls, all four of them, had squeezed on to an ancient sofa and were staring at us intently across the table. MacNeill was finishing off a raspberry lolly and Lorna was chewing gum. They appeared not to be nervous. I don't know how the other two lads were feeling, but my heart was fair hammering.

They had blacked out most of the window using some old dark green fabric and they had placed candles around, which Vic had lit with the matches that he always seemed to carry these days, and the burning wax had diluted the smell of must and age that pervaded the room. The candles flickered in the draft and gave off a warm intermittent glow and the girls' faces shone in the reflection. I thought MacNeill looked beautiful but even scrawny Monica looked passable, which was just as well because it was becoming clear that she would not be excluded from the proceedings. These girls would make sure of that.

Lorna again appeared to be in charge and she had organised things a bit like a football tournament where everybody got to play everyone else, or in this case kiss everyone else, whether we wanted to or not. There would be no excuses.

I was nervous to see who I had drawn in the first round. It was hard to weigh up the advantage of getting Monica first and out of the way and then just enjoying the rest, or whether if I did get her first I would be unable to recover. Anyway, Lorna had it all worked out.

"Right," she said, a bit like a schoolteacher, and a right bossy one at that, "we girls have discussed it and we think that this is the fairest way. I hope you agree."

Then she announced the itinerary we would all be following and I grinned to myself with anticipation at how long Billy and Vic were going to be told what to do, without kicking up a fuss.

"First to kiss will be Christine and Billy, followed by Jenny and Victor and me and Michael. Monica will sit the first one out."

"Phew," from us, not audible of course. We didn't want another wailing incident.

"Then," continued Lorna, "we will all swap and I will sit the next one out. Victor with Christine, Michael with Jenny and we will bring Monica in, and she will be kissing with Billy."

I felt Billy tighten beside me but he kept quiet.

"Then Michael with Christine, Billy with me, Victor with Monica. Any questions? No. Good. Michael with Monica, Jenny with Billy. Is that right? Oh. Well. Anyway, you all know how it works. So, now, if at the end, one of us has found one of you to our taste then I think, providing no one person is left out, we can all go round again or spend a little longer with our preferred kisser. Is that clear?"

Vic put his hand up. "What happens if one of us doesn't like kissing any of you, or one of you doesn't like any of us?"

"Anybody is free to leave the room, at any time but only after at least one kiss," said Lorna archly, conveying quite clearly that to do so would not meet with her approval, at least.

"Alright," said Vic "just so as we know."

"Right, Christine and Billy," urged Lorna. "You're first. Don't be shy."

We all watched them, in a sort of awed silence, not daring to move, as if we were watching some sacred ritual. Then Billy, like a lamb to slaughter, albeit an overtly confident lamb, stood up and walked over to MacNeill, who sat looking up at him, those clear green eyes not giving anything away. I felt a sharp stab of jealousy as his mouth moved slowly down to hers and touched just faintly, her upturned lips. Then more roughly, he pulled her up and took her back to his armchair and I saw her wince as he sat down and, then in turn, sat her down on his knee.

Vic had gone and sat beside Jenny and had put his arm over her shoulder, although she shrugged it off again. Then I was looking at Lorna and I knew then in that moment that it was me Lorna had wanted to kiss and that her face had suddenly changed, and that like a lot of people who have a hard front, underneath she was someone in need of affection. Unfortunately I wasn't the one to give it. Don't get me wrong, she was my first kiss and not a bad kisser at that, but it was MacNeill I was waiting for.

There followed, for what seemed like hours, a melee of seat-swapping and kissing, and arm-waving and grunts and laughter, as each boy took a turn with each girl. I remember kissing Monica and finding it not as bad as I thought I would.

I know Lorna got me again for a second time but for the life of me I still can't recall what it felt like. When my turn came to kiss Jenny, the prettiest out of all the girls, it was as if our lips didn't fit each other's, mine thin and hard, hers fleshy and soft. We tried different approaches but my mouth went really dry and then her expectant smile turned rapidly to a scowl of irritation. Then we got embarrassed and disentangled ourselves, our eyes studiously averted from each other's faces, desperate to be away to another part of the room.

Then it was my turn with MacNeill and she was waiting for me, tight-lipped and strict-looking, and I mistook the stern look for reluctance, which rocked me at first. Then she gave a little laugh and said, "My turn with you, Michael," and it was then that I could see that this girl I was slightly in awe of had her own nerves to contend with. She had called me by my full name, Michael, as girls were prone to do and I thought at the time how much that would have pleased my mother, although the kissing probably less so.

"Come on," she said again, "there's no escape."

"I don't want to escape," I tried to say, wanting to be romantic, but the words turned to cement dust in my mouth so I just came out with an incoherent mumble.

She presumed it was a yes anyway and put her hands up to my shoulders.

"Come on," she whispered, "let's do this properly. I've wanted to kiss you since I saw you in the road that day with your mum. The day you got back from the hospital."

"Why," I asked, my power of speech thankfully returning, "because you felt sorry for me? Because my brother had died?"

She looked at me long and hard in the eyes and I looked back.

"That was part of the reason, yes. But there are other reasons too."

"Like what?"

"Well, you didn't laugh when I said I wanted to go to university. Everyone else did, but you didn't."

"That's because I didn't think it was funny. Why shouldn't you go, if you want to? I would quite like to myself. I don't want a rubbish job like my dad, having to go away from his family at Christmas, just to earn good money. I don't want people telling me where I can go and what I can do either. That makes no sense. I want to be free to make my own decisions."

"That's another reason why I like you."

"Why?"

"Because there's more to you, than meets the eye."

I could see the others out of the corner of my eye start to break off from their own kissing to see why we were talking so much.

"MacNeill," I said. "I think we should get a move on, but I have to warn you, I'm not a very good kisser."

"I'll be the judge of that."

"Alright. Shall I just aim for your lips then?"

"Just look into my eyes," she reassured me, "and let me do the rest.

Your lips will find their way to mine of their own accord. Trust me."

"OK."

She screwed her eyes up in concentration, puckered her lips up and moved her head slowly towards me.

"Have you kissed a lot of boys?" I asked her.

Her head shot back again and a slight look of irritation came onto her face.

"None before today. But I've practised a lot on my mirror at home. Pretending to kiss Billy Fury and John Lennon." She paused and gave me a little smile to ease my nerves. "And you as well, for that matter. Now stop talking for a moment and concentrate."

She didn't have big eyes like the other girls; hers were narrower and cleverer, green not blue, and they looked in to mine and took me away. I started to feel dizzy. She sighed, and I thought for a moment that I was irritating her again, but she did it with a smile and dropped her hands from my shoulders momentarily, only to lift up my own arms, which were dangling down at my sides like a gormless ape's, and place them around her own upper body. I felt the warmth of her skin all the way through her white blouse and thin blue cardigan and I thought I would fall through the floor with the sense of it. Then she said in a soft voice, "Are you ready?" and before I could answer, her lips touched mine.

For a moment, just a second probably, I thought, *hell, all that waiting for nothing,* but then the feeling changed to a mixture of excitement and relief.

Our lips fitted! It was the best feeling I had ever had. Her lips were rose-red, I thought with lipstick but I realized it had been with the raspberry lolly that she had had when we first came in the house, because despite kissing the others she still tasted faintly of raspberry. Better than that, her lips were still cool from the ice and I could taste every outline, every piece of skin, every groove of them. To be honest I never would have believed that kissing could be so interesting. I had previously thought it would be a bit overrated; something people, and teenagers especially, did just for the sake of it. Even a bit unhygienic, like Pybus's mum had said. But MacNeill's lips had a life of their own and once they had me it was hard to get free. So we kissed and we kissed: short little pecks, long lingering snogs, wet and noisy, our skin stuck together and arms entangled, as close as we could be to one another, oblivious to all around us.

Eventually we had to stop for air but we must have been kissing for a long time because as we pulled apart and grinned at each other, something made us look around the den. The rest of them were looking at us, not doing their own kissing, just looking at us; Monica and Jenny with smiles, Lorna straight-faced; but it was Billy's look that sent a little shiver down my back. There was a look of real malevolence on his face as he looked at us, only for a second before he replaced it with something less murderous, but I saw it nonetheless. However, there was no time to ignore him, let alone respond to his glaring looks, because from the direction of upstairs there came the sound of a great crash as if something heavy like a wardrobe had toppled over, or as if half the roof had caved in. All of us stopped what we were doing and went into part panic, part laughter, jumping up and overturning makeshift tables and chairs, looking wildly for the exit points, doors and windows alike, the girls half screaming, Billy and I half laughing, half nervous.

Billy and I. Billy and I? No Vic. Where was Vic? Even in the middle of a big kissing session, Vic still felt the need to wander off. No wonder they had all been watching MacNeill and me, two of the girls were without anybody to kiss and Billy and Lorna were obviously not interested in each other, from the looks they were giving me.

"Hang on, don't panic," Billy said, his composure returning as he realised the source of the noise. "Vic's not here. That'll be him messing about trying to scare us. I thought he would be up to no good."

"I got the impression that all this kissing didn't suit him," said Jenny a bit sniffily.

Then, right on cue, Vic walked back in and we all groaned at him, but he held up his hands and protested his innocence.

"I only went out for a quick wee," he said. "I didn't make any noise."

"You made us jump out of our skins, Victor Roberts," complained Lorna.

"I tell you lot," Vic persisted, "we had better leave here quickly then, because it wasn't me who made that noise."

"Well I think we should go anyway, it's our teatime," said Lorna. "Shall we meet again tomorrow?"

Billy and Vic didn't seem that interested, or at least not as interested as they had been yesterday at the river. I felt that MacNeill and I had unfinished business so I was dead keen, but obviously couldn't show it in front of them so I kept my face deadpan. I looked across at MacNeill to see how she felt but she wasn't giving anything away either.

Billy and Vic looked at each other. "We're not sure," said Billy. "We might go down to the river, eh, Vic?"

"Oh that's alright if you want," said Lorna, "but we thought we might try something different next time."

"Like what?" asked Vic, his curiosity aroused despite himself.

The other girls squeezed each other's arms and giggled. It was obvious they were up to something again.

"What?" said Billy, irritably. Things, so far had not gone according to his plans and it was showing in his temper. "Go on tell us. You lot are a bunch of teases, I swear to God."

"If I mentioned a pack of cards," said Lorna in very measured tones.

Her girlfriends fell about with laughter; they obviously found their leader highly amusing.

"What?" said Vic. "What do you mean, cards?"

I started to feel hot again.

"Cards! You know! Playing cards," said Lorna talking slowly and showing, not for the first time I felt, that all lads, and us in particular, were a bit slow on the uptake.

"You want to bring us up here to play cards," said Billy. "What the hell for?"

Then eventually I realised what these girls were talking about.

"Not any old card game, Billy," I said.

"Oh Michael gets it," said Lorna.

"Oh yeah," said Vic, also realising.

"Well done, Vic," said Jenny.

I looked across at MacNeill but she appeared untroubled by the prospect. I wondered if, like me, she had hoped to do a bit more kissing first, but it was hard to tell what she was thinking. I hoped she was thinking of me but I couldn't be sure.

Still Billy was in the dark.

"What?" he said, his arms outstretched playing innocent or stupid, I wasn't sure which.

"Strip poker, Billy," said Lorna, finally losing her patience. "God, do we have to spell it out to you?"

The penny finally dropped for Billy. "Ohhh," he said, momentarily lost for words, "Ohhh. Oh right. What do we think, lads?"

I looked at the other girls and they were grinning at the three of us. My God, that idiot Billy wanted to discuss it as if there was any doubt in the matter.

"We'll do it," I said. Billy looked at me for a moment, thought about saying something, then agreed.

"Yeah we'll do it," he said. "Vic?"

"Alright," said Vic, "but I think we should bring Pybus. He's a brilliant dealer."

"God, we don't want to see Pybus naked," said Lorna. "Do we, girls?" They all shook their heads in unison.

"Well you won't have to," said Vic, "because he's too bloody good at cards. Better than all of us put together. Anyway, it's only fair. There are four of you and he's meant to be our mate. We can't leave him behind again."

I did have a fleeting thought that Vic, slightly out of character, was being very loyal all of a sudden, but I dismissed it. It was debatable whether Pybus would even turn up for strip poker, given his strong opposition to the relatively innocent pastime of kissing.

"Alright, bring him if you must," said Lorna. "Why don't you bring Linton too? Monica likes him, don't you, Mon?" and Monica squirmed slightly with embarrassment. "Same time tomorrow then?"

As we left the house, I found Vic and walked with him for a moment.

"Vic," I said. "Do me a favour tomorrow, will you? If I get off with MacNeill again don't play one of your tricks. It scared the hell out of those girls and spoilt the mood completely."

Vic turned, and gave me one of his withering looks.

"Two things I've got to say to you," he said with his lip curling. "One, I didn't make that noise. It may have been wild animals, it may have been other kids. Spills even. It may even have been a fookin' ghost. But it wasn't me. That's the first thing."

"What's the second?" I asked, in my best, couldn't care less, voice. I had had enough of Vic for one day.

"If you do get off with MacNeill again," he went on, all serious, "and that's a big if, well Billy boy might have something to say about it. A friendly warning, that's all. Well a warning anyway."

The next morning found us gathered at the shops on the High Road with time to kill before we met the girls at the house that afternoon. Vic was there to buy some matches so he and Billy could smoke some fags that he had nicked off his mum and he also had this harebrained idea for later, to set fire to the hayfield that led from the river up to the old quarry where the Spills hung out.

"Vic," I said to him, "that's a crazy idea. It could get out of control, and then what?"

"Don't be so weak," said Vic, "have you seen them burning the fields? It looks dead brilliant at night. Those farmers never lose control of it."

Billy laughed. "You'll set fire to the whole of Cheadle, you mad get. Then they'll put you in prison and no mistake."

"I'm not setting fire to anything, just burning a bit of old grass, that's all. If you lot don't want to come, don't bloody come then."

"If you burn their field, those Spills will come after you," said Billy. They've got a bunch of horses tied up there you know. There'll be hell to pay if you fry their horses. Ain't that right, Mike?"

But I was looking elsewhere by now because I had seen something that bothered me and I knew that I had to leave my mates and check it out. I had to convince them that I had a good reason just to up and go because I didn't want the inquisition that always comes when you want to do something different.

Out of the corner of my eye I had seen my mum get off the bus from the city centre, about a hundred yards away, and rush into the church. I knew she had been in town having her hair done, or at least having what was left of her hair teased into an acceptable style and this she wore under her familiar blue headscarf. It wasn't just her rushing into the church, although that was odd in itself, because she could not give a monkey's knacker about religion or anything to do with it. No, what was strange, even from a distance, even with those idiots going on about burning hayfields, was watching her walk in a different fashion, and through a haze of sudden dread I knew something was wrong. Although she was too far away to make out what was under her scarf and too far away even to make out the features of her face, despite all that, I knew she was crying.

So I told the others almost the truth; that I had just seen my mum go into the butcher's shop and I was going to cadge some money from her, and I shot off down the road while they carried on arguing. Then I doubled back, hiding behind other pedestrians as I walked parallel to my friends on the other side of the street, and finally reached the church that I had seen my mother go into a few minutes earlier.

It was one of those modern red-brick churches, boring-looking with a tower on top that was meant to contain a bell but I never heard a bell ringing from it, not even on a Sunday. The church was called St. Gregory's.

I studied it for a moment from the outside, gulping air as if I was going underwater and not just into a dark building from out of a sun-filled day, and then I followed my mother in. It was cool in the church, like a different climate to outside, and it was quiet. Through just one wooden door and all the traffic and the voices were gone. As my eyes grew accustomed to the darkness, there appeared great shafts of unexpected light through the stained glass high up. It shone down on my mother twenty yards ahead of me, up the central aisle, painting her old overcoat in multi-colours as she made her way slowly and respectfully towards the high altar. Much to my consternation, it looked as if she was about to fall to her knees and pray but she merely bowed to the figures there, Jesus and his disciples I think, and then sat, with her head still bowed, on a chair in the front row.

She sat there quietly for a while and I watched her from behind a wooden column at the back of the church, wondering if I should go and see her, see if she was alright because she didn't look like she was. But before I could do so, from the side of the nave a priest came in, just like an actor entering from the side of a stage. From my place in the shadows I watched this priest approach and stand in front of her. He looked young, not too many years older than our Stevie had been, although it was hard to get too close a look without giving away my position. But I could see his dark hair swept back and I could see the enamel-white of his dog collar at the neck of his long black cassock. I could hear the soft tones of his voice, its resonance, the unknown accent as he spoke to my mum and although I strained to do so, I could not hear what he was saying to her.

Then I heard a sob, just one, involuntary and guttural with despair, but any potential loss of composure was immediately arrested. The sound without doubt came from my mother and it was enough to cut through the silence of the empty church and pierce my own heart in so doing, such was the pain within it. Then the priest took her head in both his hands and held it to his stomach and then slowly he bent his own head and brushed the top of her scarf with his lips. Then in one continuous motion, his hands reached under her chin, untied the headscarf and let it fall to her shoulders.

I nearly fell over with the shock of what I saw. There was no longer any hair on my mother's head. Not one single hair. She was as bald as Yul Brynner in *The Magnificent Seven*. Her white dome shone in the light like some kind of hideous plastic football, her features underneath as if they'd been drawn on as an artist's afterthought, a mere appendage to the dominant skull. Like it didn't really belong to her. It's hard to say how I felt at that moment and when I think back it's hard to know how I remained undiscovered behind my thin wooden column; how I made no sound that would have alerted them both.

A scream would have been understandable, at the very least a groan or a gasp of shock, but from my lips that day, there was just silence. My head was full of knives and hammers and there was puke in my throat and mouth but there was nothing in my voice. It was just the shock of it, that's all. No big deal after a while, but not the first time, when you're just a kid really, and you love your mum like I did, and you're too busy with your own little life to understand or care what troubles she is going through. Then to be shown suddenly and graphically that she has lost all her lovely hair, or worse, had it all cut off, that soft silky hair that you've played with and fondled since you were a babe in her arms. That fair, thin hair which she had always felt had saved her from being just ordinary had gone and, even worse, she had become scary to look at. My own mother. Well that's a shock and I was in such a state that I ran out of that church and into the sunshine, back into the safe banality of my friends' conversation. Back in the church, although the door had slammed upon my exit, my mother wouldn't have known it had been me leaving and tomorrow she would wear her assortment of wigs, except for the blond one that looked like Hindley's hair, on her bald head, and she would be more comfortable that way until her new hair had a chance to grow back and then everything would be alright again.

That afternoon in the girls' den Vic was lighting as many candles as he could. We all wanted as much light as we could muster in that dark room with the fogged up windows. He chucked the box over to me and told me to light the ones on my side of the room.

One hand of strip poker had already been dealt and the girls had lost. We had decided to play boys against girls, it was quicker that way. If the girls lost, they were all to take one item of clothing off; the same for the boys if they lost. It was up to each individual which piece they took off. When the girls lost the first round with their stupid pairs and kings high to my flush and Vic's full house, we all thought they would balk. And they did to start with, but typically Lorna was the first to make a move. She stood up and in one flowing movement removed her jumper and folded it, would you believe, on the arm of the chair. Far from being nervous, she looked to me like she enjoyed it and she smiled defiantly down at the four of us, including the dealer, Pybus. We were all staring intently back up at her. Then in succession the other three girls took off their outer garments and laid them carefully on the back of that old sofa. MacNeill had a thin white shirt on and I could see the little bumps of her breasts underneath and it gave me the same shock as it had done at the river, she was no longer a child. Only twelve years old, or thirteen maybe, but the start of being a woman nonetheless. In that moment we all stopped talking so that all I could hear was the friction of the material passing over her skin and the asthmatic breathing of the others in the dusty, low light of the room. I smelt rotten wood in that instant and a cheap perfume that I think Lorna was wearing. I looked across at Billy and he looked like a hairy dog on a hot day. His tongue was out and he was almost panting.

The girls sat down again.

"C'mon then, deal them up," said Vic. "We haven't got all day."

"Can't we just play snap," said Billy, "this poker lark takes too long."

"Strip snap?" I joined in this time. "We're not in that much of a hurry, are we?"

"Eyes down for the next hand," said Pybus, with a big grin on his face. He was enjoying himself in charge of the cards and, by prior mutual agreement, exempt from removing his own clothing. He could relax in the expectancy of seeing us all naked, without the worry of getting naked himself, not that anybody really wanted him to anyway. From his place at the head of the table he dealt, his podgy fingers surprisingly dexterous as he flicked cards to the four girls and three boys waiting in the gloom.

"You're good at that dealing lark, eh, Pybus?" said Billy. "I expect you play at home, all happy families, you sad get."

Pybus grinned to himself. He, unlike the rest of us, was used to Billy. He understood that Billy's way of dealing with nerves was to insult people. It was like he couldn't help it and it got him into a lot of trouble. But we were all nervous, certainly the boys, maybe the girls were more used to this sort of thing. We couldn't guess what they got up to whilst we were spending long hours fishing, climbing and running from the Spills. Maybe they took their clothes off all the time. In a way I hoped they didn't. I wanted it to be an unusual significant experience, if not necessarily unique. I wanted everyone, girls included, to feel like I felt. It's not everyday that you get to take your clothes off in front of strangers and if everyone was thinking like me then the main worry when you play strip poker is that you will be the only one standing there naked, having lost every round, and the rest will all be standing there laughing while your dick shrinks with the cold. At least we boys were all in this together, but it was still the stuff of nightmares.

I was prepared to put up with these nerves because the real reason that I was still sitting there in that ghostly old house was the taste of anticipation in my mouth, as sharp as vinegar, at the thought of seeing those girls opposite take off their clothes. I had seen our Sandra several times although less so since she got older. Anyway, your own sister doesn't count. Too close to home. It's a bit like bursting into the bathroom and seeing your next door neighbour standing bare-naked in front of the mirror, which I did once because the silly cow hadn't locked the door. Why she was naked in our bathroom I'm still not sure to this day, but that aside I was traumatised rather than excited, especially after all the screaming. She was very put out and I got a clout round the ear from mum, so it became more an image to forget rather than to keep as a memory.

Watching Lorna and Jenny and MacNeill, even scrawny Monica, was a completely different experience. It was the last page of an exciting book. To see the very flesh that had sat across previous classrooms, under clothes, little bits revealed as they moved in their seats or turned around to talk to their friends or laughed or leant over to pick something from their bags at their feet. Just a glimpse of a little piece of white neck that had been hidden under hair, or a soft white forearm, or a knee. What's in a knee? What? Yet when it was the knee of Chrissy MacNeill and you were thirteen years old and she never spoke to you because you were a soft lad, then a knee was something. In the classroom once, last summer when I was still new and we hardly knew each other, MacNeill and I were kept behind to tidy up the classroom. We had to put some heavy books back on top of an old cupboard so she stood on a chair and I handed them up to her. She took hold of these books (something about Greeks and Romans I think) and she lifted them up. As she did so, her white blouse rode up and I could see the top of her grey skirt, the symmetrical pleats to the front of each hip, and above the pleats the whiteness of her skin as she stretched and, faintly visible, the creases at the start of her pelvis and the tops of her legs. I saw how flat her stomach was, how beautifully formed like a statue's, and I saw her little bellybutton, a slight hollow perfectly made and finished by an unremembered doctor at the very start of her life. There in that classroom, in that single moment, I wanted to put my lips right into that little hollow that was the beginning of her. I don't think these were normal thoughts for a twelve year old. I don't know if MacNeill had even an inkling of how much her beautiful stomach had affected me, and if she had, my name may well have been around the whole school as a sad pervert, but my mind went back to that day in the classroom. As we sat in the old house and watched Pybus deal, my expectation grew in a sudden glorious realisation that the moment I had dreamt of had almost arrived. To see MacNeill, naked top to toe, to see that stomach again, but this time the rest of her as well. My dizzy feeling from previous times returned, but I controlled it. I stole a glance at her across the table but she was whispering and giggling with her friends. Pybus had dealt once again and we all picked up our cards.

By some fluke Jenny got four nines, which beat our two pairs and king high, so just as the girls had done, now we boys stood up as one and removed our top layers. We were now bare-chested because it was a hot day and we hadn't bothered to put anything extra on. Vic glared at Pybus, and I had a sudden suspicion that something was going on between the two of them, something that at the moment was not going entirely to plan, but the girls were unsuspecting and sat in a row waiting for the next round.

They won that one too. This was getting serious. We took off our shoes, and Vic glared at Pybus again, who looked uncomfortable, while Billy just grinned. He seemed to quite enjoy taking his clothes off.

"C'mon, Pybus," I said starting to worry slightly. "Deal us some good ones."

The girls lost the next one and there ensued a big debate as to whether their shirts or their shoes should come off.

"I'm not putting my bare feet on this floor," said Lorna. "There could be all sorts living in it."

"We'll have to eventually anyway," said Jenny.

"Not necessarily," said Monica.

"Tops it is then," said Billy.

"You can shut up as well, Billy Skinner," said Monica. "Look at him, he's panting."

"Not for you," said Billy.

"Shut up Billy," I said.

"C'mon, make your bleeding minds up," Vic said impatiently. "We haven't got all day."

Lorna sighed and took her top off, followed by the other three in slow succession. They sat there in a row all wearing bras except for Jenny.

"I forgot to put one on," she said by way of explanation and instinctively she crossed her arms across her chest.

"Bloody hell," said Billy under his breath. The rest of us said nothing, trying desperately to look, whilst appearing not to. I could hear Vic cursing to himself like some old drunk, and the cards being shuffled by Pybus.

"Deal, Pybus," I said in a whisper, and as I spoke, from above our heads there was a noise of floorboards creaking.

All of us immediately looked to the ceiling and went quiet. The girls reached for their tops and held them to their chests. Billy shushed us, which was completely unnecessary because a deathly hush had fallen on the proceedings. We all strained to listen for whatever sound was coming next, but nothing came.

"What the hell was that?" said Pybus.

We waited for a few seconds more but there was no other noise.

"I don't like this place," said Monica in her, now familiar, whiney voice.

"It's alright, Monica," said Jenny, it's probably nothing.

"Yeah," said Billy finally. "These old buildings often make strange noises when the floorboards level out in different temperatures. Sometimes it can sound like footsteps."

"You're the expert, are you, Billy?" said Lorna. "What if it is somebody creeping about?"

"I want to go," said Monica, close to tears.

"If there were people in the house we wouldn't just hear one creak," persisted Billy.

"That makes sense," agreed Pybus.

"Can we get on with the game, for pity's sake?" said Vic.

"Next noise and we're off," said Lorna.

"Don't worry, we'll be right behind you," I reassured her.

"Look," said Billy, "I promise there is no one there."

I wanted to remind Billy of the time we heard the laughing behind the door but I thought this was probably not a good time to mention it. My desire to continue the game overcame my fear of the supernatural.

Pybus dealt the cards more speedily this time.

The girls lost again and there was more banter between them but their shoes came off. Then we lost and we elected to take our socks off and we were standing there in just our trousers. Two items of clothing left and then we were in big trouble.

The last round we managed to play, the girls lost again and their choice was between their bras or their trousers. They chose their trousers and I watched them undo their top buttons, unzip their zips and roll their trousers down over their legs and then step out of them, onto the cold, wooden floor. They stood there in a row in their underwear, hands by their sides, only Jenny with her hands across her bare chest, not saying anything, not acting all shy, just watching us. I looked at MacNeill and she looked at me and I don't know why but I stood up and moved a couple of feet towards her.

Then from the other side of our door, from the old corridor down which we had come in, came another noise. The sound bounced in echoes from the hall and the front door, but also from the staircase that led to the labyrinth of bedrooms upstairs. This time it was no squeak so fleeting as to believe it hadn't occurred. This noise was laughter, again not friendly, warm-hearted laughter, but mean, spiteful, hysterical laughter from several people, or at least from two or more, and it started at the top of the bare stairwell and came headlong in a rush of feet sounding like horses' hooves, as they stampeded along the bare floorboards. Down the stairs the clattering came as we all stood up in blind, half-naked terror in our little room, reaching for clothes and shoes and looking for exits. And as we scrambled in undignified chaos for our belongings, that noise came bursting through the hollow hall and along the corridor to our door. Then as the girls, especially bloody Monica, started to cry, and the boys tried to stay in control and not panic, fear like the taste of copper in our mouths, the door to the room swung slowly open.

In the doorway stood Myra Hindley and Ian Brady, and they grinned at us, teeth bared in empty skulls, like ghouls from the ghost train, the half-open door shedding only a sliver of light on to their faces. They were just like their pictures that we had seen every day for months and that were indelibly printed on our minds like macabre transfers. She, white bloated face, black make-up and that peroxide hair piled high, and next to her the strangler, the axe man, the grave digger, Brady; thin white predatory face like a weasel, black hair slicked back and yellow teeth. The two of them stood together in the doorway and surveyed the terrified group of children gathered before them, then slowly, from behind their backs, they each pulled long carving knives out and held them, points towards us, using them like a teacher would use a ruler, ordering us to keep our eyes on the floor and do exactly as we were told.

Then, strangely, they moved away from the door so as to give an escape route to some of the others. Still grinning like maniacs, they sidled away from the door, allowing first Jenny and then Monica to move round and then, pointing with their knives, directed them to the door.

"Go on, you two," whispered Myra in a deathly hoarse voice. "I'm letting you go. And you and you," she said to Billy and Vic. "Go on, get out. We don't want you."

Then Lorna and finally Pybus were allowed to leave, until only MacNeill and I were left, by this time clinging to each other in our half-dressed state, mesmerised by the lethal-looking knives waved by these intruders, waiting to be sacrificed as part of some ancient brutal ritual beyond the level of our comprehension. I felt her body against me, shivering with fear and cold whispering "please no, please no" over and over again.

I was desperately trying to make sense of the situation. It had happened so quickly. How could this be Hindley and Brady when they had only just been sent to prison. Were they in prison still? Maybe they had escaped. No how could they have escaped so soon. And together. Impossible. Then that bloody word that Vic used all the time, copycat, copycat killers came back to me. My God, what if we were in the clutches of real copycat killers. Those knives looked real enough and they looked nasty enough. Jesus Christ we were done for.

"Please let us go," I heard MacNeill say. "We won't tell on you, I promise."

"You better hurry up, whatever you want, those others will go to the police," I said, my voice shaking with fear.

Then Myra said in a familiar voice, a voice I almost recognised, "Do you know who we are?"

"Yes," I said, trying to control the wavering in my voice.

"Go on," Brady, still a dark figure hiding in the shadows, said in a weird Scottish voice. "Say our names before we chop you intae little pieces."

"You are Myra Hindley and Ian Brady," I whispered, trying to tell them what I thought they wanted to hear. Buying some time.

"Good. Do you know what we do?" Myra again, in a familiar Manchester whine.

"Yes," I repeated.

"Go on, say it," Myra persisted, still in a hoarse, but more cajoling, voice. "Don't be frightened. Say what we do."

There was just silence, while I tried to think of the right thing to say, but for the life of me I couldn't.

"SAY IT!" Myra screeched and MacNeill, on the verge of crying but too confused at this point to let go, blurted out, "You murder little children. Then you take them and bury them on the moors."

"Good," said Myra, calm again. "Now that wasn't very hard was it?" Then she turned to her partner in crime, still skulking by the door and getting harder to see as more candles were extinguished by the cold draft blowing through. Only a couple now burned. From outside the wind started to blow and it whistled through the gaps in the walls and the windows.

Then Myra said to Ian, "Come out of the shadows and let the children see your face."

I could feel my legs starting to tremble and my eyeballs getting hot. I was trying to talk to them, reason with them, beg them but no words would come except a strange squeaking sound, like that of a small animal. Like Jody's rabbit. I could feel MacNeill next to me making her own squeaking sounds amidst her soft, terrified crying, her finger nails digging into the flesh of my bare arm and her hair against my cheek as she burrowed into me. I was just on the line between panic and reason, one side of my brain contemplating saving myself and diving through the window, leaving her behind to be devoured by these monsters alone. The other side of my brain was telling me to attack them first, take the plunging of the knives into my heart and pray for a quick end, and not give them a chance to torture me, not like those other poor kids they trapped in small rooms with their sheer cunning.

Then Myra walked towards me and I started to see who it was. She came closer out of the shadows with Brady beside her and I saw who he was. I pushed MacNeill away from me and I stopped cowering and I said to her "it's alright, don't be frightened, I know who this is." Myra came towards me and with her left hand reached to her temple and grabbed a piece of her own hair. Then she pulled the hand sharply down and the big blond wig that belonged to my mother, the one she no longer wore because it looked like Hindley's, came away from her head and my sister's own mousey brown hair, moist with perspiration, lay beneath. In a moment, although the black make-up remained, the terror of her image had gone. My sister, Sandra, with a big grin on her face, stood looking at me, and her idiot boyfriend ruffled his own Beatle style back into place. They both looked us up and down and laughed out loud. "It looks like we interrupted something," she said.

MacNeill looked at me, then looked at Sandra with an anger I would not have believed she could own, had I not known what fear she had endured in those few seconds. I saw something change in her, a hardening of her mouth and in her eyes, only fleeting but there nonetheless, then she picked up her clothes and ran from the room.

I didn't run straight away. I put on my shirt and my shoes and as I did so Sandra and her boyfriend sprawled in the chairs where only minutes before we had sat playing cards. They retold to me in crowing fashion how frightened we had all been, a bunch of stupid kids, and I had to listen to that until I found my shoes. Then I don't know what came over me but I suddenly felt so angry, so pissed off with everything that had just happened, that I knew I was going to lash out. I badly wanted to hit Sandra but she was on the wrong side and I knew if I went for her the two of them would overpower me. So I settled for him because he was sitting on the chair nearest to the open door. I knew I was fast and if I got a start I could out run him so as I walked out of the door I bent down and put my face close to his. He was lying back in the chair, his face beaming up at me laughing and clucking like a chicken, and he raised his hands to fend me off, still not taking me seriously.

"Sonovabitch," I screamed at him and smacked him once on the nose with my knuckle like Jody's dad had taught us only a few weeks back when he had told us about his prize fighting days. I smacked him as hard as I could and I felt his blood instantly warm and wet on my fingers, and then I was gone, Sandra's screaming threats and his shouts of pain following me out of the house as I ran through all the others sitting around outside.

As I sped through that group, I glimpsed Pamela, Sandra's best friend, in amongst my so-called friends. They were all laughing now, their terror forgotten, their eagerness to be out of the house and not caring that they were leaving the two of us behind, already a distant memory. She had probably waited to tell them that it was all a joke and not to go to the police and everything would be alright except that it wasn't because I couldn't see MacNeill anywhere. So I ran right through them, ignoring their calls to stop, and I ran, my anger spurring me on, until eventually I came to the river.

Before I knew it I had waded across and I ran and ran up the hill into the field until I was out of breath. Then, panting hard, I sank to my knees onto the ground and lay prone amongst the sharp stalks and thistles of freshly cut grass waiting to be turned in the sun. They dug into every part of my body but I felt no discomfort. I was in Vic's hayfield, the one he had wanted to burn, and I lay on the ground trying not to cry, so angry and pissed off, my sweaty head thumping into the crook of my arm.

Then I felt the sharp edge of something in my pocket. I sat up again and reached into the pocket of my jeans. It was the box of matches that Vic had given to me in the house. I took a match out, struck it and, with the phosphate momentarily gagging me, held it lightly against a little wisp of golden grass. Then another one and then

277

another. The wisps blackened and folded in on themselves and then sprung into a miniature fiery little life. I lay there thinking about how I could kill my sister and her boyfriend, and while I thought I watched the hay grass burn, first a little blue streak of smoke, then a bright yellow flame. Then as I blew on it and fanned it with my hands it started to spread a little, moving from tuft to tuft, crackling and spitting and as fast as one clump turned black then another sprung into life. Then it seemed there were too many clumps burning and I tried to stamp them out but I couldn't and as I brought my foot down more red sparks flew up and more of the grass caught fire.

"Oh shit," I said out loud and then again louder, "OH SHIT," as I realised that quite a big patch of grass was burning away and no amount of stamping by me was going to stop it. I looked wildly back at the river, a little smoky silvery trail in the dusk, too far away to be any use as a fire dowser, beyond it my own estate and a few streets further in would be my house where my family, what was left of them, would be sitting down to tea. Any minute now, as the blaze grew ever redder, the Spills surely would come from their flats and see who had dared to set fire to their territory and threaten their horses and their land. It was time to leave.

So I ran and I ran across those shadowy fields, all the time the images that had invaded my head fuelling my panic and hatred. The images of Sandra and her stupid boyfriend humiliating me in front of MacNeill were followed by pictures of Billy and Vic, their faces grotesque in laughter. I saw pictures in my head of Jody and stupid dead Nelson, who had rescued me but not himself, and my bald-headed mum and my dad, who didn't come to see me, and then finally I saw the face of Stevie, his smiling, bleeding face that never left me.

I ran from the burning field, not homewards but parallel to the Ladybrook, through two more fields on the Spills' side, back towards the arches, at which point I could cross back over and not be recognised. When eventually I did get back across, I was suddenly engulfed by a huge weight of tiredness and I thought my head would explode with all the people inside who for whatever reason I couldn't seem to stop thinking about, people I cared for and those I didn't. I had to lie down and let it all go quiet and still. I lay down in the field to sleep and finally all their faces left me and for a short time at least I knew that I was free.

For the first time, but not the last, I stayed out all night under the stars. Not by design but because eventually I fell asleep comfortable in the long grass under the cover of the arches. I was lucky to have picked a warm night to collapse in because most other nights I would have frozen to death. Some bloke walking his dog found me, and thinking I was dead, rang the police straight away without bothering to wake me.

When the big copper arrived at my front door, with me subdued alongside him in the foggy early light, my mother, her eyes red-rimmed from crying and fatigue, peered out from the gloom of our hallway seemingly reluctant to confront the news that she had been dreading. Then when she saw me standing there, alive if not kicking, she made some kind of bestial shriek and laid into me, not just with words but with slaps and cuffs, until the very bemused copper had to drag her off. Then and only then did she hug me, clasping me to her bosom, to her familiar patterned apron, fresh tears rolling down her cheeks. I could see our Sandra behind, her face set hard, killing me with her eyes, and behind her, our George with a big smirk on his face, but I didn't care.

Mum kept saying, "Thank you, thank you," to the copper. "I thought I'd lost him," she ranted, "gone to the moors with all the others." The copper just nodded wisely as if he had seen it all before, which he probably had. In those days of roaming children and sadistic killers, hysterical mothers were two a penny in Manchester.

So he did understand and he didn't give us the copper's lecture like some of them were prone to do. For a while I was scared he was going to start on about the burning field but he never even mentioned it. He just pushed me back over the threshold of the house, glad to be rid of me I think, patted my mother on her arm and then went on his way.

I slept for two whole days and when I awoke on the third my mum told me that out of the blue Jody and his family and assorted trailers had come back to the waste ground but that she had heard the police were down there too so maybe they wouldn't be staying long. I got dressed in a hurry and ran full pelt down to the camp.

Chapter 16

THE FIGHT

When I got there, the police had already been there for some time. Early that morning, while I had been sleeping, the coppers had been knocking at their door. There were about eight of them in all, a couple of plain clothes officers, the rest in uniform, and they were going through the two caravans systematically placing goods and furniture and all sorts of personal items on the grass around. In amongst the clothing there were children's toys, ornaments, some brightly coloured crockery, bedding, papers and documents. In truth I don't think Jody's family had many possessions, but what they did have was laid out by the coppers for the world and his dog to see and I was embarrassed for Jody because of it.

It was obvious the police were having trouble finding whatever it was they were looking for because they were in and out of the trailers as if they bloody owned them. Maggie stood around, arms folded, a grim look on her face, the four little ones full of tears and snot gathered around her, shivering in the cool morning. But she did nothing and said nothing. Away from them stood Jody and his dad, man and boy together. Jody's father had anger on his face but there was resignation too, as if he had had his home turned upside down several times before. Then I looked at Jody and his face was like thunder, his eyes wide and white in the morning light and his mouth set in a snarl, like a wild dog cornered. His father held his own hand lightly on the boy's forearm and it was enough, for the moment, to restrain him.

I wanted to leave, but I was rooted to the spot. There had only been a few locals gathered when I first arrived but it was obvious that word was getting around and others were coming down to see what was going on. A lot of the crowd were sympathetic to the Gypsies; they saw no harm in them and were not threatened. But there were one or two there, a bunch of older men led by Phil Sherwood's dad who was well known as trouble on the estate, who were egging the coppers on, urging them to get stuck in and find all the goods the 'gyppos' had robbed from decent folk since they had arrived in the area.

One of the women called across to Sherwood and his mates.

"You're a brave man, aren't you, Donald Sherwood? Condemning a family with young babies like these from your place in the crowd, and all your mates along with you. Look at you, you should all be ashamed of yourselves."

Sherwood reddened and shouted back. "They're thieves, the lot of them. They had it coming. I don't know why they've come back. They know they're not wanted. Anyway, what are you sticking up for them for?"

"Because they haven't done any harm, that's why," shouted back Jeannie Croston.

"Look at them," and she pointed to the family standing forlornly in a line looking at the policemen ransacking their home. "And you ought to be ashamed as well," she said to a constable emerging from the van. "Haven't you got anything better to do? It took you long enough to get the last two, with your pussyfooting around."

The constable ignored her but a plain clothes man addressed the crowd.

"Alright, you lot," he said, "move on. Get back to your own homes." Then he turned to his men and said, "Right. Put the stuff back and let's go." There were groans from some of the coppers, which made their leader snap at them. "Go on, get on with it and make sure it goes back where you found it," he said. Then he turned to Jody and his dad and apologised. "I'm sorry we had to do that but we were acting on information. Obviously, it was wrong information. I should have guessed. If you were up to something, you wouldn't have come back, would you?"

"We work, we don't steal," said Jody's dad. "If you had asked me politely, I would have shown you around myself. All you lot have done is scare my wife and children."

"I know, I'm sorry," said the copper and I could tell that his remorse was genuine.

"Don't stop at the caravans," yelled Sherwood again from the crowd. "You want to look under the canvas on that other trailer. He's always inside that, up to no good."

The copper sighed. It was obvious he was none too keen on Sherwood but he took his advice nonetheless.

"What's under there? Please tell me that it's nothing to concern us."

"Merry-go-round," said Jody's dad. "That's all. It don't belong to me. It belongs to a Showman family. I'm painting it up for this season. That's where we've just been to. We've used it at the fairs down Gloucester way and we're going to put the finishing touches on it before the start of full season."

"Are you painting it for money?" the inspector asked.

"I don't do it for nothing," he said and then added, "but they employ us sometimes in the fair itself when it's busy. At the bigger grounds. I help them, they help us. That's how it is."

The copper nodded. "Can I have a look under the canvas?" he asked.

I saw Jody glance over to me with a sudden desperate look on his face and with his left hand make a barely discernible swishing movement. Straight away I knew what he meant. He had hidden Nelson's sword somewhere inside the merry-go-round before, and if it was found Jody and his family would be in real trouble. It wouldn't take long for this bunch of Mr Plods to add two and two and reach five. No way would a Gypsy be in rightful possession of a Japanese Samurai sword that had recently disappeared from the estate of Captain William Cairns, which was Nelson's real name, I had found out from

283

subsequent reports. He, formerly of the Royal Engineers Burma, veteran of the Siam railway and very recently deceased in the most tragic circumstances. It occurred to me also that I would have trouble convincing the inspector that I had been given the sword as a present by Nelson only minutes before he walked up the line for the last time, and that I was its rightful owner. I felt a hole in my stomach with a sudden fear and it took all my willpower not to turn and walk quickly away. But I couldn't leave Jody.

Suddenly the light of the day changed and the grey sky turned to a heavy black. It was as if that thunderstorm that had presided over mine and Jody's first meeting had returned to accompany our downfall. There were no big drops of rain this time but they would surely come, and then, as if God had switched a light on, the sun shone momentarily, saturating the colours of the fields and the wasteland. Without saying a word, Jody's father took one corner of the canvas cover and peeled it back like a waiter would a tablecloth, at the same time flicking it so it wouldn't snag on protruding features. In so doing he revealed a work of art of such colour and intricacy, of such craftsmanship and skill, that some of the gathered crowd, including the policemen, gasped in admiration.

It was the first time I had seen the ride uncovered and every horse glistened with fresh new paint, and such was the depth of colour and texture that each one seemed almost alive with its own character. It was a real work of art there on the waste ground but it was art created to be in motion and to see it being worked on a crowded and chaotic fairground, going round and round to its very own musical accompaniment, and each horse with an ecstatic child on board, would have been a wondrous sight.

Jody's dad, obviously proud despite himself, said, "It's taken me the last three weeks to paint that back up ready for this season. When would I have had time to go out thieving?"

Finally I knew where the old man disappeared to when he went behind the folds of the tent every day and why he had been keen to keep everyone away. If you can paint like that, I thought, nobody should ever take you for a thief. There would never be a need to steal. The old man could paint old masterpieces or even his own paintings and sell them for a fortune. This was the best painting I had ever seen.

The older copper in the raincoat, the one who looked like a detective, studied the merry-go-round long and hard for a full minute. Then, as he was about to go, he turned back and pointed to Jody and his siblings. "Those kids of yours need some schooling. Get them in by tomorrow or I'll be back to find out why," and he called to his men and strode off through the crowd.

Jody only lasted half a day at school and it was a miracle that he lasted that long. I was assigned to look after him, which I was happy to do, but from the moment he walked through the gates, Billy and all the others were on to him, and me. Gyppo kid, thief, robber, you name it, he was called it. Billy wasn't the worst either. Once the other kids knew, they were onto him as well.

"Whoa," said Billy in a voice of pure scorn as Jody and I waited outside the assembly hall together, "Look who's ere, the gyppo lover and his pet Gypsy."

"Shut up, Billy," I said, "give him a chance, will you? What's he ever done to you?"

Beside me, Jody looked a sight in his attempt at school uniform, which consisted of a dirty pair of grey trousers, his best white shirt which his mum had ironed for him, and a grey jumper that I had smuggled out of the house to lend to him. Mr Sutton, our form teacher, had given him a school tie, the distinct black, blue and white stripes folded somehow and just hanging there from his neck like an elaborate noose.

He hardly spoke and he stuck to me like glue as we walked the corridors to our first lesson, his mouth in a grimace of distaste at the smell of it all, the disinfectant, the polish on the wooden floors, the rush of adolescent sweat as groups of kids barged past us in waves of cursing and laughter. He shuddered at the sound of the bells and the shouts of the teachers and the slamming of the doors and he shut his eyes to try and escape it all.

"Are you alright?" I said to him as we sat together at the back of the first lesson, double English with Taff Jones, a mean Welsh bastard and no mistake. He kept an array of canes, all different shapes and sizes, at strategic places around the classroom and if anyone, anyone stepped out of turn, whether they knew they were doing so or not, they were given the stick. It could be on the hands or the arse, if you stood still. If you tried to resist or get out the way, he would hit you wherever he could. Sometimes he'd get you on the head. He didn't care. The only good thing from mine and Jody's points of view was that in Jones's lesson we wouldn't get any trouble from the other kids because they were all too scared of the teacher to play up. Well most of them were at least. Some, like Lionel Adshead and Lenny King, were too stupid to be scared of even a psychopath like Jones.

I looked across at MacNeill in the hope that she had forgiven me for the other day but she wouldn't look me in the eye, just kept her head bowed over her desk, doodling with her pencil. I took some comfort from the fact that she was ignoring everyone else as well, Lorna included, and that maybe if I talked to her in the break and explained that I had nothing to do with Sandra's trick she would forgive me. I really hoped so. I found myself, for the first time since I had arrived at this school, caring more about her opinion than I did about Billy's.

Today Jones was intending to do something on current affairs. He had brought in a load of newspapers from the past week and most of the copy seemed to be about the Hindley and Brady trial that had happened a few days back just down the road at Chester assizes.

"Right, you lot," said Jones in his Welsh accent. "We're going to do a little bit of current affairs today and I'm going to see just how much you lot know about what is happening in this wonderful world of ours."

I looked at Jody next to me and he had his head in his hands but was actually paying attention to what Jones was saying. He was studying the pictures that Jones had pasted up on the board, especially the big one of Hindley that everybody knew. Her malevolent features gazed down at us from the blackboard, with that look of callous indifference, the peroxide hair piled up, the grey skin, the predatory black eyes that had enticed children to their deaths. I shivered at the sight of it, but Jody stared intently at her with a quizzical look while Jones continued to paste up pictures from the case all over his blackboard. Some unlucky kid was going to be told to clean all that sticky tape off later.

Jones continued his little commentary.

"These pictures that you see before you," he turned around to look at us while with one hand he held a picture of Brady to the board, "are from probably the most notorious court case that has ever been heard. Yet it all took place, all of it, the crimes and the trial, not far away from where you are sitting now. I expect you not only to have read about it already, but to write about it now."

All of a sudden Jody whispered in my ear, the first time that I had heard him speak since we had got into the school.

"Who's that woman in the picture?" he asked me, his left hand cupped over his mouth to hide his words from the class.

"Where? What woman?" I said, taken aback by this sudden interest from him.

"There," he said louder this time in his impatience, and with his other hand he pointed to the blackboard. "That evil-looking cow with the blond hair, that yer man is plastering all over the place."

"Oh her. That's Myra Hindley. She's the one that murdered all those kids." I saw his blank face. "Jesus, Jody, you must have heard about Hindley and Brady. It's been everywhere – on the telly, in the papers. You can't get away from the bloody thing."

"What, she's a murderer?" he asked me. "She murdered children?"

"Yes," I replied, getting tired of his questions. "At least she helped the man to do the murders. Got the kids for him. As good as doing the murders I reckon because they would have trusted her. As a woman and all that. Anyway, why are you so interested all of a sudden?"

He paused for a moment then looked at me. I could see him close to in that moment and I can still remember how he looked all that time ago. His hair patted down with brylcreem in a vain attempt by his mum to smarten him up for his first day at school, the line of his eyebrows and his narrow but clear blue eyes. His nose broken several times but still neat despite that, and his mouth full of broken and chipped teeth and rarely open as a result. That and his natural reserve and suspicion of others, making his smile a rare thing. I saw his face properly now for the first and last time, because in school behind a desk with me he was unusually captive and still. Outside in the fields he was free and running and climbing; his face and character were not for studying. But I studied him now and I could see that something was bothering him.

"Who's that little girl then?" he continued in a whisper, pointing to another picture on the blackboard.

I saw that he meant the picture of Lesley Ann Downey. A face I'd seen a thousand times; on the TV, in the newspapers, plastered all over south Manchester by her desperate family, on lampposts, in newsagents. Curly black hair, chubby cheeks and a sweet, innocent, shy smile. Sometimes I'd seen her in my dreams. When I dreamt of bad people and the moors and the half-lit streets round our way. When I heard my mum and all the other mums then I saw her face again.

I told Jody who she was. A victim who had been taken from a fairground on Boxing Day 1964, and who had been tortured and murdered by those evil people, and who had been buried for months on the moors while her mother had been driven nearly mad with grief.

I looked across at the Gypsy boy and I saw his eyes bright with curiosity.

"Why are you so interested?" I said, my own curiosity aroused by the dramatic change in him.

"Because I saw her," he said, "at the fair over Ashton way. A while back. A couple of Christmases back."

"Are you sure?" I asked him, slightly sceptical. "There's hundreds of kids, especially at a fair."

"No it was her," said Jody. "That one in the photo. I know because she was on her own and when she looked at me I thought she was going to ask for directions or something. I was in a hurry to get back and help my dad on the ride because I was due a clout for being so long, as it was. So I rushed past her. She was by the waltzer, standing on her own. She didn't look scared or anything. I don't usually take notice of your lot but there was something about her. I couldn't understand it at the time and it nagged at me for a bit, and then I forgot about it."

"Bloody hell," I said, and then Taff Jones whirled around from his place at the blackboard and looked directly at me and Jody. The rest of the class turned around as if choreographed, to stare at us as well. I could see Billy and Vic grinning at me from the other side, waiting for the action to start.

"You two have been talking for two minutes now to my knowledge, without any permission granted by me. Would you like to stand up and address the whole class, and tell us what is so important? Come on now," he persisted, his voice taking on a dangerous tone. "We all want to hear your story, don't we, class?" I used to hate it when these teachers tried to include the whole class in their victimisation. A lot of teachers were bullies too, it seemed to me, and usually I would face up to them, but I was still shaking as I rose alone from my seat, lightly touching Jody's shoulder as I did so, to keep him in his.

"It was me sir," I said. "I was talking about the murderers to him."

"Stand up, boy," said Jones to Jody and Jody stood up alongside me.

"You're the Gypsy boy, am I right?" said Jones.

"Yes," replied Jody, no trace of fear in his voice.

"So you haven't quite got the hang of the rules yet. Is that so?"

"Not yet, no."

"Despite this idiot here," and he looked at me as he said it, "who has been given the onerous task of at least telling you the basics. Like don't talk unless the teacher tells you to. Address the teachers as sir at all times. That sort of thing."

"Yes sir. Sorry sir," I said hurriedly, praying that Jones would just leave us alone and turn back to his blackboard.

"Be quiet," he snapped, "I'm talking to your friend, not you."

He stared at Jody then and I could see that he was considering what to do next; whether to punish us or let it go. Finally Jones spoke again.

"Tell me, Gypsy boy, what was it that was so important that you had to say. I am intrigued because normally young Gibson here never breaks the rules, so it must have been extremely fascinating. Go on, speak up."

Jody looked at me then and I could see that he was starting to get annoyed so I said, "It's alright, Jody, you tell the teacher what you told me. He'll be interested, I'm sure."

Jody looked at me and I nodded vigorously at him in encouragement, so he took a deep breath and started to speak in his soft low voice, a mixture of all sorts of accents that he had picked up on the road.

"That picture of the young girl on the board," Jody said "Lesley or whatever her name is. I was telling him," he said indicating me, "that I saw her."

"Oh yes, where was that boy?" said Jones, not convinced.

"Over Ashton way it was, at a fairground. We were there two winters ago, with the merry-go-round. My dad was working that and I was also helping my Uncle Joe on the dodgems. Then I saw her."

"Yes, go on," said Jones. I could see his eyebrows raised, a sure sign that he was sceptical. But I could also see he was interested in what else Jody had to say, as were the rest of the class, who had all turned round to face us.

"Well as I said," Jody continued, "I was walking back in a hurry to my dad's ride and I saw this girl, the one in the photo over there," he said, pointing at the blackboard. Well she... this Lesley, was standing on her own. There was nobody around her, which was unusual. She didn't look much more than a kid and it was freezing cold, snow in the air, but she was just standing there. I thought she might ask me something as I rushed by her. She sort of opened her mouth to speak but then closed it again. She must have thought better of it like. I nearly stopped but I knew my dad would be waiting for me to get back so he could go and have his own tea."

"Go on," said Jones and the class all murmured their approval.

"Well she was still on my mind. I don't know why. So I kept half an eye out for her, from where I was standing like, just minding the carousel. I could see her in her dark coat, through the snowflakes, standing by the waltzer.

"Then I lost her for a while. I had almost forgotten about her. The ride got really busy. Saturday night as well as Christmas and I had my work cut out."

Jody paused and raised his eyes from the desk only briefly before looking down again.

"Then I saw her one last time."

"Where?" asked Jones, interested despite himself.

"I took a break and I ran over to my Auntie Lily's trailer for some food. After that I walked back through the fair past all the stalls, past the rifle range, you know, dawdling like because I wasn't that keen to go back. Then I saw her again," and again Jody pointed to the picture of Lesley Ann pasted up on the blackboard.

"This time she was not alone though. She was with someone else."

Jones turned theatrically to his blackboard and with one arm pointed at the pictures on the board, the one of Hindley and the other one, equally infamous, of the thin grey-faced man with the black quiff and the bulging evil eyes, Ian Brady. Pictures to make your blood go cold.

"Now I suppose you are going to tell us all that you came face to face with the evil Myra Hindley and Ian Brady and that you survived to tell the tale. Eh, lad. Is that it?"

"No not them," said Jody looking at Jones with scorn, almost contempt because he may have been a Gypsy and illiterate but he knew an arrogant fool when he saw one. "No I didn't see those two at all, not this time anyway."

The class groaned and I was aware of my own disappointment in amongst them, and slightly embarrassed for Jody because of the emptiness of his story.

"No she was with a couple of blokes, teddy boy types, dark hair and dark jackets." Jody ignored the groans and the catcalls, stood his ground and finished his story.

"I couldn't make out their faces properly but I know it wasn't him," said Jody, nodding towards the picture of Brady. The girl was between them and they were rushing out towards the edge of the fair. I got a glimpse of her face one last time. She looked alright. Not happy but not scared. The snow was coming down by now. I thought it was her brothers come to fetch her home and I remember thinking. About time, little kid like that. That was the last I saw her."

They were quiet then, the sea of different shaped heads that were Taff Jones' English class 3C, all staring at Jody intently, looking for a sign that he was lying to them. Even Jones was quiet for a moment but then he said, "Is this true boy?" Then I saw Jody hesitate for the first time as he started to realise that the interest shown by Jones and the class was uncommonly keen. I saw him gulp for air suddenly, having to think. It was unlike him to reveal so much and I could see that he wanted to backtrack. There was some significance to his story that Jody hadn't quite grasped.

"Because, young man," said Jones in a very serious voice, "if what you have said is true then I am going to have to bring the police in to talk to you. You may be a vital witness and I would be failing in my civic duty if I didn't inform them straight away."

"Police?" said Jody, a deep tremble in his voice that I could hear even if nobody else could.

"Only right," said Jones the bully.

"What for? I only saw them, I didn't do owt. Even then I can't be sure."

"He's lying, sir. He's having us all on," said Billy Skinner.

"I shall be the judge of that," said Jones, "not you, Skinner."

Then Jones turned to Jody again. "Are you lying to us boy?"

I could see the confusion in Jody's eyes and I didn't know how to help him. He was damned either way. Jones had scared him with his promise to tell the police and the alternative was to back down with the story and lose face. I felt responsible, at least in part, because I had encouraged him to tell but he was going to cop it from the other kids, I knew it.

"I can't be sure," said Jody, "and if I lie to the coppers they'll be after my dad again."

"So did you exaggerate your story," asked Jones, "to try and impress us?"

I was sure Jody didn't understand the literal meaning of 'exaggerate' but he understood a get-out clause when he heard one.

"If you mean did I dress it up a bit then the answer is yes," he replied and the class jeered him.

"Told you," said Billy, "he lied. They're all the same these gyppos."

"Shut up, Billy," I said, "he didn't want to say anything in the first place. Jody, it's alright." I turned to him, getting agitated to the side of me. "The trial is over and they're both in prison for life. There's no more that can be done. Isn't that right, sir? Police wouldn't bother now. It's all over. Remember, you all made him talk. He didn't want to."

"It's a shame he did then, isn't it?" said Vic.

"I didn't mean to," said Jody.

"All the same, gyppos," said Lenny King from the back of the group. "They lie and they thieve, that's a fact of life. That's what my dad says."

"Yeah and my dad," said Billy.

"My dad says that about the Welsh," said a reckless youth at the back of the room, but Jones didn't hear him which was lucky for the lad concerned. He would have lost the skin on his arse, had our teacher not been more preoccupied.

"Right, that's enough," Taff Jones finally pronounced. "I'm sick of hearing what you and your fathers think. None of your views are worth a tinker's cuss in the great scheme of things so you can all get back to your work and we shall forget what the young man said, shall we? Go on."

Finally the class turned around again and Jones went back to his board.

"Right, you lot," he said. I've pasted all the relevant headlines and the pictures on the board from this terrible crime. After break what I want you to do is, using what you've read yourselves and already know from talking to other people, write it up as if you were journalists writing a newspaper report. Those of you who have trouble reading and writing," at this juncture he paused meaningfully and looked around the class, "like you, Skinner, well do the best you can. Go to break then get on with it when you come back." Then Jones turned meaningfully to me and Jody still at our desk at the back. "You two can see me at the end of break outside the headmaster's office. We'll see what Mr Catchpole makes of your storytelling. NOW GET LOST, ALL OF YOU!" he bellowed, and the classroom emptied.

After that lesson, as we walked out towards the playground where I knew they would be waiting for us, I felt angry with Jody, I couldn't help myself.

"Jesus Christ, Jody," I said. "Why did you say all that? There was no point. It could have been any little girl, and that lot know it. Now they think you lied to them."

Jody turned to me angrily. "Everything I said about seeing that little girl was the truth. Why would I lie? She's the girl in the photo and I saw her that night at the fair. But I had to pretend I lied because that teacher was going for the coppers. You didn't think of that, when you told me to tell that teacher, did you? You didn't think he would get the police on us, did you?"

Jody was right, I couldn't deny it. "No I didn't," I admitted. "I'm sorry. I shouldn't have got you involved."

Jody paused and looked ahead. On the tarmac up ahead stood a group of lads, Billy at the fore, Vic alongside him and others like Lenny and Pybus on the fringes, for once not playing football as was the custom at break time, just standing, waiting for Jody and me to come out to them. Jody looked at them and smiled his little half smile.

"Anyway," he said to me. "You don't know the half of it."

"What do you mean?"

"I mean there's more to the story. I ain't lying either."

"Go on."

"That blond woman in the photo. Hindley?"

"Yeah. Hindley."

"I saw her at the fair before. Not that night. But a month or so before, when we were the other side of Manchester. It was definitely her."

"How can you tell?"

"Because I spoke to her. She was as close as I am to you. Evil-looking cow. I was running between rides again going to help my Uncle Joe and she stopped me and asked me if I had seen her puppy. A little black thing it was. She even showed me a picture of it. I said I hadn't seen it."

"What did she say?" I asked. I had never seen Jody so deadly serious or heard him talk so much for that matter.

"She then offered me ten bob if I'd help her look for it. I couldn't believe it. I was proper tempted, I can tell you."

"Did you help her?"

"She then said she had seen it last over by the road and would I go with her to look. So I said I would have to be quick because I had work to do but we would give it a try so I walked over with her towards the road. It was dark away from the fair, away from the lights and the music and I couldn't see as much. The streetlights weren't that bright either. I said to her, 'Aren't you going to whistle for him or call him?' and she said, 'He's too much of a pup to know my call or whistle. He's only a couple of weeks old. He doesn't even have a proper bark yet.' So I said back to her, 'Well you ain't going to find him here, missus. Not in this light.'"

Jody looked at me and shrugged. "I was thinking what are you doing letting a little pup like that out in this weather anyway, but I said nowt. Then she said to me, 'Look I have my car right here. We could have a quick drive round the streets. I'm sure we'll find him.' It was one of those cars like the coppers drive around in, so that put me off it straight away. Although that wasn't what stopped me."

"What stopped you?"

"It was the man inside the car. I could see his face through the window. Just sat there he was, just waiting. Why isn't he helping to look for the dog, I thought, if it's so bleeding precious? Then he got out and started to walk towards us. Straight away there was something about him. Something not right. He spoke strangely in a funny accent, but that wasn't all it was."

"It was that man in the photo, wasn't it?" I said. "It was that man Brady, the one that Jones was talking about. The evil one."

"Yeah," said Jody. "It was the man in the photo alright. I was only a little kid when I saw this man, and I didn't know much about anything, but what I did know was who best to stay away from. There was something about him."

"What did you do, Jody?" I asked, already knowing the answer to my own question, realising that he would have had the common sense to do what the other children hadn't done. He wouldn't have been here talking to me if he hadn't.

Jody paused a second, looked at me with a sideways glance and said, "I ran for it. I saw this man come towards me and I turned round without saying another word and ran. I could hear them shouting behind me, the woman and the man, and I heard him cursing and I ran faster than I had ever run from anything in my life. I didn't stop until I was safely back inside the fair. Normally if I run I feel ashamed but not this time. I couldn't have explained it before just now when I saw all those photographs, but from the moment I ran, I knew I had done the right thing."

He looked at me again.

"I don't care what this lot think," he said, gesturing towards the lads still looking at us, waiting for us to come out into the open. "I don't really care if you believe me or not, because I know what happened, and what I just said is the truth."

"Yeah, Jody," I replied. "I know it's the truth."

In the playground, as I feared they would, Billy, Vic and some of the others gathered around Jody, calling him a liar and other choice things. I tried to protect him but I knew that this lot wanted blood, that Billy wanted to fight Jody and that no amount of reasoning from me would help the situation. Jody showed no emotion either way, he looked neither scared nor angry. In fact, those eyes of his had almost glazed over and I remembered where I had seen that look once before. With the three Spills on the far side of the river when he ate the rabbit's liver and they had ridiculed his name, his eyes had glazed over then and I knew that he was preparing to fight.

Word had got around and our small group had turned into a large crowd. Thankfully MacNeill and her friends were nowhere to be seen. I knew that sooner or later a teacher would appear to see what the fuss was about and Billy knew that he didn't have much time either. I looked at the two of them starting to circle each other, big bulky Billy and this skinny little Gypsy kid.

"You should leave him alone, Billy," I said "look at the size of him compared to you."

"He shouldn't have such a big gob then, should he?" said Billy. "It's time he had a lesson."

"He's got every one against him," I said.

"Because he's a mouthy get," countered Billy, "and when I've done with him – I'll have you next."

Now normally at those words my stomach would have lurched and I would have felt like shaking, if not on the outside then certainly inside in my guts. But I no longer cared what Billy or Vic or any of them thought or were going to do. I was no longer scared. I didn't care if he battered me but I would make damn sure that I hurt him back as he did it.

"I'll fight you first, Billy," I said.

There were roars of laughter from the assembled throng.

"Shut up," said Vic, beside himself. "He'll snap you like a stick. I tell you what, pal, you need to remember where you come from. You're getting obsessed with this gyppo."

I ignored Vic.

"You're picking on him because you know you can beat him. You're just a bully and bullies are cowards."

But for the first time Jody stepped in and he held my arm. "This is my fight," he said. "It's been coming for a long time and I'm ready." Then Jody turned to Billy and took him on. He looked him in the eye and spoke directly to Billy for the first time since the day of the storm.

"Come on then," he said, "we all know how good a talker you are, let's see how good you fight." Then Jody immediately went into a boxer's crouch, knees slightly bent, up on the balls of his feet almost dancing, hands forming fists and up to his face for protection.

Billy, with his own hands up but only chest high, smirked at his opponent's stance.

"Is that how they teach you Gypsies to fight?" he said with a mean grin. "Well have a bit of this," and he swung his right hand in a looping arc towards Jody's bobbing head.

Billy struck quite quickly for a big lad but not quite quick enough to get Jody, who swayed out of the way. The punch went by with a whoosh and the crowd whooped with delight but the look in Jody's eyes changed again. He knew how close he had come to being poleaxed by the first blow and he knew he had to concentrate. Billy came again at a rush, trying to grab and hold Jody because he knew that was another way for him to gain a quick victory. His brute strength would crush any resistance out of the smaller kid in very quick time and then he could punch him into oblivion, to his heart's content.

This time Jody was more prepared and he danced away in retreat from Billy's swinging arms, but as he did so he swung his own right hand and caught him with a peachy little shot on the side of the face. It hadn't been hard but almost immediately it turned his opponent's red skin redder and started to make Billy lose his temper.

Jody was moving up and down and across, looking all the time at Billy, who was circling, his own fists clenched tight and waiting to strike.

"Stand and fight, you coward," said Billy and Jody jabbed him twice with his left hand. The first was too short, the second got him smack on the end of his nose, immediately drawing a flow of blood.

"Bloody hell, Billy," said Vic from the side. "Hit the bastard."

"I'm trying to but he won't stand still," said Billy, and I could hear the sudden doubt in his voice.

"Stop chasing him," said another, I think it was Lenny. "Let him come to you."

Billy threw another right which missed then a left which caught Jody on the shoulder. It made him rock back for a moment and Billy lurched forward, fists flailing, thinking he had him. He was met with a flurry of punches from Jody, a combination of four or five at such speed they were a blur, that all smacked into Billy's head with sickening slaps. They stopped him in his tracks and for a few moments before Jody was to unleash again, Billy looked at his opponent with a mixture of anger and confusion. Then slowly his head bowed until it reached down to his chest and then his whole body doubled in the middle and his arms, with fists still clenched, covered up his head but made no more effort beyond that to resist.

But he was still on his feet and Jody wanted him on the floor. Even though Billy was essentially beaten, his victor wasn't finished. Carefully, calculatingly, Jody walked around the doubled up body of his opponent, circling him like a craftsman would his handiwork. Then seeing an opening and a need for some finishing touches, he sent in a left and right uppercut, again with that dull slap of knuckle on skin, deep into the buried flesh of Billy's face. Then another two hard brutal punches that made the crowd grow uneasy and begin to think about intervening, which finally made Billy, with cries of pain, fall onto the hard tarmac floor. Jody went to pick him up. He wasn't finished and it had been too easy. But this was no longer defence or even retribution, whatever the justification for it. This was going towards humiliation.

All the hurt and suspicion, all the police raids and Don Sherwood's catcalls, all Jones' snide arrogant disdain, all of the other lads and their calls of gyppo liar and worse were all being taken out on Billy's stupid, misguided hide. Just as I couldn't watch Jody's humiliation so I couldn't watch Billy's either, and I stepped in.

I put myself between Jody and Billy, now half back up on his knees, and said, "That's it, no more, Jody."

But this was a Jody I didn't know, hadn't seen before. His eyes were wild and there was spittle on his lips and he was breathing hard with exertion. It was him against the world, me included. For that split second as I intervened, I was no longer a friend and I thought he was going to hit me too.

"I haven't finished with him," said Jody. "You'll get out of the way if you know what's good for you."

"I won't let you, Jody," I said. "I'll fight you if I have to."

That made him stop for a second, and he laughed at the stupidity of my challenge.

I could feel the crowd of lads encircling again, sensing another beating, tasting more blood, this time mine. There were still no bloody teachers on the scene to save me.

So with a heart beat in my ears and with goosebumps on my skin, I crouched down into the same stance that Jody and his dad had taught me when we were sparring round the caravan a few weeks back, and I prepared to fight. Or at least to get hit, I wasn't sure how much fighting I was going to be allowed to do.

Jody crouched too and he looked me in the eyes, just as he had done to Billy, and he looked at me long and hard as we circled each other. Then just when I thought the first pain was coming, when I braced my whole body to take one of his shots, Jody stood up and smiled. But it wasn't a friendly smile.

"You see, when it comes down to it," he said directly to me, ignoring all the other people gathered, "no matter what you say, we stick with our own."

Then Jody stood for a moment looking at the crowd around him, then with one last look of contempt at Billy who was still on the ground, he turned and walked across the square and out of the front gates of the school. Then, true to form, the teachers started to arrive now that the fighting was over. A few lads clapped me on the back for facing up to him but I suspected Jody had let me off the hook. I know he could have beaten me to a pulp and for one moment had been mad enough to do so. But he chose not to. Eventually I came to realise that he had shown me some kind of mercy in that playground.

After school I rushed down to the waste ground but, as I expected, Jody and his family had gone again, this time in more of a hurry because there was still a small fire smouldering in its circle of stones and a couple of paper bags full of rubbish. I wandered around the patch of ground where they had been, looking for a sign from Jody, but there was nothing and again I felt almost a sense of betrayal that he had left yet again without even a goodbye or anything. I wondered whether all the time we had spent together had meant anything at all to him.

Then I remembered the sword, Nelson's sword, and where we had agreed to hide it until the fuss died down.

We had hidden it, wrapped in polythene, inside a little cluster of dense hawthorn shrubs about a hundred yards from the trailers after the police had got so close to finding it under the merry-go-round. Jody wanted it even further away than that because he knew the trouble it would cause for his family if a dead man's sword was found near his home but I had persuaded him not to get rid of it altogether.

But I had changed my mind about that sword. I started to see implications for my own family if the sword was found in my possession. It didn't matter that the others had seen Nelson all but donate it to me on his last day on this earth. Besides, I doubted if any of them would back up anything I said now anyway. But it was more than that. Something more sinister. I tried not to be superstitious but Nelson had owned the sword, had endured a miserable and isolated existence before eventually dying violently under a train. Then he gave the sword to me and in that short time my brother had died, my dad had left home and my mother's hair had fallen out. Then Jody had the sword and the police had pulled their camp apart and humiliated them all in front of a large crowd.

It was something that Nelson had said when we had seen him at the arches on his last day, the day before we went back to school; something about bad men owning it. His words came back to me and I no longer coveted that sword. It may only be coincidence but I could see only trouble with the damn thing and I wanted to get rid of it once and for all.

In the hazy light of a midsummer evening, hungry for my tea but prepared to wait, I pulled that sword from the shrub, still inside its polythene, and I ran the line of the river downstream. I ran for a mile and carried it tight to my body, wedged under my arm and down the side of my leg. I carried it past where Billy caught his fish and fed it to Linton, past the pool where we saw the girls, past the rope swing where I saw my first Spill. Then down around the double bend to the factory, to where the tunnel was. As I ran, I looked across to the Spill's territory, gleaming in silvery and black light like a magical place, the flats at the top of the hill like ancient white castles, but I knew that was a mirage, a false illusion enticing me in where there was danger and hostility, and I shuddered at the thought of being up there.

Where I was going was not much better though. I got to the entrance of the tunnel that led to Liverpool, where the Ladybrook became the Mickerbrook and where Billy and I had last seen the Indian disappear as he had fought his battle with the giant eel.

I still felt his presence all around and heard his voice deep and somber and regretful. It was close to dark now and I knew I had to hurry. I only dared walk into that tunnel for a few steps before taking the sword from under my arm. Then I threw it into the dense, languid water of the brook and it sunk slowly down into the black sludge beneath, never to be discovered except when it was too late and they couldn't accuse me or Jody of burgling Nelson's home after he had gone under a train. I threw it to where I was convinced the Japanese soldier wouldn't find it in his pursuit of honour, and to claim what was rightfully his. But most of all I threw it where the headless ghost of Nelson's saviour, Captain Mac, wouldn't find it, as he wandered aimlessly and bitterly in his quest for revenge against the sword's owners, whoever they were and wherever they happened to be these days.

Chapter 17

MANCHESTER
The End 2002

At the hospital later that same evening I took out the scarf and unfolded it in front of our George and our Sandra. They looked puzzled and were on the verge of asking what I was doing but I wasn't in the mood to explain in detail, so I just said that Mum had always treasured these two pieces and I thought it would help her to hold them. I just left it at that and neither pursued it. They were tired too and just wanted it over and that suited me. I was happy to explain to my own son and this I did.

The first piece was the gold watch that had belonged to my mother, the one that Stevie had rescued from the pawn shop in Rusholme on the day he died. He had shown me for the first time how the sides were interchangeable just by flicking the winder. On one side the familiar watch face that I saw every day on my mother's wrist, and then on the other side, when you reversed the face, the gold plated back with an inscription that was small but still clearly legible. It said, "To Amy with love, Daddy, 1926." It had always amazed me that something so plain and simple could mean so much to my mother; that was until she told us the history of it. The words had been a dedication from her own father, who on the birth of his daughter had given her his most prized possession, the watch that had been his one constant possession throughout the Great War of 1914–1918, to the point where he had come to see it as some kind of talisman. It had been the only real thing of monetary or sentimental value that he had owned and it was always a source of great comfort to my mother that he had loved her so much as to give it to her. However, when he had insisted on going to war again in 1939 at the age of forty two, he had left the watch behind with her and he had died in France in 1940, only months into the campaign. My mum, to our knowledge, had not been the superstitious type but according to Stevie she had always felt a strong sense of guilt because he had given the watch to her and not kept it for himself. This guilt tempered the pleasure of ownership but heightened her possessiveness of it, and yet she had been prepared to risk that possession for her children, as we had found out that day outside the pawnbrokers. When Stevie died with the watch in his hand, I realised in later years when I was old enough to understand, that for my mother it was not merely a treasured possession but beyond that, almost a religious icon, something spiritual, a symbol of his last material connection to earth.

The other piece that I had found was the old silver photo frame and enclosed within, a small black and white photo of a handsome young man in his army uniform, the date 1918 inscribed in small white letters at the bottom of the picture. This was my mother's father, my own grandfather, a solemn smile on his features, a thousand questions in that smile left unanswered. In the other frame once there had been a picture of my mother but she had replaced it with another. When I had found it in her desk I had gasped at the sudden realisation of it. I had not seen the other photo before, but I should not have been surprised that she had put the two together so my shock was not in the fact the picture was there. No, my shock was at how much I had forgotten of the beauty of the young man in the image and how intense the rush of love that flowed up and filled me at the sudden memory of him. A love for my brother that I thought I'd let fade through the passing years. I placed the frame on the little locker next to her bed and arranged it so that her solemn father in his uniform and her grinning first born son in his favourite light blue shirt could both look down on her and welcome her into their world.

My mother died that night with the old watch and its inscription entwined around her bony fingers where I had placed it for her. I'm not sure if she realised that it was there but it comforted me at least because I knew how important it had been.

At the very moment she passed away, I was asleep in the chair next to her bed. I was dreaming of her though. Dreaming of the day in 1966 when we walked together into the back streets of Manchester after leaving the hospital, to look for my father. On that day we couldn't find him and in my dream a generation later nothing had changed in that respect. We walked to the address we had been given by him, number thirty two Sebastopol Street, and there was no house there, no house and no grumpy landlady to send us on our way. So in my dream we walked round and round the same block of terraced houses, looking for number thirty two, surrounded on all sides by bombsites except for a little general store and newsagent's on one corner. Sitting outside the newsagent's was my big brother Stevie, and he had glasses on with one of the lenses blacked out like they used to do in those days to try and make the weak eye stronger. Stevie never wore glasses so I haven't a clue why he had them on in my dream. Still. Around and around we went and each time we went past the newsagent's Stevie would say, "Have you found him yet, our kid?" and I would have to say no, over and over. And Mum and I kept walking round the block looking for him and we never found him. So eventually, tired and really pissed off, I sat down on the steps next to Stevie and started to cry and Stevie, still with his stupid glasses on, put his arm around my shoulder, which he did all the time in real life, and then he kissed me gently on my forehead, which he had never done in real life, at least not to my knowledge. That's as far as my dream went because his kiss woke me up.

So deep was my sleep that when I awoke I thought that Stevie was with me and like a fool I cried out, "What was that? Who kissed me? Stevie, is that you?"

In the shadows of the low lighting that the nurses kept on at this time of the night I could see both George and Sandra looking at me like I had gone mad. They had been asleep too and they stared at me then at my mother, who seemed very still.

Only Alex had been awake, his pale features and big dark eyes, sleepless for most of forty eight hours, showing concern for me as I tried to get my bearings. He was standing, gangly legs in blue jeans, his fair hair sticking up as if he had been startled, which in fact he had been. He was moving from one foot to the other as if he was on hot bricks, which he was prone to do on those rare occasions when he was frightened.

"It was me, Dad," he said, "it was me that kissed you. I kissed your head to wake you. You were all asleep only seconds ago and Gran died. She gave just a small sigh and I think she went and I didn't know what to do. I wanted to wake you gently," and his voice started to break.

I stood up and looked down at my mum at rest, her beautiful white hair framing her face, her eyes closed, and the watch still in her hand, ticking away. Then I walked across the room to where my son stood in a state of grief and shock, too close for any thirteen year old to be to a loved one no longer living, and I held his beautiful sad head close to my chest and buried my face into the back of his neck.

EPILOGUE

This story just told, I told to my son in that short time we had together while waiting for my mother to die. On a couple of walks we took down to the river and beyond I told him about Billy and Vic and the gang, and the Spills and Christine MacNeill and all those adventures we had in that year I turned thirteen and I lost my brother, and my father too, but in a different way.

The path to the river had been different to how I remembered it, with the trees bare and the leaves flicking and crackling off the ground in the east wind of a November day. The views were clearer and you could see further, not like in the summer months when the foliage was dense and green and the birds were around and the noises were strong and musical, not this wintry silence that we walked in now. In a way it was a good time to show him the places that I had spoken about; we found the rope swing, what was left of it, almost straight away, whereas in summer I would have taken a few wrong paths. After all, it had been over thirty years.

However, the walk I did that day with Alex I knew pretty well because I had covered every inch of it in my head a thousand times. It was the walk I had planned, in my imagination, to take with MacNeill after she had asked me to that day I got back from the hospital. I had promised I would show her all the secret places, but after what happened we never got round to it. As Alex and I stood looking at the frayed ends of the rope swing, a long time out of use it seemed, and he was asking me how nasty the Spills had seemed that day, I was thinking of how I would have dared MacNeill to climb on that rope and swing out into the middle of the river like the boys did and then dip her toes into the deep milky flow of the Ladybrook, as she came in perfect form like a gymnast, back round the old tree. I know she would have taken the dare because she was that kind of girl.

If things had worked out I would have shown her the seven arches and we would have lain down together in the long grass under the deepest one, counting all the bricks and trying not to run for it when the trains went overhead.

Alex and I walked the length of the Ladybrook upstream as far as the seven arches but they didn't look so big or imposing and less trains seemed to go over now. I told the story about Nelson and he was incredulous. I felt at the time that I might have told him too much.

"He saved you from drowning then he nearly murdered you."

"He didn't want to kill me, just show me the sword."

"Dad, he was drunk as well as mad. He could have beheaded you."

"I know," I replied morosely, feeling uncomfortable at the memory.

"You're lucky to be here," said Alex. "That makes me lucky to be here."

"Yes it does," I agreed.

"Did he really get killed by a train?" he looked up to the parapet as he said it. "Up there."

"It was a good way for him to go," I said. "I think the war had done for him."

Alex nodded then grinned. "I liked that story about his head going to Stockport on the front of the train."

"All true."

"Did he really bleed on you all?"

"No," I replied. "Just on Billy."

"What happened to Billy?" asked Alex "What happened to them all for that matter?"

We had moved down again from the arches to the shallow river crossing near where Jody and his family had parked their caravans and to where the Spills, with the white-haired girl leading them, had crossed in pursuit after our ambush at the quarry had backfired. I found myself pleased by his interest.

"Well quite a few I just don't know. As I told you, Nelson died and the older people like Sid and the Red Indian Milkman and the Jewish magician and even Jody and his family came into my life and then left it just as quickly, without so much as a goodbye. I have no idea where they all are now although I imagine Jody at some fairground somewhere, running the rides or even trading horses. He was good with horses."

"What about the milkman?" said Alex.

"Never saw him again although every milk float we saw after that, we had to duck down in case he was driving it. I hoped for ages that the milkman found his father and went back to America because he was out of place over here with his big hunting knife and no proper lakes or forests.

"I never saw the white-haired girl again although I confess I looked for her from time to time and strangely nobody else knew where she had gone either. Later on I got friendly with a couple of Spills and even they couldn't tell me who she was. It was almost like she didn't exist, but in a strange way I felt as close to her in the middle of that battle as I've felt to anyone before or since. I can't really explain it.

"I rode with Sid a few times up to the hills but eventually he got another job on another building site and I never saw him again and the Jewish man moved but we never played around his house afterwards so I couldn't be sure when he moved or where to.

"The children are different. I don't know what happened to all of them, but quite a few will still be around here, doing mundane jobs, with kids themselves, getting drunk on Friday nights, going to United or City at the weekend, if they can afford it."

"What about your gang," asked Alex, "what happened to all of them?"

"Well Linton became a copper," I said.

"No surprise there then," he said, and I grinned at him and agreed.

"No it was always his plan. It's a family tradition, you could say, but actually he did pretty well. He made chief inspector and he can't be far off retirement. He works in the Midlands, round Birmingham. Actually, it's Linton that keeps in touch and tells me what the rest of them are doing.

"Pybus moved to Yorkshire and runs a couple of butcher's shops up near Doncaster somewhere. Still looks the same, according to Linton, never lost his puppy fat, and instead of that tight, red football shirt over his belly, he wears a tight blue and white striped apron. He stands outside his shop greeting all his customers."

"Vic did pretty well for a while. He started up his own business as soon as he left school, buying and selling cars. Ten years of that and he was a millionaire by all accounts. A millionaire in your mid-twenties, can you believe that? Anyway, he expanded into all sorts of other areas, always judging exactly the right market, always getting lucky. He bought a couple of pubs, a scrap metal yard and quite a few terraced houses to rent out. Proper empire he had and one million went to five and by 1990 Vic was worth over ten million quid. He was enjoying himself as well. He had a lovely wife and two lovely children who were devoted to him. Executive box at Manchester United, home in Alderley Edge and a villa in Spain, all the usual trappings. Life was good for Vic. Then he bought an aeroplane."

"An aeroplane? What for?"

"Well, according to Linton, he learnt to fly so he could do more business, more quickly and further afield. He flew all round the UK, all round Europe, he even flew himself and some colleagues to Moscow on one occasion."

"I'm waiting for something to happen here," said Alex. "Things are going too well for Vic. Something has to give."

"Very astute of you, Alex," I acknowledged. "Something did give. Not for the first time in his life, but probably for the last time, Vic went missing."

"Missing?"

"Yes. While flying his plane from Manchester to Dublin apparently. Went down in the Irish Sea, or so they think, at least he never arrived in Dublin. They never got a mayday call and the searches never found any sign of wreckage. In typical Vic style he had disappeared, except the old Vic that I knew had always reappeared, sooner or later."

"Maybe he was up to something," said Alex, who seemed to have got to know Vic pretty well after the stories that I had told him. "Maybe he wanted to disappear. People do."

"Yes," I agreed, "that's what I said when Linton told me. But Linton, who as usual knew everything that was going on, said that Vic's wife was in the plane with him, but that his little children had stayed at home. So effectively his children became orphans even though they never found any bodies. Even someone as ruthless as Vic Roberts wouldn't leave his own children behind forever in the care of someone else, small as they were, no matter how much he wanted to disappear. No, as sad as it seems, Vic and his wife are at the bottom of the Irish Sea."

"So what about Billy, what happened to him?"

"Well, according to Linton, Billy is big in local politics. He is a Labour councillor in Manchester and is applying to become a Labour MP for the area of Manchester South or somewhere in the area. I think they run into each other from time to time, Linton and Billy, in a professional capacity at least. I shouldn't think they would socialise with each other. They probably talk about fishing, when they do meet." I chuckled to myself at the thought.

"Do you ever see him?"

"Only once since we left school. In a pub in Manchester by chance. We said hello, that's all. Remember, I left Manchester when I was eighteen to go to London and I never lived here again, so I was never around. Billy got into a bit of trouble when he first left school, got in with the wrong crowd, stealing cars, drinking alcohol. He even went to prison at one point, so Linton said. But he snapped himself out of it, got a degree in politics when he was about twenty eight and has done well since. He could be a good politician with some real experience behind him, if he's given a chance. That's providing he's sorted out his little weakness for causing trouble with everybody he meets, and that is if the media leave him alone. They could have a field day with his criminal past."

"You could all have been a gang again," said Alex as he and I walked down through the building site, which didn't look so new now, past where the farm and the orchard had once been, to go and stand for a moment outside MacNeill's old house, like I had done on a few early mornings thirty years ago when Billy and I had worked for the milkman.

"What do you mean?" I asked.

"Billy would have been the MP. You're the writer, you could write all his speeches. Linton would be his protection officer. Pybus would be his personal butcher and Vic would have flown you all over the country in his aeroplane."

"Well, leaving aside the fact that Vic is at the bottom of the sea and wouldn't necessarily be my first choice of pilot anyway, it seems that everything would be revolving around Billy Skinner again." I turned and grinned at my son. "Wouldn't work," I said matter-of-factly. "It would be too much like old times for everyone's liking."

"Pokey little place," he said, staring up to the same window, without the yellow curtains, that I had stared up to all those years ago when doing the milk round. We were at Chrissy MacNeill's old house in Cheadle Avenue on our way back to my mother's old house.

"That's why she was so desperate to leave it," I said, remembering her brave declaration to Mr Sutton and the whole class, when she had set herself up to be laughed at.

"But she did manage it eventually. She did go to Manchester University and she did get a degree but she exceeded even her own expectations and became a lawyer. After a very short time working she didn't need the contacts to move her family because she had the money and she moved the whole lot of them, her mum, dad and all her little sisters and brothers out to a nice big house in New Mills on the edge of the moors. She was a determined girl; I could see that even when she

313

was thirteen years old. That was one of the things I liked about her."

"Were you ever friends?" asked Alex.

"No not really," I said, trying not to sound too regretful. "She moved to the grammar school soon after and we never spoke much again. Just the odd shy 'Hello' when we met or 'How's school?' that sort of thing, very polite. I wanted to say more, even offer to show her the river, but I always thought she wouldn't be interested now she had new friends and a new school. She once told me she had to work much harder at her lessons and didn't get much free time to hang around with Lorna and Monica. I was on my own more then as well. I had split up from Billy and the others. Then, as I said, when I left school, I moved to London and we lost touch. She studied, became a lawyer, had her own family and was very happy by all accounts. Then Linton told me that five years ago, she got breast cancer. She would have fought hard against it I think, from what little I knew about her character, but she died three years after that, in 1999. She left a husband and three teenage kids. It made me sad when he told me that, I can tell you. She was only forty five."

I turned away from MacNeill's old house and started to walk back, up through the unchanged streets, past houses that looked ragged and uncared for, up to the cutting that would take us back onto the estate with the paid-for houses, where my family had lived.

"That's a shame," said Alex as we walked.

"I know," I agreed. "She was too young. No age really."

"Not just that," he continued. "I meant it's a shame that you never properly talked again. Never went to the river together; all that's pretty stupid, if you ask me. You were both messing about not talking to each other, trying to be cool. Where did that get you? You were both on your own, and together, as friends, you could have been happier. That's all I'm saying."

In the summer after Stevie died we went for a holiday to the sea, our first proper holiday in several years. I don't know where mum found the money, but we caught an overnight train down to Exeter and stayed at a guest house on the south coast of Devon near to a beach and a little fishing port. We had been a couple of times as a family when Stevie was alive, but on this occasion it was only mum, me and our George. Sandra had decided to stay at home. As soon as we had unpacked, I ran down to the harbour to watch the sail boats going out and the fishing boats, bursting with their overnight catches, coming in.

It was a day full of promise, perfect for sailing, a blue day with a good breeze and lots of yachts going out of the narrow stone mouth of the harbour. I stood and watched a few being prepared for sea on the broad slipway, a constant trilling of the wires against the masts and violent slapping sounds as the sails, all colours – reds and blues and yellows – flying in the breeze like a giant's washday, were raised, the little flags at the top of them spinning furiously. The harbour was full of bustle, like a scene in one of those old B-movie pirate films, only in this scene, instead of buccaneers and slave traders, the characters were weekend sailors. One man in particular was observed by the crowd with a mixture of amusement and annoyance. He wore one of those little mock navy caps emblazoned with a gold anchor from under which emerged tufts of frizzy brown hair that joined without a break one of those beards that has no moustache. He looked like a bully and acted like a bully. He criticised his long-suffering wife for letting go of the boat as it threatened to drag her into the shallows with it. He criticised one son for getting in his way and criticised the other son for standing around with his hands in his pockets and all this humiliation dealt out in the safe knowledge that he had an audience of fifty day-trippers or more leaning on the rail above the harbour. But this man didn't know (how could he) that this crowd that he thought he was impressing with his seamanship were silently wishing him a slow death by drowning. He pretended that he was a man of the sea but really he was a teacher from Taunton and the more that he berated and bullied his sons, the more he risked losing another trickle of familial love, never to be recovered even with the passage of time. But he was not alone. There were another twenty like him. This area was well known for it. The whole basin reverberated to their loud, round, plummy accents. The local men had seen it all before. They leant on the harbour rail smoking their pipes and smiling enigmatically at the chaos going on around them; old faces full of sun and salt, their strong rope-like forearms burnt black.

I walked around to the sea wall, solid blocks of hard granite-like stone, hewn from local quarries, this wall had held back the sea for centuries and kept the harbour safe. On a previous holiday, Stevie had played a game on this very wall. He would have been fourteen and I would have been eight. We had walked past the yachts in their yards and past the trampolines, the children bouncing high, loose-limbed like rag dolls, screeching like the gulls that circled above them. Then, starting at the beginning up the stone steps, where all the hippies sat around and played their guitars, we would close our eyes. We would stand for a few seconds getting our bearings and then we would see how far we would dare to walk before we opened our eyes again. We never cheated. We would walk, hands outstretched, reaching for the furthest point. In that summer we knew the wall better than anyone. Better than the lovers who came every day and sat at the far end looking out to sea. Better than the fishermen. Better than anyone. We didn't just know its lines and its shape and the sight of it, we knew its feel and its sounds and smells and its taste. We could smell the fish being landed on the quayside and we learnt to discern what species dominated the catch. When the wind blew from the other side of the wall then the smell of the seaweed that had been washed up on the shingle beach obliterated any other smell. Sometimes it was tarry on really bad days, like raw sewerage, its pungent blasts souring our lips and stinging our skins. Those days were thankfully rare.

As the wall progressed, the top started to slope away so that illusion of security fast disappeared. It could still be walked upon but there was a feeling of being dragged towards the sea. When the waves crashed in as they can do, especially after September has passed by, then it could be dangerous to walk along that sloping spine beyond a certain point. Playing blind man's buff, even on a fine day, caused us to drop to our knees quite soon and feel our way around. The texture of the wall was rough on our fingers. Something almost volcanic like granite, pockmarked and porous like cinder but very hard. We spent almost all our time there on the wall and by the sea that lapped or thrashed at its edges. The sea wall was our domain and we lived on it and around it like human anemones wavering and bending with the currents but refusing to shift.

In that summer of 1966, the year Stevie died, I can remember my father arriving one afternoon out of the blue, and he took me to the little aquarium at the end of the harbour. It was housed in an old low-slung, tar-painted shed that had once been a boat house. There was an old man on the door and he charged us a shilling to go in. Before we went in, I made some bemused tourist take a picture of the three of us together, me in the middle of my mum and dad. I suppose in a way I was trying yet another way of bringing them back together, a happy threesome preserved in posterity, none of us smiling although my mum was trying. Then my dad and I left the hot day and went into the cool dark room of the aquarium, for that was all it was, as if we were going into the ghost train at the funfair or into a picture house. There was not much to see. The indigenous fish of the English Channel, that's all. There were grimy tanks containing small black blennies, bulbous heads and feathery gills, and various slugs and crustaceans. But in pride of place was the conger eel, lying at the bottom of the tank, as thick as my young arm and twice as long, eyeing me malevolently, fascinating me because the proud claim on the tank said that he could sever a man's arm if the mood took him and he had been caught only ten miles out to sea. I thought of the Red Indian and wondered if he would have liked the sea as much as he liked the lakes and the rivers.

We wandered around the tiny aquarium, close together in its dark corners peering into green slimed tanks. We only had one fraught, unsatisfactory conversation whilst in there.

"When are you coming home, Dad?" I asked him.

"Not yet, son." He looked at me quickly and then turned away, avoiding eye contact.

"When then?" I persisted.

"Trouble is, Mike," he said, "when I'm there, all we do is fight, your mother and I. We make each other unhappy and you kids too. Perhaps it's better that I'm away."

"It's not better for me. Please come home."

"We'll see. I can't promise anything."

"Please try, Dad. I know it's hard. Please try."

"I will. I will." He squeezed my hand to placate me. He was keen to get back out in the fresh air. "Come on," he said. "Your mother will be wondering what's happened to us."

When we went out into the light I could see my mother sitting on the quayside, wearing her blue headscarf, her face turned up skyward, eyes closed absorbing the sun's rays.

He touched her lightly on her arm.

"You were quick," she said.

"Not much to see," he replied, "was there, boy?"

"The eel was good."

"Yes. Yes, you're right. The eel made it worthwhile."

My mother stood up and faced us directly for the first time. Her eyes were red as if she had been crying. In her hand she held a white handkerchief tightly. My mother rarely cried these days, crying for Stevie had made her bone dry. She saw me looking at her closely and said, "Michael, I want you to say goodbye to your father. He has to go back to the North and we won't see him for a while. Go on, say goodbye."

"Please don't go," I said. "Stay another day. We could go mackerel fishing."

"I'm sorry, son, I have to work," said my dad, who hardly ever worked, or so my mother said.

"Michael, please don't make it harder than it already is," she pleaded with me, the tears coming back into her voice, and the threat of those tears made me relent.

"OK OK," I said, not wanting an argument. "Goodbye Dad," I said, adding as an afterthought, "Thank you for showing me the eel."

My dad laughed. A sad laugh, I thought. He held out his hand and I shook it, like a man.

"Goodbye, son," he said and he bent his head and kissed the top of mine. "Be good. Oh and say goodbye to your brother for me. Tell him I'll see him soon."

My mother rummaged in her handbag, took out her sunglasses and gave me a lost little smile as she put them on. "Walk on love," she said "I just need a quick word here. I'll see you by the steps at the end. Go on. There's a good boy."

"Hey, boy," my dad called out as I started to walk away. "Don't forget to send me one of your photos." He indicated the camera around my neck.

"I will, but I won't know where to send it. Mum will have to post it when she knows where you are."

"Don't worry, we'll send him a copy," she said. "Now go on, I'll meet you at the end."

So I walked on my own round to the steps at the beginning of the wall where the trampolines were. George was still bouncing, I could see his curly head and hear his high-pitched laugh as he strived for ever greater height, the more complicated aspects of life passing him by, for now at least.

Eventually, my mother came round the long curve of stone, and with the light low in the west and her face in shadow, she took our hands without a word and we walked back to our guesthouse. Before we turned the corner round to the boatyards, I looked back to the end of the wall and saw him standing there, a tall, slight figure in his long overcoat, dark hair blowing in the breeze. With a jolt in my heart I could see that he no longer followed us with his gaze, as other men would have done. Instead of watching his family pass all the way out of his view, he had turned around again, in sorrow or relief I could not be sure, and I watched him then, with the sea behind him, in that sunset of bloody red diamonds. In the last moments that I had as a boy, the very last seconds that I had of being unsure, of faltering, of relying on others, I watched my father.

I watched him, not looking inland for the people who loved him, but looking away, looking out to sea.

319